A Handbook for the
Technical and Scientific Secretary

About the Author

George Freedman is the manager of the Materials and Techniques Engineering Group of the Microwave and Power Tube Division of the Raytheon Company, Waltham, Massachusetts. He is technical editor of the magazine *Semiconductor Products and Solid State Technology,* and is also the editor of a series of books entitled *Materials and Techniques for Electronics: Devices and Systems* that is now in preparation.

Mr. Freedman holds several patents on materials, electron tubes, and semiconducting devices, and has also published many papers on these subjects. He received his B.S. in physical metallurgy from the Massachusetts Institute of Technology in 1943 and his M.A. in physics from Boston University in 1952. Since 1964 he has also held the position of Lecturer at the Harvard University School of Dental Medicine.

A HANDBOOK FOR THE TECHNICAL AND SCIENTIFIC SECRETARY

GEORGE FREEDMAN

BARNES & NOBLE, INC.   NEW YORK

Publishers   Booksellers   Since 1873

Dedicated (in alphabetical order) to the ladies who in the last twenty years have somehow survived the ordeal of being my secretary:

Anne
Arlene
Betty
Carolyn
Gertrude (2)
Janet
Jeannine
Jeannette
Joanne
Linda
Louise
Marjorie
Marion
Marilyn
Mary (3)
Nancy
Peggy
Rosella

Preface

This book is designed to help the secretary who works for a scientist or an engineer. Its goal is to serve as a guide for improving the quality of her work, and, incidentally, to increase the pleasure she may derive from it. At the same time, if it is successful, it will also satisfy and give pleasure to another person, the engineer or scientist for whom she works. This book differs from most guides to the secretary in that it is written by one who has never been a secretary and never expects to be one. I have been and am the employer of a secretary, and see her from the employer's point of view. Since I am the one to be satisfied by what she does, I consider myself well suited to write a handbook for her. So, without any apologies, I wrote it, and here it is.

This book is based on the premise, in which I sincerely believe, that a secretary can always do a better job when she understands what she is doing than when she doesn't. Does this mean that the secretary to a chemist should know chemistry? Well, she is his closest working associate; it would certainly help for her to know some. If a secretary is typing mathematical or chemical equations all day, and many secretaries do, she is usually working with what is for her meaningless gibberish. That is a terrible predicament to be in, and a terrible way to earn a living. But, it is really not difficult to explain what a mathematical or chemical equation is to one who has the level of intelligence required to be a good secretary. Anyone who has the ability to type and take shorthand and organize complex reports and handle people and the telephone in a busy office (usually with a level of tact and skill that puts most Ph.D.'s to shame) is quite capable of understanding, for example, that a chemical equation is merely a shorthand way of telling how certain materials combine to form other materials. Once the chemical equation takes on that meaning, it loses many of the qualities of gibberish. So, early in my engineering career I began the policy of explaining to my secretaries just enough of what the material they would have to handle was about so that it would have some meaning and interest for them. This method always seems to have worked; that is, it always seems to have helped both my secretaries and me.

The material in this book is presented in two parts. This first part is a treatment, in "secretarial" language, of the basic scientific disciplines of chemistry, mathematics, and physics, and there is also a chapter on electricity and electronics. Throughout, I have tried to keep in mind that only "enough" would be given, so the secretary would not feel overwhelmed by complex details involving unfamiliar subject matter. Every topic is treated from the point of view of how the material should be composed on a typewriter. Many times the statement is made, "this is how he will say it (into a dictating machine or in 'live' dictation), and this is how you will write it."

The second part of the book is meant to serve both as a guide to some secretarial techniques and as a reference. The techniques covered are ones that are necessary to the effective performance of a technical secretary, but which are not normally included in her training. Primary among these is the use of drafting tools for making simple sketches and graphs. Since I believe that the best guide to effective performance is provided by examples, a generous number of these, in a variety of technical fields, is given. The remaining portion of Part II consists of a set of glossaries that the secretary will be able to use as a supplement to her dictionary, as swift, easy-to-understand references. The glossaries contain prefixes, suffixes, abbreviations, names of important scientists, some foreign alphabets, and, most important, a dictionary of technical terms, with definitions given in as few words as possible. Defining naphthalene as "a chemical compound" may be very incomplete for the scientist, but, in most cases, it is all his secretary needs to know to do her job.

I think that it is also worth saying a word about what is *not* in this book: First, whatever the secretary should know *anyway* has been left out. There is no advice on what to wear to the office or how to file or get plane tickets or deal with visitors or keep reminder notes. I am sure that a secretary can handle these matters far better without my recommendations than with them. Also, I have made no attempt to treat every field of science and engineering. An understanding of the basic physical sciences should help the secretary with most fields. Also, in line with the philosophy of not treating what is not understood, the biological sciences are not covered since I have never studied them.

I would like to acknowledge the patient and tolerant aid of my wife who has made many helpful suggestions in our discussions of the material, and has helped me greatly with the choice of words and manner of presentation. I also wish to acknowledge the kind aid and comments given by the many secretaries of the Raytheon Company of Lexington, Massachusetts, who have sub-jected the book to prepublication tryouts. Many of the examples of typical typed pages in the various fields of chemistry, mathe-matics, physics, and electronics that appear within the text are extracts from actual technical reports written by engineers and scientists employed by the Raytheon Company (and typed by their secretaries). The company's permission to use this material is gratefully appreciated.

George Freedman

Wayland, Massachusetts
June, 1967

To the Secretary
How to Use This Book

The best way to use this book is first to read Part I from the beginning to the end. Then repeat the process for the material that relates most closely to the work being done in your office. By the time you have gone through a portion of the text for the second time you should have very little difficulty with it. If anything still remains unclear, any scientist or engineer in the group for which you work should be able to help, and most will be glad to.

Regardless of what kind of office you work in, you should give particular attention to the chapters on mathematics and physics. No matter what your employer's specialty is, he will always use the language of mathematics and physics. If chemistry is completely missing from your place of work, you might omit the chapter on chemistry. By the same token, you might leave out the chapter on electricity and electronics if these subjects are not discussed in your office. But, this book will really serve you best if you read all four chapters in Part I. It is inevitable that an electronics engineer will sometime in his career find himself talking about chemicals, and eventually even a theoretical physicist will discuss electronics. Notice that each section is followed by a short summary which can help you review the most important concepts covered in that section (or give you an idea of what is included in a section you may have skipped).

Just reading the chapters in Part I is not enough, however. You must also do some practicing. Look over some of the memos and reports that you have worked on in the past. Compare the way you presented the material with what is suggested here. Retype some of the crucial sections, making corrections and changes in accordance with your newly acquired knowledge. Always keep in mind the two bits of advice that you will meet over and over again in this book: plan a page so that it is neat and pleasing to look at, and use your common sense. Now you will also be able to read over the text of the memo or report to get its meaning (not its detailed, exact, scientific meaning, but the general drift of what it says). This rereading will enable you to catch many small errors that you would not have been able to see before.

Part II of this book is for reference. Become familiar with the seven glossaries and develop the habit of referring to them. Glossary 7, which contains short definitions of scientific and engineering terms, should help you clear up many problems you may have about the meaning, spelling, or pronunciation of unfamiliar words.

Contents

Preface   vii
To the Secretary—How to Use This Book   x

Part I: What the Technical Secretary
Should Know about Science and Engineering

Chapter 1. Chemistry   3
   Introduction   3
   The Chemical Elements   3
   Chemical Combinations   6
   More Grammar of the Chemical Language   16
   Physical (Unchemical) Chemistry   22
   Electrochemistry   26
   Organic Chemistry   31
Chapter 2. Mathematics   36
   Introduction   36
   Numbers   36
   Geometry and Trigonometry   55
   Algebra   65
   Calculus   80
Chapter 3. Physics   88
   Introduction   88
   Mechanics   89
   Hydraulics   96
   Acoustics   99
   Optics   102
   Heat and Thermodynamics   109
   Crystallography and Crystal Physics   112
   Modern Physics   118
Chapter 4. Electricity and Electronics   134
   Introduction   134
   Electrons in Circuits   134
   Ohm's Law   143
   Electrical Waves   145
   Magnetism   150

Components 155
Radio Tubes 162
Transistors and Other Solid-State Devices 168
Transducers 174
Electronic Systems 176

Part II: Techniques for the Technical Secretary
and Glossaries of Technical Terms

Techniques for the Technical Secretary 187
   The Secretary as Draftsman 187
   Some Additional Words about Typewriters 191
   Some Examples 192
Glossaries of Technical Terms 201
   Glossaries 1 and 2. Prefixes and Suffixes 201
   Glossary 3. Technical and Scientific Abbreviations 204
   Glossary 4. The Chemical Elements and Their
      Abbreviations 208
   Glossary 5. Frequently Encountered Names of
      Scientists and Engineers 209
   Glossary 6. The Greek and Some Other
      Foreign Alphabets 211
   Glossary 7. The Secretary's Glossary of
      Scientific and Engineering Terms 216
Index 297

Part I
What the Technical Secretary
Should Know about Science and Engineering

Chapter 1
Chemistry

Introduction

In spite of what you may have heard, it is difficult to tell a chemist from other people. It is even difficult to tell a chemical office from, let us say, an insurance office. This is so because the chemist's fuming test tubes are usually far down the hall, in the "lab" or the "distillation room" or some such place. The office looks like any other. But if you work for a chemist the material you will work with will be very different from what you would see in an insurance office. Every business and profession has its own specialized terminology, its "jargon," with which the secretary must become familiar. Suppose you have just accepted a job working for the engineering department of a chemical company. Your new employer calls you into his office on your first day of work. Your pad and pencil are ready. He dictates: "After the reaction proceeded to completion the resulting precipitate was desiccated, oxidized to a higher valence state, and caused to sublime by placing it in an autoclave...." This is a chemist's special language. It is neither foreign nor difficult, only different from what you have been accustomed to. However, with a few new rules of grammar and a growing new vocabulary you will find the chemical work both fascinating and easy.

This chapter approaches "chemistry for the secretary" in six major sections. Each section contains explanatory text, some examples, and a short summary. You may find the summaries to be all that you need, or you may decide to skip a section entirely because your employer never deals with that branch of chemistry. This is quite all right. Just be sure you make a mental note of the section you left out so that you can refer to it if you ever do need it.

The Chemical Elements

What Is an Element?   Every material in the world, solid, liquid, or gas, is a chemical. How many chemicals or different materials do we know about? Millions. It is the job of the chemist to know about them: how to make them, how to "unmake" them, and how to make them into other materials. He can know all this because these millions of materials are only different combinations of about one hundred basic building blocks, or *elements*. In a similar manner the thousands of words in the English language are made up of only twenty-six letters (or elements).

Some chemical elements are named after men *(columbium, einsteinium, fermium, lawrencium, mendelevium)*, places *(europium, germanium, americium, francium, polonium, californium, berkelium)*, mythical gods *(mercury, uranium, neptunium, promethium, thorium)*, and so on. Some names are descriptive, for example, *tungsten* comes from the Swedish *tung* (heavy) and *sten* (stone); and the name *radium* was chosen by Madame Curie (who discovered it) to indicate that the material gives off a great deal of nuclear radiation. Some elements have two names; for example, tungsten is also known as *wolfram* after the mineral from which it is refined, wolframite. Some have two spellings: *aluminum* in the United States and *aluminium* in the British Empire. More than half end in *-um* or *-ium*.

Some elements are found in greater quantities than others. One reason we build automobiles out of the chemical element iron rather than the chemical element platinum is that there is much more iron in the world than platinum. For the same reason, statues are more usually made of bronze (an alloy of the elements copper and tin) than of another metal which is also yellow, gold. If the elements of the world were made into a pie with a slice for each element proportional to the amount of that element, then the whole arrangement would look like Figure 1. One element, oxygen, makes up about half of the earth and another element, silicon, makes up about another quarter. This should not be surprising if you think about it, since most of the world is rocky and sandy, and rock and sand are just chemical combinations of silicon and oxygen. (There is certainly a great deal of rock and sand in such places as the Himalayan Mountains and the Sahara Desert.) This leaves about a quarter of the earth available for more interesting things, to which we will now turn.

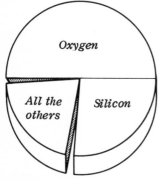

Figure 1. The chemical elements.

Abbreviations for the Chemical Elements. The names of the chemical elements are simply nouns and as such are commonly written as ordinary words, *without* capitalization. However, when it is desired to represent them in short form, they are symbolized in a rigidly prescribed manner by abbreviations consisting of either one or two letters. At all times the first letter is capitalized and if there is a second letter it is *never* capitalized. Thus,

aluminum is written   Al
calcium is written   Ca
oxygen is written   O
hydrogen is written   H

Do not be fooled into always using the first letter of an element's name to represent it, however. For example, silver is neither Si nor S but rather Ag (Si is silicon and S is sulfur). Furthermore, tungsten is written W, and antimony is written Sb. A list of all the elements with their symbols is given in Glossary 4, in Part II, p. 208.

The Atom. An atom is simply the smallest unit of an element that can exist and still have enough personality to be recognized as the element it is. One might call an atom the "elemental" part of the element. Just as there are about a hundred different kinds of elements, so there are necessarily only about a hundred different kinds of atoms, one kind for each element.

We often talk of "an atom of carbon," or use a sentence like, "One atom of carbon combines with two atoms of oxygen to form carbon dioxide." *Atom* comes from a Greek word meaning "indivisible." Thus, if you had a piece of iron and you cut it in half, threw one half away, cut the remaining piece in half, and repeated and repeated this process thousands of times, soon the remaining piece of iron could be seen only with a powerful microscope. After that it would be too small to be seen even in that way. Ultimately, assuming your cutting apparatus could reach the end (not of its ability to cut, but of the capacity of the iron to be further subdivided), the smallest particle of iron remaining, one which could not possibly be subdivided, would be the iron atom.

Summary

1. All the materials of the world, whether solids, liquids, or gases, are made up either of pure chemical elements or of combinations of chemical elements.
2. There are only about a hundred different chemical elements: iron, chlorine, copper, zinc, nitrogen, helium, carbon, hydrogen, uranium, and about ninety-one more.

3. The atom is the smallest amount of a recognizable element that can exist. It is extremely small. If you have a diamond ring that weighs one carat; it has approximately a thousand million billion atoms of carbon in it.

4. Each of the elements has its own prescribed abbreviation consisting of one or two letters. The first letter of the abbreviation is always capitalized, but if there is a second letter it is never capitalized. Refer to the list in Glossary 4 (p. 208) to find the correct abbreviation for each element.

Chemical Combinations

Compounds and Molecules. If you associate with chemists you will one day hear the expression, "cookbook chemist." It will be applied to someone—a chemist—in a disparaging way. We should pay a little attention to this term, however, because it is pertinent to the subject of this section. The fact is that cooking is chemistry. In cooking, chemical materials (the recipe ingredients) are mixed together; chemical processes occur; and these processes are speeded up by the application of heat. In the end out of the oven appear some different materials, which are call by such unchemical names as cake, stew, and beef stroganoff. What is wrong with being a "cookbook chemist"? Nothing, really, except that most chemists want to write their own cookbooks and recipes and not just follow the directions of another chemist-cook. The chemist who is content to follow the procedures set up by others has his value too, but he is the "cookbook chemist."

Now what happens when the cook, housewife or chemist, cooks? Atoms (or groups of atoms) combine with each other to form new groups of atoms. The finished product is known as a *compound.* Webster says that "a compound is a distinct substance formed by a union of two or more ingredients in definite proportions by weight." That is a straightforward enough definition for either chemist or secretary.

In our everyday lives we do not see uncombined elements very often. This is so because most elements have a tendency to combine with each other. In the natural course of events over the passage of history, most elements have already entered into some kind of combination with other elements. The chemist can sometimes "uncombine" them and recombine them into new materials. By such procedures the chemist has created materials such as nylon, gasoline, plastic, glue, and the fluorescent material that glows in a fluorescent bulb or television tube. Nature is also constantly practicing chemistry, for example, by manufacturing chlorophyll in green plants, corroding steel into rust, tarnishing silverware, and turning bronze statues green.

Occasionally we see some things that are elements not in combination with anything. A diamond is pure, elemental carbon; the mercury in a thermometer is just the element mercury; and the helium in a carnival balloon is pure helium. However, most of the things we see around us are compounds rather than uncombined elements. Table salt is a combination of sodium and chlorine; water is a combination of hydrogen and oxygen; rust is a combination of iron and oxygen; and so on. The processes of combination, which we have considered up to now as forms of "cooking," are more scientifically described as *chemical reactions*. This is a good name because, as they combine, the elements influence each other, cling to each other, and act on each other; in short, they "react."

An atom of sodium will react with an atom of chlorine to form a compound called sodium chloride. An atom of oxygen will react with two atoms of hydrogen to form water. Of course, what really occurs is that trillions of atoms react with other trillions in forming trillions of the new combination. To understand how this happens we need a new word: *molecule.* Just as the smallest particle of an element is an atom, the smallest particle of a compound which still retains all the character of the compound is a molecule. Take that same sharp knife you used on the iron bar, and take something that is a chemical compound, for example a piece of nylon cloth. Pull out one thread, cut it in half, throw one half away, and keep on cutting in half and throwing half away. In the end, the smallest possible piece left which is still nylon—if you could get a piece that small—would be a nylon molecule.

It is important to remember that even when trillions of atoms are reacting, they do so *in proportion,* just as Webster pointed out. That is, to form water there must be twice as many atoms of hydrogen as atoms of oxygen in the reaction. Otherwise the result would not be water. It would be something else. This reaction is illustrated in Figure 2.

26 billion trillion   +   13 billion trillion
atoms of hydrogen (react with) atoms of oxygen

to form   13 billion trillion molecules of water
(H_2O)—or just about one drop !

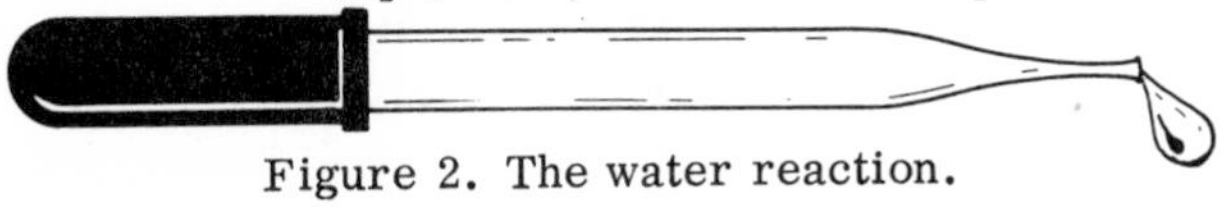

Figure 2. The water reaction.

Symbols and Numbers in Compounds and Reactions. Now that we have discussed three major chemical concepts — the element, the chemical reaction, and the compound, we are ready to get into the actual reproduction of chemical text. Remember, you will have very little trouble if you understand the few principles that provide the reasons for writing in this way. Consider the analogy to the English language. If the element is the "letter," then the compound is the "word," and the reaction is the "sentence."

When words (compounds) and sentences (reactions) are constructed in this chemical language the letters of the English alphabet are supplemented by a system of symbols. Most of the symbols are familiar, and all of them are reasonable. These symbols do two things for the chemist. First, they are a shorthand system whereby he can represent much in a small space; and second, they impart a "feel" for what he is trying to represent. That is, arrows show directions, numbers show how much, parentheses show groupings, lines show connections, and so on.

Chemical symbols are international like those of music. They can be read in any nation regardless of its language. Every year there are many international chemical conferences. The fact that everyone uses the same rules to write compounds and reactions makes these meetings practical and useful in spite of the fact that the different scientists attending frequently do not understand each other's languages. Let us now examine these symbols and the rules for their use.

The Coefficient. You have probably heard water referred to as "H-two-O" or you may have seen it written as H_2O. This is one chemical compound that is often represented in ordinary nontechnical text in accordance with the rules of the chemical language. "H" and "O" we know to be the prescribed abbreviations for the elements hydrogen and oxygen. What is the "$_2$" doing there? The numbers written with compounds are known as *coefficients*. Their purpose is to signify how many atoms of each type are present. They appear after the element to which they apply. If no number is written it means that the number one (1) is implied. Thus H_2O represents the compound water, that is, it is the formula for water, and it consists of two atoms of hydrogen combined with one atom of oxygen.

There is another kind of coefficient. It is written in front of the formula for a molecule. For example $3H_2O$ means three molecules of water. It should be clear that the "$_2$" was written *inside* the formula and the "3" was written *in front* of it. The numbers that appear inside or at the end of a formula refer to the number of atoms of a given element, and the numbers that appear in front of the formula refer to the total number of molecules of the compound. In the example, $3H_2O$, there are three molecules of water. Since each molecule contains two atoms of hydrogen and one atom of oxygen, in $3H_2O$ there are necessarily 3×2, or six, atoms of hydrogen, and 3×1, or three, atoms of oxygen.

Some examples of compounds that you will undoubtedly come across are listed for your examination. Make sure that you understand the use of the numbers (coefficients). Check the explanation given with each one.

NaCl — the compound *sodium chloride* (table salt): one atom of sodium, one atom of chlorine

CO_2 — the compound *carbon dioxide* (dry ice): one atom of carbon, two atoms of oxygen

$KMnO_4$ — the compound *potassium permanganate*: one atom of potassium, one atom of manganese, four atoms of oxygen

$2KMnO_4$ — *two* molecules of the compound *potassium permanganate*, consisting of a total of two atoms of potassium, two atoms of manganese, and eight atoms of oxygen

SiO_2 — the compound *silicon dioxide* (beach sand): one atom of silicon, two atoms of oxygen

CH_4 — the compound *methane*: one atom of carbon, four atoms of hydrogen

C_2H_6 — the compound *ethane*: two atoms of carbon, six atoms of hydrogen

$7CH_4$ — *seven* molecules of the compound *methane*, consisting of a total of seven atoms of carbon and twenty-eight atoms of hydrogen

Coefficients inside a formula (which apply to the individual atoms) are always written as *subscripts* placed half a carriage turn below the line. Thus, H_2O is written as shown and *not* "H2O." Coefficients in front of a formula (which apply to the entire molecule) are always written at the normal level. Thus $3H_2O$ is written as shown and *not* "$_3H_2O$." Notice also that no spaces are employed between coefficients and the molecules to which they refer. Thus, $3H_2O$ is *right*; "3 H_2O" is *wrong*. An example (reproduced from an actual research report) that illustrates some typical compounds as typed by a technical typist is given in the first column of Figure 5 of Part II (p. 190).

The Radical. Parentheses are used in chemistry (and in mathematics) as a technique for saying "this group of numbers or symbols or letters go together." In ordinary English, in fact in the preceding sentence, a group of words within parentheses also has the connotation of an "insert," with the implication that the sentence would be almost as meaningful if the insert were not there. However, in chemistry (and in mathematics) if the group within the parentheses were taken out, the meaning would be drastically changed. Such a deletion could even make a chemical statement meaningless to a chemist.

A group of chemical elements surrounded by parentheses is called a radical. So, in addition to its other meanings, in chemistry, a radical is a group of atoms that "go together" as a group and *behave as though they were one atom.* Such a group is represented within parentheses, and all the rules for the use of coefficients apply to it exactly as if the group were a single atom.

The following examples illustrate this:

In the compounds $Mg(OH)_2$ and $MgCl_2$ the radical (OH) is treated exactly like the atom Cl; it happens that in combination with Mg two atoms of Cl are needed to make a complete compound, and in the same way two of the radical (OH) are needed. So we use the coefficient "$_2$" after each of them to indicate this.

Another molecule which has a radical in it is $Al_2(SO_4)_3$. The group of elements (SO_4) is known as the "sulfate" radical. Radicals are given particular names because they have certain characteristics. Notice that in the above compound, this radical happens to have a coefficient inside the parentheses, "$_4$," and another one outside, "$_3$." This violates none of the rules we have given. All it means is that the sulfate radical contains one sulfur atom and four oxygen atoms, and in the particular case of aluminum sulfate, given here, the sulfate radical is taken three times.

There is one inconsistency in the use of parentheses to indicate radicals. When a radical is taken only once, it is a matter of choice whether or not the parentheses are written. Thus for the molecule magnesium sulfate both $Mg(SO_4)$ and $MgSO_4$ are correct. A radical does not have to appear at the end of the formula for a molecule. The ammonium radical (NH_4) appears at the beginning of the expression $(NH_4)_2CO_3$, while the cyanide radical (CN) appears at the end of the expression $K_4Fe(CN)_6$. The use of parentheses to designate a radical is a signal to the chemist who will read the technical material which you reproduce. It is important to use parentheses correctly. When the chemist sees the parentheses he says to himself, "Aha, a radical!"

The (OH) radical is probably the one you will see most often and it is known as the *hydroxyl* radical. Every compound which contains a hydroxyl is called a *hydroxide*. The chemist knows that in certain ways all hydroxides behave similarly to each other. So by simply writing (OH) in a molecule you have told the chemist a fairly involved fact with significant implications to him. But the hydroxyl radical is only a hydroxyl if it is written (OH), or if only one is taken, OH; HO and (HO) are *not* the hydroxyl any more. Also, never leave the parentheses off when they should be on. See what happens to $Mg(OH)_2$ when the parentheses are removed—it becomes $MgOH_2$, and an oxygen atom is lost in the process. At the same time we have invented a new compound. But it is a "paper combination," because $MgOH_2$ happens to be a compound that no chemist has ever been able to make, nor does it occur in nature. Suppose you put the oxygen back in, but without the parentheses. Then you would have MgO_2H_2 instead of $Mg(OH)_2$, and there would be the same number of Mg's, O's, and H's in each formula. But MgO_2H_2 is still wrong because it does not send the chemist the right signal. He only recognizes that the molecule in question is a hydroxide when he sees the (OH) radical. Then he knows that the material being discussed has all the properties of hydroxides (also known as *alkalis* or *bases*); that is, it will not attack most metals, it will react readily with acids (certain compounds which will be described later), and in a water solution it will tend to be soapy and slippery. By the way, $Mg(OH)_2$ is the chemical formula for "milk of magnesia."

To sum up, it is important that when a chemist wants parentheses to be placed in a certain manner, he gets just what he asks for. Otherwise, his meaning could be completely changed. *Arrows and Equal Signs.* In describing how a compound is formed we have defined the chemical reaction. In effect, most of the time, a chemical reaction says, "this combines with that to form something else." The chemist has to say this so many times, just substituting different atoms and molecules for "this," "that," and "something else," that he has devised a way to do it with a minimum of words. This is the *chemical equation*.

An equation states that something is equal to, or at least is equivalent to, something else. Every time you use the word "is" you are saying something in the form of an equation. The perfect equation (using words and not symbols) is Gertrude Stein's immortal statement to the effect that

"A rose is a rose . . ."

How true. This sentiment can also be expressed in the convention for equations as:

rose = rose

Or if we invent the symbol Ro for rose:

Ro = Ro

Another statement for equality is the one that describes the ingredients for making a cake:

eggs + milk + sugar + flour = cake

The use of the equal sign seems warranted because the cake in the end has in it only what you put into it, no more and no less. If you put in three eggs, it still has three eggs, not four and not two. But they are not eggs in their original form any more; they have become something else.

If we try to represent the act of "becoming," the equal sign is inadequate. The chemist likes to use an arrow. He would write the recipe for a cake as

eggs + milk + sugar + flour → cake

or perhaps it would look more like

3Eg + M + Su + Fl → C

If the chemist were a magician he could reverse the process and recreate the original ingredients as shown in the next equation.

cake → eggs + milk + sugar + flour

In other words, "unbecoming" is a kind of becoming too, although the chemist prefers the more descriptive word *dissociation.*

The chemist may prefer to reverse the order of the statement and reverse the direction of the arrow

eggs + milk + sugar + flour ← cake

It will still say the same thing. This is perfectly all right and is a matter of choice with him. Make sure you do it just as he wants it.

Let us now dispose of the cake and treat chemical reactions by the rules we just discussed. In the reaction

$$Na + Cl → NaCl \qquad (1)$$

we are saying that one atom of sodium added to one atom of chlorine becomes, or "gives," one molecule of sodium chloride. Using other chemicals for the same sort of reaction

$$2H + O \rightarrow H_2O \tag{2}$$

we have just formed water from its ingredients. You can say the same things with a different arrangement by reversing the direction of the arrow and the order of the statement. Thus,

$$NaCl \leftarrow Na + Cl \tag{3}$$

(sodium chloride *is given* by sodium and chlorine); or

$$H_2O \leftarrow 2H + O \tag{4}$$

(water *is given* by hydrogen and oxygen).

Reactions (3) and (4) are the same as reaction (1) and (2). They say the same things. Just as in ordinary English, (1) and (2) are in the "active voice" and (3) and (4) are in "passive voice." But even though the meanings are the same, *do not improvise.* If the material is presented as (1) and (2) do not give it back as (3) and (4).

The directions of the arrows are very important:

$$H_2O \rightarrow 2H + O \tag{5}$$

says something very different from reactions (2) and (4). This is so because the act of "becoming," or "giving," or "resulting in," always happens in chemistry in the direction in which the arrow points, and not in the other direction. Equation (5) tells of something breaking up, dissociating. Equations (2) and (4) tell of things doing the opposite, things getting together, combining in order to form something new. Be careful where you point your arrows!

Unfortunately life is not always as simple as pictured in Equations (1) through (5). It is rarely all black or all white. This is another way of saying that not all chemical reactions go just from left to right. Sometimes the same reaction is equally happy to go from right to left at the same time. This is known in chemistry as the state of chemical equilibrium. When a reaction is equally likely to happen in either direction the chemist has an easy way out. He simply uses two arrows, one pointing each way. If the water reaction were this kind of reaction it would be written

$$H_2O \rightleftarrows 2H + O \tag{6}$$

which says that it may go either way equally readily. It is then a matter of choice for the scientist or engineer whether he writes the reaction with arrows or with an equal sign, as in Equation (7):

$$H_2O = 2H + O \qquad (7)$$

Even though (6) and (7) say the same thing, the choice of which to use must be made by the chemist and not by his secretary.

There is one other important feature of equations which can be expressed by the manner of writing the arrows. This is another circumstance that can be described as neither black nor white. I refer here to reactions that can happen either way but are more likely one way than the other. Take the case of the water reaction. Equation (8) shows hydrogen and oxygen combining to form water; at the same time the water is dissociating to form hydrogen and oxygen — but the tendency to form water is stronger than the dissociating tendency. The chemist shows such reactions (which have a preference) by using a long arrow and a short arrow together; the longer arrow indicates the direction of the preference. In the same way Equation (9) delivers the opposite message from Equation (8):

$$2H + O \rightleftharpoons H_2O \qquad (8)$$

$$2H + O \rightleftharpoons H_2O \qquad (9)$$

Sometimes the chemist chooses to keep all the arrows the same length but to draw the preferred direction of the equation with a heavier line:

$$2H + O \rightleftharpoons H_2O \qquad (10)$$

$$2H + O \rightleftharpoons H_2O \qquad (11)$$

Equation (10) says the same thing as Equation (8), and Equation (11) says the same thing as Equation (9).

Always draw arrows with a ruler and a black ball-point pen. Always put the arrow going from left to right on top. Make the arrows neat and symmetrical, like this →. In the chapter on mathematics (p. 36) there is more detail on this subject.

This is also a good place to mention that symbolizing techniques like the arrows just discussed are used in different ways by different scientists and engineers. For example some people dislike arrows altogether and will use only the equal sign. Fashions change and some older men will use symbols different from the ones younger men use. But scientists are flexible; they always seem to recognize what is meant whatever equation symbol is used. It will be your job to accustom yourself to the method preferred by your employer, and to do it that way.

Balancing Equations. As far as a chemical reaction is concerned it is always written according to the law that you only get out of something what you put into it. You cannot make a pound of cake with a half pound of ingredients. In the same way, the chemical reaction—even if it does not go all the way—must be balanced in the sense that the *same* number of *every* type of atom must appear on each side of the equal sign or arrow. So reaction (12) is wrong because it says that as $KClO_3$ dissociates into KCl, $KClO_4$, and O_2, one extra K, one extra Cl, and three extra O's are created:

$$KClO_3 \rightarrow KCl + KClO_4 + O_2 \qquad (12)$$

$$\left.\begin{array}{l} 1K \\ 1Cl \\ 3O \end{array}\right\} \rightarrow \left\{\begin{array}{l} 2K \\ 2Cl \\ 6O \end{array}\right.$$

If we were to start out with two $KClO_3$'s instead of with one, everything would be all right, as shown in Equation (13):

$$2KClO_3 \rightarrow KCl + KClO_4 + O_2 \qquad (13)$$

$$\left.\begin{array}{l} 2K \\ 2Cl \\ 6O \end{array}\right\} \rightarrow \left\{\begin{array}{l} 2K \\ 2Cl \\ 6O \end{array}\right.$$

Since the same number of atoms appears on the left side of the reaction as on the right side, it is said to be *balanced*. As this was not the case for Equation (12), it is said to be *unbalanced*. Unless the chemist unbalances an equation on purpose in order to explain a principle, as we did here, *chemical reactions must always be written balanced!* Another example is given in Equations (14) and (15). The unbalanced equation

$$MnO_2 + HCl \rightarrow H_2O + MnCl_4 \qquad (14)$$

when balanced is

$$MnO_2 + 4HCl \rightarrow 2H_2O + MnCl_4 \qquad (15)$$

It is not suggested that as a technical secretary you attempt to learn how to balance equations in the sense of converting (12) to (13) or (14) to (15), because it sometimes becomes quite tricky. Rather, you should form the habit, as part of proofreading or checking, of making sure that the number of atoms of each type is the same on both sides of an equation. Remember: if it does not balance, it is *not* an equation! Your employer will be grateful to you for pointing out any error of unbalance. It may even save him some future embarrassment.

Summary

1. Under certain favorable conditions atoms combine with each other to form combinations of atoms that are known as *chemical compounds*. The smallest particle of a compound that can exist is called a *molecule*, and the process of chemical combination is known as a *chemical reaction*.

2. The ingredients of a compound are always present in a given proportion. The same ingredients taken in different proportions form different compounds.

3. The numbers used in writing the formulas for compounds and reactions are known as *coefficients*. There are two kinds of coefficients. Those which indicate how many atoms of any given kind there are are written as *subscripts* after the symbols for the pertinent atoms, for example H_2O; those which indicate a total number of molecules are written in front of the formulas for the given molecules, for example $2H_2O$.

4. A group of atoms that behave as if they were one atom is called a *radical*, and is shown enclosed in parentheses. The same rules for the use of coefficients apply to radicals as to individual atoms, for example $Al_2(SO_4)_3$.

5. A chemical equation is the shorthand method employed by a chemist to write a *chemical equation*. It expresses a change, and lists all the molecules that go into the change and all that result from the change. It looks like

$$A + B \rightarrow C + D$$

where the letters stand for the formulas of molecules, and the arrow indicates the direction of the reaction. In this case, A and B react to form C and D.

6. A reaction may go either way ($\rightarrow$ or $\leftarrow$); or equally easily in either direction ($\rightleftharpoons$ or $=$); or somewhat more easily one way than the other ($\rightleftharpoons$ or $\rightleftharpoons$), which may also be expressed by a combination of heavy and light arrows ($\rightleftharpoons$ or $\rightleftharpoons$)

7. There must be exactly the same number of a given type of atom on both sides of every equation. That is, every equation must be *balanced*. As part of proofreading, check all equations to make sure that the number of atoms of a given type is the same on both sides.

More Grammar of the Chemical Language

Introduction. The language of chemistry, like all languages, has its own words. To talk and read and write in this language you must learn these words. Fortunately your task will not be as difficult as learning French or German, where you should know at least 5,000 words in order to function effectively. In the chemical language you will get along fairly well if you are familiar with the names of the chemical elements (only about a hundred, remember, and in any job you will find only about twenty-five of these commonly used) and the names of the more common prefixes and suffixes. In addition there are a few (perhaps a dozen) important names of groups or kinds of chemicals and an equal number of names of chemical concepts or ideas which you should know. This will be your basic vocabulary. Everything else is "extra" and can be looked up (in a technical dictionary or in the glossaries in part II) when you have any questions.

The most important thing to remember about chemical words is that most of them are made simply by adding a syllable either to the front or to the end of a word. Word beginnings and endings thus mean a great deal to the chemist. In the great majority of cases, the word which will receive the prefix or suffix is one of the chemical elements. Consider the word "chlorine," which is commonly encountered. You will find yourself listening to, writing, typing, and proofreading such variations on the word as:

chloride	trichloride
chlorate	perchlorate
chlorite	chloric
chlorous	

As soon as you have accustomed yourself to "-ide," "-ate," "-ite," "-ic," "-ous," "tri-," "per-," and a few others, you will be grateful to know that most of the unfamiliar chemical words will then seem familiar to you.

As an example take another chemical element, iodine:

iodide	tri-iodide
iodate	periodate
iodite	iodic
iodous	

And so it goes through most of the chemical material you will meet. Most chemical words are just the elements with prefixes and suffixes added. You will see a never-ending array of "permanganates" and "oxides" and "aluminates" and "sulfites" and "antimonides" and "bismuthates" and "tetrafluorides" and so on. Remember: never mistake an "ite" for an "-ate," or an "-ic" for an "-ous!" To a chemist such a mistake might be as serious as confusing Sgt. with Gen., or R.N. with M.D., or Miss with Mrs. As an example with which you may be familiar consider carbon *mon*oxide and carbon *di*oxide. Carbon monoxide is a poisonous gas, but carbon dioxide is something we breathe in all the time without harm. Let us now examine the more common word beginnings and endings, showing some of the logic behind their use.

The Suffix -Ide and the Simple Numerical Prefixes. Some chemical prefixes and suffixes are applied to compounds in order to make them "conversational." For example, it is easy to convey a feeling for the compound $SeCl_4$ by writing it out and by reading it—but how do you *say* it? And how do you *hear* it? Even in chemistry we do not communicate entirely with formulas and symbols. Should we say, "a compound of one atom of selenium with four atoms of chlorine"? By the correct use of word endings and beginnings it is possible to express and describe the molecule in question in a much shorter way.

The compound $SeCl_4$ can be "said," or verbalized, as "selenium tetrachloride." We have made use of the prefix *tetra-* and the suffix *-ide* to describe the element chlorine; "tetra-" is a prefix meaning four and "-ide" is a suffix meaning something just a little more complicated.

Let us talk about "ide" first. The suffix "-ide" applied to the end of the name of an element indicates that that element is in chemical combination with the element that precedes it. The suffix indicates that we have a compound of two elements, and is applied to the second of the two. Thus:

InSb is indium antimon*ide*
ZnS is zinc sulf*ide*
NaF is sodium fluor*ide*
KI is potassium iod*ide*
LiBr is lithium brom*ide*

The prefix "tetra-" is one of a class of numerical descriptive word beginnings. The most commonly encountered members of this class are:

mon-	one	tetra-	four
di-	two	pent-	five
tri-	three	hexa-	six

Therefore CO_2, which has two oxygen atoms is a *dioxide*, carbon dioxide to be exact. In the same way MnO_2 is manganese *dioxide*; AlF_3 is aluminum *trifluoride*; and $PtBr_4$ is platinum *tetra*bromide.

The "More" and "Less" Pairs. The simple numerical prefixes in the preceding section gave exact numbers: one, two, three, etc. Some other word attachments simply tell "more" or "less," or may make up a list like:

> more
> more yet
> still more
> even more than that
> a lot more yet
> a lot more, indeed
> a great deal but still not most

Such a list is known as a series. The simple numerical series, mon-, di-, tri-, etc., tells exact quantities and is called *quantitative;* the list indicating "more," "still more," etc., is not so exact and is known as *semiquantitative.* When we consider atoms in chemical compounds as being "more" or "less" we generally refer to oxygen. Almost everything combines more or less with oxygen and the quantitative and semiquantitative prefixes and suffixes tell how much more or less. In radicals the amount of oxygen can be described as

> -ite is less
> -ate is more

Thus

> (SO_3) is sulf*ite*
> (SO_4) is sulf*ate*

In the sulfite there is less oxygen than in the sulfate. Another example is that of the radicals of nitrogen and oxygen, where

> (NO_2) is nitr*ite*
> (NO_3) is nitr*ate*

When these radicals are used in compounds we should experience no difficulty:

> $K_2(SO_3)$,   potassium sulf*ite*
> $K_2(SO_4)$,   potassium sulf*ate*
> $Na(NO_2)$,   sodium nitr*ite*
> $Na(NO_3)$,   sodium nitr*ate*

However, the rule gets a little special when the compound is an *acid.* In general, you may think of acids as those compounds that begin with H (hydrogen). (There is more to it than that, but it is not necessary for you to be concerned with anything more than this simplified rule.) Since the compounds HNO_3 and H_2SO_4 both begin with H, they are acids. The special part of the rule is that in acids

-ite becomes -ous
-ate becomes -ic

Then, just like -ate and -ite

-ous is less
-ic is more

Thus the suffixes that tell the same things are different for acids than for other compounds. This is best shown for the sulfur and nitrogen compounds given above. Turning them into acids, they become:

H_2SO_3, sulfurous acid
H_2SO_4, sulfuric acid
HNO_2, nitrous acid
HNO_3, nitric acid

Other Prefixes and Suffixes That Tell How Much. There are many more suffix and prefix combinations than have been mentioned. Here are a few of the more important ones. You do not have to know all of these but you should at least have a feeling for why they are used. Most of the time they are used to show differences between compounds that are made up of the same elements but in different proportions. Such a series of compounds is known as a *chemical family*. Just like in a human family, the "ingredients" of the members may be the same, but some are fat and some are thin. The prefixes and suffixes merely indicate the amount of "fatness" or "thinness." Consider the families of the acids of sulfur and of the potassium compounds of sulfur, where the relation of the number of atoms of hydrogen or potassium to oxygen is different in every case. Prefixes and suffixes are used as follows:

*hypo*sulfur*ous* acid, $H_2S_2O_4$ potassium *hypo*sulf*ite*, $K_2S_2O_4$
sulfur*ous* acid, H_2SO_3 potassium sulf*ite*, K_2SO_3
sulfur*ic* acid, H_2SO_4 potassium sulf*ate*, K_2SO_4
*thio*sulfur*ic* acid, $H_2S_2O_3$ potassium *thio*sulfate, $K_2S_2O_3$
*per*sulfur*ic* acid, $H_2S_2O_8$ potassium *per*sulf*ate*, $K_2S_2O_8$

The "hypo-," "thio-," "per-" group tells something about the numbers of certain atoms in the compounds. (It is not always clear just what, but only that there are different amounts.) Another series is

meta-,	some
pyro-,	more
ortho-,	most

where in the phosphoric acids

*meta*phosphoric acid,	HPO_3
*pyro*phosphoric acid,	$H_4P_2O_7$
*ortho*phosphoric acid,	H_3PO_3

the "meta" acid has as many atoms of H as of P; the "pyro" acid has more atoms of H than of P; the "ortho" acid has still more atoms of H for every atom of P.

There is also a two-prefix series you will meet fairly often:

hypo-,	less
hyper-,	more

You know these prefixes in ordinary English. A person who is *hypo*thyroid has less thyroid than he needs; and one who is *hyper*-sensitive is more sensitive than most people. The meanings are the same when these prefixes are used with chemical words. Thus, $Na_2S_2O_4$ is the compound sodium *hypo*sulfite—it has less sulfur than usual; and H_2O_2 is hydrogen *hyper*oxide—it has more oxygen than water, H_2O (it is also known as hydrogen peroxide).

Summary

1. Most chemical words are constructed out of a basic word, and attachments that are added before the word (*prefixes*) or after the word (*suffixes*).
2. The most common use of prefixes and suffixes is to show the differences between chemical compounds that are all made up of the same elements.
3. *Quantitative* prefixes show exact amounts and *semiquantitative* prefixes show relative amounts.
4. You must be careful in reproducing prefixes and suffixes. Changing only one letter can make a serious difference in the meaning of the text. When in doubt, consult the glossary of prefixes (p. 202) and of suffixes (p. 203) in Part II.

Physical (Unchemical) Chemistry

Physical Changes and Chemical Changes. Things are always changing in science. They can change in only two ways — chemically or physically (or both together). Up to now we have discussed only the chemical way. All other changes in materials must be physical. What do we mean by this ?

Consider an iron nail. Suppose you leave it out on your window sill. After a week in the sun and rain you will find that the nail is covered with a red, flaky coating — rust. The iron of the nail has combined with the oxygen of the air to form iron oxide (rust). This is a chemical change, and Equation(16) is the chemical reaction that describes it:

$$4Fe + 3O_2 \rightarrow 2Fe_2O_3 \qquad (16)$$

But suppose you tried to hammer the nail into a piece of wood and you bent the nail. The nail is changed from what it was before; but the change is not chemical, it is *physical*. It is not chemical because the nail still remains iron. The iron has not combined chemically with anything. The nail has merely changed in shape. A change in shape is a physical change.

So is a change in size. Suppose you cut the nail into three pieces. Nothing changes chemically, only physically. There are now three pieces of iron, not just one.

A change in polish is a physical change too. Suppose you polished the nail with fine sandpaper and made it shinier. You would then have changed the nail physically, not chemically, since you would still have the same chemical, iron; it would only be shinier than before.

A change of temperature is also a physical change. Suppose you put the nail into the oven and heated it up. You would only have changed it physically, not chemically. You would have made hot iron.

Changes of State. There are a few physical changes that are a little more difficult to separate from the chemical but not too difficult if you apply the test for a chemical change: "Was there any chemical combination of elements or compounds to form new compounds ?" If the change did not involve such combination (or dissociation) it was not chemical. Let us look at these other physical changes, which are known as changes of *state*.

There are three physical states, or conditions, of matter: solid, liquid, and gas. Everything on the earth is either solid, liquid, or gas, under ordinary conditions.* Consider the nail in the oven again. If the oven were an industrial furnace, you could heat the iron to such a high temperature that it would melt. Would it still be iron? Yes. It is liquid iron. It has undergone a physical change of state. It has *melted* (or *fused*), which means that it has gone from solid to liquid. If we let the furnace cool down, there will be another physical change of state: the iron will change from liquid to solid. The word for this physical change is *freezing* (or *solidification*). We can even heat the iron so hot that the liquid will change to a gas and drift away—but it has not changed chemically. It is still iron. When a liquid changes into a gas, that physical change is called by another name that is familiar to you. That change is known as *boiling* (or *vaporization*).

Another change in the state of matter is *condensation*. This is where a gas turns into either a liquid or a solid. You see condensation when your eyeglasses "steam up" as you go from the cold dry air outside into a hot damp room. Still another physical change of state is *sublimation*. This word may mean something quite different to the psychologist, but to the chemist it means changing directly from solid to gas, without ever becoming liquid. Not all materials sublime easily, but one with which you may be familiar is solid carbon dioxide, CO_2, which you also know as "dry ice." The "smoke" you see coming off it shows the solid CO_2 becoming *gaseous* CO_2. This is still a physical, not a chemical change.

We see water change physically more than any other material. We see it freeze into ice cubes in the refrigerator; we see it boil off into steam as we heat it. But through these changes it does not change chemically—it remains water, H_2O. The changes from one physical state to another are illustrated in Figure 3.

The Physical Change of Dissolving. One of the most important things we can do with water (and many other materials too) is called *dissolving*. When you put sugar into water the sugar seems to disappear. Actually it is still there; there has been no chemical reaction, there has been a physical change, *solution*. The sugar has *dissolved* into the water. When something dissolves into something else, as sugar does into water, the substance dissolving (the sugar, in this case) is called the *solute*; the substance into which the dissolving is taking place (here, the water)

---

*Some scientists consider that there is a fourth state of matter, *plasma*, but it exists only at very high temperatures, such as those in the interior of a star.

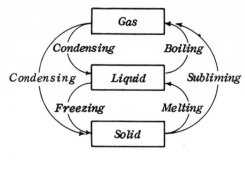

One material can be in any one of three physical states, and can move back and forth between states any number of times by: melting, boiling, subliming, freezing, or condensing.

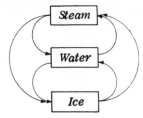

Figure 3. Changes of state.

To make a cup of tea, take one tea bag, one teaspoon of sugar, and one cup of boiling water.

Add the tea bag and the sugar to the water. It turns "tea color," and the sugar disappears. This is physical chemistry.

You have made a solution. The sugar and the tea are solutes. The water is the solvent.

Since much more sugar can be dissolved into this cup of tea, the solution is dilute. If about seven more teaspoons of sugar were added, the solution would be concentrated.

Figure 4. Solutions: a cup of tea.

is the solvent, and the whole mixture is called a *solution*. Water dissolves so many things that it is called "the universal solvent."

The opposite of dissolving is *precipitating*. Coming back to sugar and water, it is possible to boil away the water, leaving the sugar behind. When much of the water is gone, the sugar begins to appear as a solid again. As the solid crystals appear we say the sugar is precipitating out of solution. The sugar that has precipitated is known as a *precipitate*. Precipitating is therefore "undissolving."

Solutions can hold only so much dissolved material. Beyond this amount the solute "precipitates out" of the solvent. When we boiled away the water there was soon so little water that it could not hold all the sugar; we had exceeded the amount of solute it could hold; we had exceeded the solubility limit of the water for sugar. (This is also called the *saturation point*.) When a solvent has very little of the solute in it and can hold much more, we say it is *dilute*. When we add more solvent to the solution (more water to the sugar and water, for example) we are diluting the solution. On the other hand, as we add more solute (the sugar) we are *concentrating* the solution. Getting rid of some of the solvent (as in boiling it away) is also concentrating. Some of the physical things that happen in solutions are shown in Figure 4.

Representing Physical Changes in Chemical Equations.   When a chemist wishes to show that a chemical reaction has resulted in the formation of a solid, a liquid, or a gas, he usually does so with different combinations of arrows, symbols, underlines, and overlines:

solid,   ↓ or (s) or _____

liquid,   (l),

gas,   ↑ or (g) or ‾‾‾‾‾‾

Thus in each of the following equations

$$AgNO_3 + HCl \rightarrow AgCl\!\downarrow + HNO_3 \qquad (17)$$

or $$\qquad AgNO_3 + HCl \rightarrow AgCl(s) + HNO_3 \qquad (18)$$

or $$\qquad AgNO_3 + HCl \rightarrow \underline{AgCl} + HNO_3 \qquad (19)$$

we state the same fact: that in the reaction between silver nitrate and hydrochloric acid in a water solution (water is always understood to be present) a mass of solid matter—silver chloride, AgCl, will appear. Such a solid material is said to have *precipitated out of solution*. It is a precipitate and we know that it is because we have used the symbols for a precipitate, the arrow, ↓ , the (s), and the underline, _____. (Your boss may even prefer some other way of showing these conditions that he may consider to be more descriptive—although these are the most commonly used—but they will all tell the same story.)

Another reaction involving a physical as well as a chemical event is shown in Equations (20), (21), and (22):

$$H_2SO_4 \rightarrow H_2O + SO_2 \uparrow \qquad (20)$$

or $$H_2SO_4 \rightarrow H_2O + SO_2(g) \qquad (21)$$

or $$H_2SO_4 \rightarrow H_2O + \overline{SO_2} \qquad (22)$$

where sulfuric acid is shown to dissociate into water and sulfur dioxide gas. The gas actually bubbles out of the solution in the way that carbon dioxide bubbles out of ginger ale. We show this with the arrow, ↑ , the (g), and the overline, $\overline{}$.

Summary

1. You must know the difference between a *chemical change* and a *physical change*. In a chemical change elements rearrange themselves into new chemical arrangements (compounds). In a physical change substances take on different forms, but they remain unchanged chemically. In a physical change something may become: differently shaped, cut up into different sizes, smoother, rougher, hotter, or colder, but it remains the same material.
2. A *change of state* is a special kind of physical change. The three normal states of matter are *solid, liquid,* and *gas.* The actions that take place in going from one state to another are: freezing, melting, boiling, condensing, and subliming.
3. *Dissolving* is a special kind of physical change. The substance that dissolves is the *solute*; the substance into which the solute dissolves is the *solvent*; and the mixture of solute and solvent is the *solution.* The amount of solute in the solvent determines whether the solution is *dilute* (less solute) or *concentrated* (more solute). If the solute "undissolves," or comes out of the solution as a solid material, the solid is called a *precipitate.*
4. In a chemical equation, the physical state of a chemical is shown as follows:

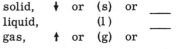

```
solid,    ↓  or  (s)  or  ___
liquid,           (l)       ___
gas,      ↑  or  (g)  or  ‾‾‾
```

Electrochemistry

Sciences overlap and go into each other's territory. Thus some engineers specialize in a field that is a combination of several fields. Usually this makes little difference to the secretary. She must just produce material which adds the terminology of one kind of science to another. Sometimes, however, the combination makes it necessary to bring in a totally new way of writing what is happening in order for the scientist to express what he means clearly. Electrochemistry is one of these combined fields. If your boss is an electrochemist, he is a chemist and an electrical engineer both at the same time. This means that he studies the electrical properties of chemicals and chemical reactions. Does it seem hard to believe that chemical reactions can be electrical? Think of the battery in your car or in your portable radio. The battery is a container which holds a few chemicals together. These chemicals slowly and continuously react together, and as a result of the reaction electricity is created. Finally, when the reaction is over the battery is "dead."

Static Electricity. Let us start with *static electricity.* You find static electricity in your comb after you have combed your hair; your comb will then pick up little particles — paper, dust, or dandruff. It is static electricity that makes your nylon clothing cling to itself, and it is static electricity that shocks you when you touch a doorknob after a long walk down a carpeted hotel corridor.

Opposites Attract.   All electricity is either positive or negative, and as far as we know there is the same amount of positive as negative electricity in the world. Just as with males and females, there is an attraction. Any positive charge is always seeking to meet up with and get attached to any negative charge, and vice versa. When they finally do meet and join up, the chemist says, "the charges are satisfied."

In the case of your clothing that becomes statically charged, the movements of your body cause different layers of cloth to rub against each other and to "rub off" some negative charges of electricity from one layer to another. This means that one layer gets more negative than it was before, and that the layer that lost its negative charges is left with a quantity of unsatisfied positives. Thus one piece of clothing is *negatively charged* and the other is *positively charged.* Since they crave to be "satisfied" by each other, they stick together.

All About Ions.   Many chemical compounds are formed because the elements that react to form them combine (or move or cling together) as a result of static electricity, in just the same way that layers of clothing stick together.

Some atoms have a positive charge and some have a negative charge. Thus sodium chloride, NaCl, is made up of a positively charged atom of sodium and a negatively charged atom of chlorine. It happens that when chlorine is charged electrically it always charges negatively, and in the same way, sodium always charges positively. Bromine also charges negatively and potassium also charges positively. Since opposites attract, compounds like

NaCl   NaBr
KCl   KBr

are common and natural. But compounds like

NaK   ClBr

are neither common nor natural. This is so because in the first group a positively charged atom is joined or bonded to a negatively charged one. But to form the compounds in the second group, two positively charged atoms would have to bond to each other, and they cannot. Neither can two negatively charged atoms join to each other.

An atom that is charged electrically is known as an *ion*, and compounds made up of ions are known as *ionic compounds*. The compounds are then held together by the love of positive for negative electricity. They are said to be held together by the *ionic bond*. If we wanted to show the bond for NaCl pictorially we might draw it as in Figure 5*a*.

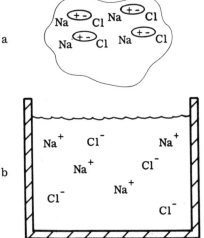

a

b

Sodium chloride is made up of charged atoms of sodium (Na$^+$) and chlorine (Cl$^-$). Since they are charged, they are ions, and they are held together by the ionic bond: that is, the attraction of positive for negative electricity.

"Free," unbonded ions of sodium and chlorine in water. The water has broken the ionic bonds, and the ions wander freely in the water solution.

Figure 5. A grain of salt: (*a*) held together by the ionic bond and (*b*) dissolved in water.

Not every compound is an ionic compound. There are three or four other kinds but you do not have to worry about them at this time.

Ions in Water Solution. Most ionic compounds dissolve easily in water. The dissolving occurs because the electrical forces holding the solid material together are weakened by the water to the extent that they are no longer strong enough to hold the atoms together. Since the electrical forces have been weakened this much, the separate atoms or radicals of the compound (radicals can be ionized too, just like individual atoms) freely mix themselves with the molecules of the water. In effect, the ionized atoms seem to "disappear" into the water, which is another way of saying that they have *dissolved*. Since water can easily break ionic bonds we say that water easily dissolves ionic compounds. Sprinkle some salt into a glass of water. The salt disappears; it has dissolved ionically as shown in Figure 5*b*.

But even though the ionic bond has been separated, the ion has not changed. It is still an ion. It is simply in water solution. The next section gives a simple and logical way of indicating that a material is an ion dissolved in water.

Writing Ionic Compounds and Equations. The signs "$+$" and "$-$" are used to indicate ions. These signs are written after the atom or radical to which they apply, in order to show that the separate parts of the compound are ionized in a water solution. The signs are always written as superscripts.

Thus sodium chloride in water solution may be written

$$Na^+ Cl^-$$

and nitric acid may be written

$$H^+(NO_3)^-$$

Some compounds demand more than one electrical charge on a particular ion in order to be "satisfied." For example, in $CaCl_2$ one calcium ion joins with two chlorine ions. This arrangement is correct because the calcium ion always has two charges. So the compound is written ionically as

$$Ca^{++}2Cl^-$$

In other words the number of charges in an ionized compound *must balance*. There must be as many positive charges as negative charges. The number of charges on an ion is known as the *valence* of the ion. The charges associated with the ion are written as superscripts after that ion, one "$+$" or one "$-$" for each charge. (It is also possible to show more than one charge with a written number. Thus Ca^{++} could have been written Ca^{+2} or Ca^{2+}; but be sure to remember that charges are *always* superscripts.)

Once an ion is dissolved in water and is free of its "mate" of the opposite charge, it is treated like a compound in its own right, and its coefficients are moved to the front of its symbol.

This is done for the case of calcium chloride dissolving in water in Equation (23):

$$CaCl_2 \rightarrow Ca^{++} + 2Cl^- \tag{23}$$

This is the only new procedure or rule that you must learn in order to write electrochemical equations. All other equation rules still apply. Taking an earlier example, you may rewrite Equation (15):

$$MnO_2(s) + 4HCl \rightarrow 2H_2O + MnCl_4 \tag{15}$$

as an electrochemist would like to see it:

$$MnO_2(s) + 4H^+ + 4Cl^- \rightarrow 2H_2O + Mn^{++++} + 4Cl^- \tag{24}$$

Note that Mn^{++++} may also be written Mn^{+4} or Mn^{4+}. Note too that the compound MnO_2 did not dissolve in water; it was a precipitate to begin with and it was not ionized. Only after the chemical reaction with the hydrochloric acid did the manganese become ionized with four charges, and as a consequence of being ionized, it dissolved. Without the acid it would have remained undissolved in the water, like a brown mud.

It is important that you realize that either equation, (15) or (24), is correct. The chemist chooses the way he prefers to write it depending on the information he wants to convey. A reproduction of a page of inorganic chemistry using electrochemical symbols is shown in Figure 7 of Part II (p. 193.)

The Battery. Now that you know something about electrochemistry you can understand a little more about how the battery in your car or portable radio or flashlight "makes" electricity chemically. It does so by finding a way to remove some of the electrical charges from certain ions (by making them into unionized precipitates), and to lead these charges down some wires into the devices that need electricity to run. The electrochemist has discovered the chemical reactions that make this happen; when he wants to describe such reactions in written form he uses the symbols for charges, the superscripts " + " and " - ," which have been described in this section. The battery is only one product that uses the principles of electrochemistry; there are also many others that you will encounter if you work for an electrochemist.

Summary

1. Chemical compounds are held together by electrical forces. The field of chemistry that studies the electrical properties of chemicals is called *electrochemistry.*
2. All electrical forces are of two kinds: *positive* and *negative.* Anything that has some positive or negative electricity on it is said to be electrically charged. An atom or radical with electrical charge on it is called an *ion.*
3. Positive and negative charges are attracted to each other. If two pieces of cloth have opposite charges they attract each other and stick together. They are said to be held together by *static electricity.* When ions with opposite charges hold together they are said to be joined by an *ionic bond.*
4. Compounds that are held together ionically are easily dissolved by water. After dissolving the ionic bond is weakened, and each ion moves around freely in the water solution.
5. When you write the formula for an ion, you write the number of charges it carries as a superscript of plusses (+) or minuses (−), one plus or minus for each charge of electricity. For example, the formula for ionized sodium nitrate may be written $Na^+(NO_3)^-$. When an element or radical occurs more than once in an ionized compound the coefficient that tells how many times it occurs is written in front of it. For example, the compound $Ca(NO_3)_2$ when ionized is written as $Ca^+ 2(NO_3)^-$.
6. In *ionic equations* ions are written with plus signs between them, as: $Na^+ + (NO_3)^-$; $Ca^+ + 2(NO_3)^-$.
7. In an ionic compound all electrical charges must balance. That is, there must be as many positive charges as negative charges. In an ionic equation, the total number of positive charges on one side of the equation must be the same as the total number of negative charges on that side.

Organic Chemistry

Everything That Lives. There is one other field of chemistry that is important for you to know, *organic chemistry.* Organic chemistry is the study of the chemical compounds of the element carbon. This is a special branch of chemistry for two reasons: (1) Most living things (or things which once lived) are made of compounds of carbon—and this includes you and me. Furthermore, most of the things we eat, wear, use as fuel, and use as medicine are organic chemicals. (2) Carbon usually joins to other elements to form compounds in a peculiar way which involves *four* joints, or *bonds,* for each atom of carbon. Such bonding makes carbon chemistry different from the chemistry of most other elements.

Structure. What do you need to know as a secretary to an organic chemist beyond what we have already described in the preceding sections? Essentially only one new thing. This is the technique of writing compounds and equations *structurally*.

Carbon Has Four Arms. It was said above that carbon bonds to other elements with four joints. That is, the carbon atom behaves as though it has four hooks or arms with which to grab other atoms. These are not ionic bonds but some of the same thinking applies. The chemist often likes to show the carbon atom diagrammatically not as a C alone, but as the atom with its bonds. So, C may become

$$-\overset{|}{\underset{|}{C}}- \quad \text{or} \quad \overset{|}{\underset{\diagdown}{C\diagup}} \quad \text{or} \quad -C\equiv$$

The bonds are just shown as lines of length equal to about three spaces of typing. It is the chemist's decision whether he makes use of the structural technique or not. He can also use dots instead of lines, but lines are more common and more clear.

The Hydrocarbons. There is a compound of carbon with four hydrogen atoms which is called methane. It may be written like any other molecule as

$$CH_4$$

But if the chemist so desires he may write it structurally, with each one of the carbon atoms shown grasping a hydrogen atom:

$$\begin{array}{c} H \\ | \\ H-C-H \\ | \\ H \end{array} \qquad\qquad \begin{array}{c} H \\ \bullet \\ H\circ C\cdot H \\ \bullet \\ H \end{array}$$

with line bonds   with dot bonds

The structural way of writing a chemical compound shows more to the chemist than the more conventional technique of just indicating the elements with their coefficients. The structural method actually gives the chemist a model of how the different atoms are arranged. This information is valuable to him. For example, an arrangement for methane (which is all wrong) but which attempts to show the compound as if it had a different structure, might look like this:

$$
\begin{array}{c}
\text{H} \\
| \\
\text{H} - \text{C} - \text{H} \\
| \\
\text{H}
\end{array}
$$

It is still CH_4 but it is not methane any more. Part of what makes methane unique in its chemical behavior is the fact that the hydrogen atoms all take up positions around each carbon atom as though each were a point of the compass, north, south, east, and west.

Methane is one of a family of compounds of carbon and hydrogen which are, logically enough, called *hydrocarbons*. All the members of the family form a series made by adding more and more CH_2 groups:

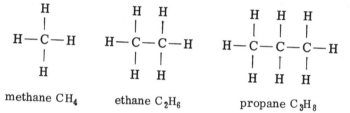

methane CH_4 ethane C_2H_6 propane C_3H_8

There are additional members of the family, in order: butane, pentane, hexane, heptane, and so on. The formulas of each can be shown structurally in the same way, although one of the senior members of the family, pentatriacontane, $C_{35}H_{72}$, would take a rather large piece of paper.

Drawing Bond Lines. When compounds are written structurally, the bond lines should be drawn in neatly with a ruler and a black ball-point pen or with a drafting pen using india ink. Never resort to free-hand drawing of these lines! One of the worst things a secretary can do is to prepare a poorly drawn or inked typewritten page. So long as the typewriter puts down the lines of text in neat rows, the reader feels that there is an orderliness and correctness about what he is reading. But let something be added to the text that is not put down by the machine and the whole effect can be spoiled. This is particularly evident with organic molecules that are more complex than the ones we have discussed.

The Benzene Ring. Consider the compound benzene, C_6H_6. Here the atoms are arranged in a hexagonal pattern (known as the "benzene ring") and some of the bonds are double. (Remember, this is really a model of the way the different atoms take up positions in the actual molecule of benzene.) Note that every carbon atom still has four bonds leading from it, no more and no less. (In organic chemistry, if carbon appears with another number of bonds, someone has made a mistake.)

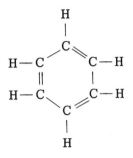

benzene C_6H_6

The Structural Equation. Keeping in mind what we show when we write a chemical formula structurally—namely, how the atoms are positioned relative to each other, as well as what they are and how many there are of each—we can even write equations structurally. For example, the conventional equation

$$2CH_4 \rightarrow C_2H_2 + 3H_2 \qquad (25)$$

is written structurally:

$$\overset{\displaystyle H}{\underset{\displaystyle H}{\overset{|}{\underset{|}{H-C-H}}}} + \overset{\displaystyle H}{\underset{\displaystyle H}{\overset{|}{\underset{|}{H-C-H}}}} \rightarrow H-C\equiv C-H + 3H_2 \qquad (26)$$

No one is going to win any speed prizes doing this sort of thing. Still, typing pages of structural organic chemistry is a part of the job of a technical secretary. Reproducing this material on a typewriter is difficult only when one is not used to it. Success is dependent on understanding what you are doing and on showing care and concern for detail. It is important to remember that every bond line and its position are important. Before typing, take a few minutes to apply some common sense to planning the page. It will do some good to plot the layout with a ruler and pencil, meanwhile setting up a rule for the number of spaces to be used for a bond—three is good. A well-planned page will have equations neatly and centrally placed and not squashed at one end. Another good tactic is to draw plusses and bonds "in a line" with one setting of the ruler. (See the page of organic chemistry text reproduced in Figure 8 of Part II, on page 194.)

Summary

1. Organic chemistry is the study of the chemical compounds of the element carbon, which include all materials that are alive or have been alive. It is like all other chemistry, but there is also one new factor: organic compounds may be shown *structurally* (they don't have to be but they may be, and they often are).
2. In a structural formula, elements are written in locations that are assumed to be in the same relationships to each other as those that are found in an actual molecule. They are then joined to each other (whenever there is such a joining) by straight lines called *bonds*.
3. *Carbon always has four bonds.* That is, four bonding lines are always drawn starting from each carbon atom. They may be drawn in any direction.
4. Some examples of structurally drawn carbon compounds are:

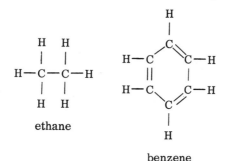

ethane

benzene

5. It is possible to write equations structurally by showing each compound in the equation structurally.

Chapter 2
Mathematics

Introduction

This chapter is for someone who is not a mathematician, who has no interest in becoming a mathematician, but who works with mathematical words and symbols. The material treated here is used by every engineer and scientist. The subject matter is probably the most important you will meet in this book. It is also the most complicated. Yet as you go through it, you will see that what you have to know about it is not really difficult at all.

Numbers

Fractions. As you probably remember from somewhere, fractions are numbers that look like 1/2 or 36/59 or a/b. The most important thing to remember about fractions is that they should be written so that the reader recognizes them for what they are. It should be perfectly clear to him that he is being presented with a fraction, that it begins "here" and ends "there," that "this" is the *numerator* (the top part) and "that" is the *denominator* (the bottom part). Mathematical text may be so complex and so crowded on a page that parts of the material may run into other parts and confuse the meaning. In writing fractional expressions I recommend that you *take plenty of room*. That is the best way to avoid confusion.

Then there is the issue of how to write a fraction. Should you write: 1/3 or $^1/_3$ or $\frac{1}{3}$ or $\frac{1}{3}$ in small case (if available)? All are correct. There is no standard of correct usage. Use the form which your employer prefers. I prefer the form 1/3 for small fractions in the middle of written text. When an expression becomes involved, however, it is better to treat it as follows: Break it out of the text altogether and display it on a separate line. Use a horizontal line between numerator and denominator. This line is to be drawn neatly with a ruler using a black ball-point pen or a draftsman's ruling pen. Thus, if you are rattling along in a welter of words and suddenly come upon the fraction

36

$$\frac{19.876 + 2ad - x^2}{54.4 \ (x - 1 + y)}$$

treat it as I just treated it.

Decimals. A decimal is just a fraction whose denominator is 10, or 100, or 1,000, or 10,000, or any other number made up of 1 followed by 0's. You may not have thought about it, but you have used decimals many times before. You use them every time you get change from a dollar. A penny is 1/100, or a *hundredth*, of a dollar, also written 0.01 dollars or .01 dollars. (Here we have a choice of whether to hang that somewhat useless and meaningless zero to the left of the dot called the decimal point. If it serves any purpose, it is to emphasize the presence of the smallest mark we can make, the dot. I think it is better to use it.) Also, a dime is 1/10, or a *tenth*, of a dollar, or 0.1 dollars. Although all these ways of stating the given fractions are equivalent, the term decimal is usually reserved for the ones that look like 0.01 and 0.1. Decimals are very important to you because the scientist usually uses them about as often as he uses the words *and* and *the*.

It will be easy for you if your boss dictates using the word *point*. For example, he might say, "The angle of declination is thirteen point four seven degrees." You would then write, "The angle of declination is 13.47°." But what if he said, "The angle of declination is thirteen and forty-seven hundredths degrees." He is liable to use this second form, and he will still expect you to write the sentence the same way. Since you cannot expect your boss to use the word *point* all the time, you must know the rules for reproducing the correct number from the spoken word. The rules are as follows:

1. The little decimal point rules the roost. Everything rotates around it. All numbers to its left are whole numbers. All numbers to its *right* are *decimal* parts of whole numbers.
2. The first number to the *right* of a decimal point is called a *tenth*, and whatever that number may be it represents so many tenths. So "seven-tenths" is 0.7 and "two-tenths" is 0.2.
3. The second number to the right of the decimal point is called a *hundredth*, and whatever that number may be it represents so many hundredths. So "seven-hundredths" is 0.07 and "two-hundredths" is 0.02. You see, just to get that 7 and that 2 into the second position so that they may designate hundredths we add a zero between the decimal point and the number. That is clear enough. But the thing that seems to confuse secretaries is translating larger amounts of hundredths from words to

numbers. Consider the angle of declination again. Remember, in 13.47 the forty-seven hundredths was written as ".47." That is the key to the whole thing. You use the word hundredth for the number after the decimal point as long as the *last digit* is in the second position to the right after the decimal point.

4. And so it goes. If we see *three* numbers to the right of the decimal point we are talking about *thousandths, four* numbers indicate *ten-thousandths, five,* indicate *hundred-thousandths,* and so on.

5. Finally, remember that these words sound alike even though a world of difference separates them. For example, a *thousand* is a million times more than a *thousand*th— so listen when you take dictation.

The Decimal Point

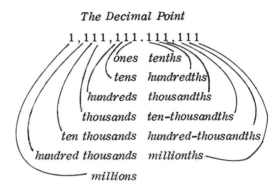

Figure 1. The decimal point rules the roost.

Figure 1 should make this clear. Note that it takes more digits to the left of the decimal point to show whole numbers than to the right to show related decimals. For example, to show the number one hundred and forty, 140, it takes three digits; but to show fourteen-hundredths, 0.14, it takes only two digits to the right of the decimal point. The number 0.140 uses three digits on the decimal, or right, side, and that makes the number one hundred and forty thousandths, while one hundred and forty thousand uses up six digits, 140,000.

Here are a few examples to pin down the issue of decimals and their translation from spoken words to written symbols. These are presented first as they would be spoken and then as they would be written using numbers and decimals.

1. Two hundred thirty-three and seventy-one ten-thousandths:
233.0071

2. Thirty-five thousand and thirty-five thousandths:
$$35,000.035$$
3. Sixteen and one-tenth:
$$16.1$$
4. Sixteen hundred and sixteen hundredths:
$$1,600.16$$
5. Three-thousandths:
$$0.003$$
6. Thirteen-thousandths:
$$0.013$$
7. Seven-hundred-and-thirteen thousandths:
$$0.713$$
8. One hundred and thirty-one thousand:
$$131,000$$

Exponents. Probably the most important concept you must understand in order to reproduce mathematical material correctly is that of exponents. A typical example of a mathematical expression that contains an exponent might look like

$$4 \times 10^{12}$$

The ^{12} is known as an exponent; it is also known as a *power,* and it must always be written a half line up, as a superscript, or it will not be recognized as an exponent. (By the way, it also helps to write exponents with small case if your typewriter has such type.) The number to which the exponent is applied is called a *base.* In this case, and probably in most cases you will meet, the base is 10. But this need not necessarily be so:

$$a^b \times c^d$$

and $$934 \times 7^5$$

are examples of exponential expressions where the base is not 10. Another thing to remember about exponents is that they can be anything: numbers, letters, even long mathematical expressions.

Positive Whole-Number Exponents. When an exponent is a positive whole number it means that the base is to be multiplied by itself the number of times indicated in the exponent. Thus the number 10^2 represents 10×10, which is 100. In the same way, 1,000, which is $10 \times 10 \times 10$, may be written 10^3. You may go on and on with this as shown in Table 1. Our original example, 4×10^{12}, is, therefore, simply a way of writing

$$4 \times 10 \times 10 \times 10 \times 10 \times 10 \times 10 \times 10 \times 10 \times 10 \times 10 \times 10 \times 10$$

which equals 4,000,000,000,000 (4 trillion).

Table 1. Raising Ten to a Power

	Multiply Together	It Looks Like	You Say It
10^1	one ten	10	ten
10^2	two tens	100	one hundred
10^3	three tens	1,000	one thousand
10^4	four tens	10,000	ten thousand
10^5	five tens	100,000	one hundred thousand
10^6	six tens	1,000,000	one million
10^{18}	eighteen tens	1,000,000,000,000,000,000	one billion billion

How would your boss say it? He might say

four times ten to the twelfth

or four times ten raised to the twelfth power

But either way he will expect you to write it as 4×10^{12}.

You should understand that multiplying a number by a power of 10 that is a positive whole number is like adding zeros. For example, the number 9 becomes 90 when multiplied by 10:

$$9 \times 10 = 9 \times 10^1 = 90$$

and 9 becomes 900 when multiplied by 100:

$$9 \times 100 = 9 \times 10^2 = 900$$

The exponent of the 10 tells you how many zeros to add to the original number.

You do not have to start with a simple number like 9. You might have a number with a decimal point in it like 3.789. Then the number 3,789,000,000 may be dictated as "three point seven eight nine times ten to the ninth," which you will type as

$$3.789 \times 10^9$$

and you will know that it means three billion, seven hundred and eighty-nine million. In cases like this one, the rule is that the exponent of the 10 tells you how many places to the right to move the decimal point.

All this raising to a power is nothing but a shorthand, a means of making the handling of numbers easier. This shorthand is often referred to as *scientific notation*.

Squares and Cubes. The exponents [2] and [3] have special names. Anything raised to the second power is called "squared" and anything raised to the third power is called "cubed." This all makes sense, because if you have a square, as in Figure 2a, and you want to find its area, you multiply the length of one side by itself and you get the square (or "squared") area. Since any base to the second power must also be multiplied times itself, the result is equivalent to the area of a square with a side equal in length to the base. Similarly, any base to the third power is equivalent to the volume of a cube with a side equal in length to the base (see Figure 2b). Thus,

$$5^3 = 5 \times 5 \times 5 = 125$$

The words *squared* and *cubed* are important to you as a technical secretary because your employer uses these words automatically, without thinking, when he wants you to write the exponents ^{2} and ^{3}.

Taking Roots. Raising to a power is only half of the story. Suppose you wanted to do the opposite. You can be sure that any scientist who has learned to do and express something one way also wants to be able to do it and say it in reverse. In fact he will point out to you that if you do something the reverse way, and then reverse that, it is right side up again. "Raising to a power in reverse," is "taking a root." In our preceding example, where 5^3 was equal to 125, the cube root of 125 is simply 5. We have reversed the process.

As a technical secretary you must know the rule that pertains to writing a root so that the engineer or scientist recognizes that *this* is a root and *that* is a power. A root may be indicated by using the root sign, $\sqrt{}$. For example, "the seventh root of 95" is $\sqrt[7]{95}$. The root sign appears on some typewriters and you can order it from a typewriter company as an "extra letter" if you use it frequently. Otherwise just draw it in neatly.

Now the "square root" of 25 is 5 and may be written

$$\sqrt[2]{25} = 5$$

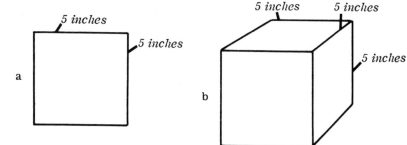

a — 5 inches, 5 inches

b — 5 inches, 5 inches, 5 inches

The area of this square is
5 x 5, or 25 square inches.

The volume of this cube is
$5 \times 5 \times 5$, or 125 cubic inches.

Figure 2. Squares and cubes.

Table 2. The Negative Exponent

ten	10	10^1	one-tenth	10^{-1}	1/10	0.1
one hundred	100	10^2	one-hundredth	10^{-2}	1/100	0.01
one thousand	1,000	10^3	one-thousandth	10^{-3}	1/1,000	0.001
ten thousand	10,000	10^4	one ten-thousandth	10^{-4}	1/10,000	0.0001
one hundred thousand	100,000	10^5	one hundred-thousandth	10^{-5}	1/100,000	0.00001
one million	1,000,000	10^6	one-millionth	10^{-6}	1/1,000,000	0.000001

which is the reverse of $5^2 = 25$. But in this case only, the second, or square, root, we have our choice of putting in the number or not, so $\sqrt[2]{}$ is the same as $\sqrt{}$. The cube root of 125 is written:

$$\sqrt[3]{125} = 5$$

which is the reverse of $5^3 = 125$.

That is all there is to it. You can take the 79th root of 609,234. Or the 609,234th root of 79. These will look like:

$$\sqrt[79]{609,234} \quad \text{or} \quad \sqrt[609,234]{79}$$

The Fractional Exponent. Another way to represent a root is to show it as a fractional exponent. If 10^7 is the seventh power of 10, $10^{1/7}$ is the seventh root of 10. The $1/7$ is an exponent just like the 7 is. In fact, it turns out that mathematically, "raising to a fractional power" is the same as "taking a root."

$$\sqrt[19]{842} \text{ is the same as } 842^{1/19}$$

and $\qquad\qquad \sqrt[7]{10}$ is the same $10^{1/7}$

Which of these do you use? Ask your boss. He probably has a preference.

Negative Exponents. There is one more fact about exponents— they may be negative. That is, it is possible to put a minus sign into an exponent. The rule in such a case, for example 765^{-4}, is:

$$765^{-4} \text{ is the same as } \frac{1}{765^4}$$

That is, the minus sign may be removed by writing the number, with the exponent positive, as the denominator of a fraction whose numerator is 1. The negative exponent has a special significance when used with the base 10. It becomes another way of expressing decimals, as should be clear from Table 2.

It is important for you to know and understand Table 2. You should know that the first column is equivalent to the second and third columns, and that the fourth, fifth, sixth, and seventh columns are equivalent and equal to each other. But you only write the one your employer wants you to use. If he does not always say which he wants you to use, you will soon sense the way he prefers to show these numbers.

Occasionally the base to which an exponent is applied is so long and complex, there may be some confusion about whether the exponent is meant to apply to all of it or just to the last portion of it. Whenever that happens, you may use parentheses. That is, you may put the base into parentheses if you feel that it will get rid of this kind of ambiguity.

Some Examples.   Look these examples over and make sure you understand them (first "tell" it, then "show" it):

1. Four and sixteen-hundredths squared:
$$(4.16)^2$$

2. Sixty-one hundred two point oh one to the one-third power:
$$(6,102.01)^{1/3}$$

3. The thirteenth root of one and fifty-three thousandths:
$$\sqrt[13]{1.053}$$
   [may also be written as $(1.053)^{1/13}$].

4. Two thousand two hundred and eighty-three hundred-thousandths:
$$0.02283$$

5. Seven and three-tenths to the minus five:
$$(7.3)^{-5}$$
   [may also be written as $\frac{1}{(7.3)^5}$].

6. Seventeen times ten to the three:
$$17 \times 10^3$$
   (may also be written, if your employer prefers, 17,000).

7. Seventeen times ten to the minus three:
$$17 \times 10^{-3}$$
   (may also be written, if your employer prefers, 0.017).

8. Six times seven to the eighth
$$6 \times 7^8$$

Logarithms and Antilogarithms.   Some odd things happen when you multiply or divide numbers which contain exponents. If the numbers being multiplied or divided together have the same base, then *you add exponents to multiply and you subtract exponents to divide.* Here is an example:

$$10^3 \times 10^2 = 10^5$$

The exponents 3 and 2 were added: one thousand (10^3) times one hundred (10^2) is one hundred thousand (10^5 or 100,000).

Divide one thousand by one hundred:

$$1,000 \div 100 = 10$$

It may also be written as:

$$\frac{10^3}{10^2} = 10^1$$

where we have subtracted the exponents.

There is not much advantage here, but consider multiplying 17 times 91:

17 is also $10^{1.2304}$

19 is also $10^{1.9590}$

and adding exponents, you get the answer

$$10^{3.1894}$$

Look up that number in a *Table of Logarithms* and you find that

$$10^{3.1894} = 1,547$$

Also, if you multiply out 17×91 you get the same answer, 1,547. The word *logarithm* is used to describe the exponent; for example, "the logarithm of 1,547 is 3.1894." In the same way

the logarithm of 100 is 2

the logarithm of 1,000 is 3

the logarithm of 10,000 is 4

and so on.

The scientist must always have a way to "get back." He needs a word for doing the opposite of what he has just done. To go backwards he uses the *antilogarithm*. If the logarithm of 1,547 is 3.1894, then

the antilogarithm of 3.1894 is 1,547

Just say it backwards and add the prefix, "anti-."

In mathematical expressions, the abbreviations "log" and "antilog" are used to tell the reader "take the logarithm or antilogarithm of this or that number or expression." Then log x or antilog y become like any other numbers and may be incorporated into equations like this one:

$$3y^{n-2} = 4 \times \log(x - y) + y^7$$

One final word, the term "log" almost always means "to the base ten." You can take a log to any other base, but then you write what that base is as a subscript. If you mean to the base 2, you must write:

$$\log_2 193$$

which is the logarithm of 193 to the base 2.

A base that is used as often as 10 in scientific work is the number 2.1783'.... It is a number that cannot be written exactly but goes on and on. (Mathematicians call such numbers "irrational.") It has a special meaning to the mathematician and is known as the "natural base." The symbol for it is the letter e. Logarithms to the base e ($\log_e$) are known as natural logarithms, and are often abbreviated "ln." Everything else, as far as the secretary is concerned, is the same; so the equation

$$1 - 2x + \ln(a + b^2) = y^2$$

is a perfectly good equation.

Precautions. One thing should be clear now. The meanings of exponents are one thing, writing them is another. You must operate in a situation where the typewriter carriage must always be made to go half lines up and down, and where occasionally the exponent will be a more complicated number than the base to which it is applied. How can one do this neatly? There is no question that it is easiest when the exponential numbers are small case. But not every machine has small-case type. So follow these rules:

1. Be careful.
2. Practice laying out mathematical expressions using exponents until you have the neatest and most logical arrangements.
3. Always remember that the reader must recognize easily which part of a mathematical expression is the base and which part is the exponent.

Some Special Numbers and Symbols.   You may have seen the book for children by Dr. Seuss entitled *On Beyond Zebra.** It deals with the alphabet after Z. The alphabet after Z is the sort of concept that appeals equally to children and to mathematicians. Dr. Seuss made up fascinating letters like "Yuzz" and "Wum" for the alphabet after Z. The mathematician lets us down, because when he needs more letters after Z he merely goes to other alphabets. That is why later in this book (in Glossary 6) you will be familiarized with the Greek alphabet and with a little bit of Hebrew. But when it comes to representing some special numbers and some special things we do to numbers, the mathematician is a little less restrained. I shall not burden you with all of these special symbols, but only with those you will encounter most often.

∞, *The Infinity Symbol.*   There is nothing better than Latin to help in understanding how words are made. Take the word *infinite.* The "in" says that it means the opposite of *finite*—just as *inconsequential* is the opposite of *consequential.* What about *finite*? Webster says that anything that is finite has "definable limits." It comes from the Latin *finitus* (finished) which in turn comes from the Latin *finire* (to finish). Thus, anything that has an end is finite; anything that has no end is infinite. In mathematics,

---

*New York: Random House, 1955.

certain things may be said to be infinitely large or infinitely small; they may go back infinitely far in time or space, or may go infinitely far forward in time or space or imagination.

Engineers and scientists think of the infinite so frequently that they have created a symbol for it, and they treat it just like a number. The symbol is ∞ and it is used (it would seem) as casually as the number 2 or 8. It is most easily written on a typewriter as two small letter o's jammed together. Some typewriters will have the symbol on the keyboard, which is a convenience. Do not hesitate to draw it in freehand when that is the only way to make a complex equation look neat. It is just an 8 on its side. But *never* confuse it with an 8!

Δ, *The Increment.*   An *increment* is an *increase.* If you used to weigh 120 pounds and you now weigh 125 pounds, your weight increment (or increase) is five pounds. If we call your original weight W, then, mathematically,

$$W = 120$$

If the mathematician wishes to say you have gained five pounds, he will say that your incremental weight (ΔW) is five pounds. Or

$$\Delta W = 5$$

where the Greek delta, Δ, indicates an increment. Thus, if your weight at first was 120, we can now call it W_1, and if your new weight is W_2, we can construct the mathematical sentence (or equation):

$$W_1 + \Delta W = W_2 = 125 \text{ pounds}$$

When you gain five pounds, you have acquired a positive or plus increment of five pounds. On the other hand, if you lose five pounds you have had a negative increment, called a *decrement.* A decrement may also be symbolized by Δ since it is only a special kind of increment.

In any event, be familiar with the triangular symbol for increment or decrement. If it is not on your machine, draw the symbol neatly when you need it. It may be helpful to use the underline key on your typewriter as the base of the triangle. It is a matter of choice with you how you do it, but do not do it carelessly. *Do it neatly!*

!, *The Factorial Symbol.* Perhaps the mathematician chose the exclamation mark, !, to be the factorial symbol, in wonderment that anything so ridiculous as the mathematical operation it describes should be useful. This symbol, applied to any number, says to multiply by themselves all the numbers that you can count up to that number. For example,

factorial seven is 7!

and it is the multiple multiplication: one times two times three times four times five times six times seven, or

$$1 \times 2 \times 3 \times 4 \times 5 \times 6 \times 7 = 7!$$

and if you take the trouble to multiply it all out,

$$7! = 5040$$

Here the factorial symbol can be a most useful mathematical shorthand.

When your employer gives you the term *factorial* in dictation, he may say it either before or after the number to which it applies. That is, he may say "factorial seven" or "seven factorial." Get used to how he says it. In either case the symbol is always written *after* the number to which it applies.

Σ, *The Summation Symbol.* The use of Greek letters is explained in detail in Part II (see Glossary 6, p. 211). We will now discuss only Σ (called sigma), the Greek capital *S*. When used in mathematical text, the capital sigma is a shorthand symbol meaning "take the sum of." Since *sum* begins with *s*, the choice of the Greek *S* makes sense. Usually the summation sign Σ tells you to add numbers in sequence just as the factorial sign tells you to multiply numbers in sequence. It is written with the limits of the sequence to be added shown at the top (the larger number) and bottom (the smaller number) of the sigma. This is best explained by an example:

$$\sum_{n=3}^{n=9} n$$

is a shorthand way of saying "the sum of the number *n*, where *n* is the series of numbers running from 3 to 9." Therefore:

$$\sum_{n=3}^{n=9} n = 3 + 4 + 5 + 6 + 7 + 8 + 9 = 42$$

The numbers at the top and bottom of the summation sign are known as the *limits of summation*. They may be written as little equations as above ($n = 3$, $n = 9$), or with the $n=$ understood and left out; thus

$$\sum_{3}^{9} n = 42$$

is equivalent to the preceding expression. The letter which stands
for the numbers does not have to be n. Any letter your employer
chooses to use is all right.

Now you know how to *write* summation expressions and what
they *mean*. But how will your boss *say* them when he is dictating? He will say them in a variety of ways, but generally it will
come out something like: "sigma of y between 16 and 33," or
"the summation of y between the limits of 16 and 33." You will
put on the printed page:

$$\sum_{16}^{33} y$$

That is all there is to it, except that if your machine does not
have Greek letters on it (many technical typewriters do), you
must write in the sigma with a black ball-point pen, *neatly!*

i, The Imaginary Number. Numbers can have both a real and an
unreal, or imaginary, part. The mathematician might say, "It
may be imaginary, and I may not know what it means, but the
least I can do for it is to give it a name or symbol, just as though
it were real and easy to understand." The most important imaginary number in mathematics is designated by the ordinary letter
i. When you write an i in a mathematical expression, it stops
being a letter of the alphabet; it becomes a number, a number
which can be treated just as if it were 5 or 37 or anything.

Of course the deeper implications of this symbol in mathematics need not concern you here. Even scientists and engineers, who use imaginary numbers, are not sure that they really
understand what i means—but they do use it.

Briefly, this is how imaginary numbers come about. You know
that $\sqrt{16}$ means "the square root of sixteen"; and $\sqrt{16} = 4$ because 4 times 4 is 16. That is simple enough—but what is $\sqrt{-16}$?
What multiplied times itself is -16? This is a puzzler because
by the rules of multiplication plus times plus is plus, and minus
times is also plus. Something multiplied times exactly itself can
never be minus—unless it is imaginary. That is why $\sqrt{-16}$ is an
imaginary number. Now $\sqrt{-16}$ may also be written $\sqrt{16} \times \sqrt{-1}$ and
still mean the same thing. That is

$$\sqrt{-16} = \sqrt{16} \times \sqrt{-1}$$

$\sqrt{16}$ is real enough: 4. Only the $\sqrt{-1}$ is imaginary. So we can say

$$\sqrt{-16} = 4 \times \sqrt{-1}$$

Where 4 is the real part and $\sqrt{-1}$ is the imaginary part of $\sqrt{-16}$. The expression $\sqrt{-1}$ is written usually as i; thus

$$\sqrt{-16} = 4i$$

Prefixes That Make Numbers Larger and Smaller. You recall from the chapter on chemistry the importance of prefixes and suffixes in enriching and extending the meanings of words. In chemistry these word attachments may be qualitative (descriptive) or quantitative and semiquantitative (referring to amounts). Mathematical prefixes are almost entirely quantitative; they tell exact quantities. Some of the prefixes make numbers much bigger and some of them make numbers much smaller. In this sense, some prefixes are like raising to a power and some are like using decimals or raising to a negative power. Table 3 lists the most commonly used prefixes and the symbols which may be used as abbreviations for them.

These prefixes may be inserted in written text in front of a physical quantity being described numerically. A typical use might involve the electrical term volt where the text may talk of "3,000 volts." We already know that this may be represented as 3×10^3 volts. So, in accordance with Table 3, we may also write it as 3 kilovolts. In other words, a kilovolt is a thousand volts. If it is desired to represent the text in a shorter and more symbolic form, again in accordance with Table 3, we can make use of the symbol "k." Thus three kilovolts may be written as "3 kV." Which one do you use? The one your employer requests.

Here the rules that were listed in the section on decimals are brought back to your attention. Remember the difference between

Table 3. Number Prefixes

Multiplier	Name of Prefix	Prefix Symbol	Alternate Prefix	Alternate Prefix Symbol
10^9	giga *or* beva	G *or* B	kilomega	kM
10^6	mega	M		
10^3	kilo	k		
10^{-3}	milli	m		
10^{-6}	micro	μ		
10^{-9}	nano	n	millimicro	mμ
10^{-12}	pico	p	micromicro	$\mu\mu$

Table 4. Some Quantitative Prefixes

Physical Unit Being Described	Prefix	Multiplier	Symbolic Represen- tation	Complete Name
volt	milli	10^{-3}	mV	millivolt
ton	mega	10^6	Mt	megaton
ampere	micro	10^{-6}	μA	microampere
second	nano	10^{-9}	nsec	nanosecond

thousan*d* and thousan*dth*? A thousand volts is a *kilo*volt; a thousandth of a volt is a *milli*volt. Three thousandths of a volt is the same as three millivolts or 3 mV. The very same argument holds for all the other prefixes and for any other unit we may want to describe other than volts. Thus we talk of *mega*ton hydrogen bombs (equivalent to a million tons) and *micro*amperes (millionths of an ampere, another electrical unit) and *nano*seconds (billionths of a second). These words may be presented symbolically in conjunction with abbreviations of the units being used, as shown in Table 4. A few precautions you should observe are as follows:

Consider the prefix letters used with regard to whether they are capital or small letters: "M" stands for *mega* or millions; "m" stands for *milli* or thousandths. That is quite a difference and you could turn the world upside down merely by substituting "M" for "m."

Notice the symbol for *micro*. It is *not* the small letter *u*. It is the Greek letter μ which is pronounced "mew." The way to tell the difference is by that little tail which starts the letter in Greek. If your machine does not have a Greek μ, it will be up to you to draw it in.

Subscripts and Primes. One of the simplest ideas you will meet is that of the subscript; however it is still easy to get terribly confused with this idea. (You will be confused if you are not careful and if you are not neat. We can of course say this ⌐ ¬t most of the reproduction of mathematical text.) We use a ⌐ ¬t to describe a mathematical symbol or mathematical expr ther in terms of its position in a series or in terms of wh⌐ belongs to *this* series or to *that* series.

Suppose your engineer-employer is writing a scientific treatise. He may be looking into some very unlikely matters; just for fun, let us say that he is investigating the effect of the conditions on the moon on different types of pies. He must first create a symbol for the concept "pie." The engineer reporting on this

research will start with the definition phrased quite straightfor-
wardly:

"Let P = pie"

There can be no mistaking his meaning, nor that he chose P instead of p. Now he cannot investigate merely one piece of pie; he
knows that it is necessary to look at much pie of many varieties
and at many per variety before he can draw conclusions about
pie. He will study pecan pie, Boston cream pie, cheese pie, and
apple pie. These he now labels with subscripts which are written, respectively, as p, BC, c, and a. Since they are indeed *sub-*
scripts, they are written one-half line down. Then the various
categories of pie may be designated thus:

$$P_p = \text{pecan pie}$$
$$P_{BC} = \text{Boston cream pie}$$
$$P_c = \text{cheese pie}$$
$$P_a = \text{apple pie}$$

But this is not all. As we all know, there are regional differences in pie. Pecan pie is very different in Arkansas from the
way it is in South Carolina; cheese pie from the Lower East Side
of New York is different from Montana cheese pie. One might
think that Boston cream pie is made only in Boston, but this is
not true—there is a variety that is made on the island of Manhattan without any cream. Apple pie is made all over America;
our investigator chose apple pie as made in Colorado, Maryland,
and Louisiana. Now we need more subscripts.

Adding subscripts should now be no problem to you yet it is
possible to get into trouble at this point. This is because our
scientist now may request that you put subscripts onto your subscripts. In other words, Boston cream pie from Boston may be
differentiated from Boston cream pie from Manhattan as follows:

Boston cream pie from Boston = P_{BC_B}

Boston cream pie from Manhattan = P_{BC_M}

This could go on indefinitely. It helps a little to put all the subscripts on the same level and it may be allowable to do this; but
P_{BC_B} really tells us more than P_{BCB} even if it is a little harder
to write.

Now, the manner in which our researcher pursued his investigation was to subject seven of each of the categories of pie to
the temperature extremes they would see on the moon—350°

Fahrenheit during the day and $240°$ Fahrenheit below zero at night—through 4 days and nights. Then he had his laboratory assistant eat 400 milligrams (400 mg) of each pie in the experiment in order to get his reactions. Now *you* have a problem. You have to take the dictation and type the final report. There is really nothing to it; you must just be careful, especially in sentences like,

$$\sum_{n=1}^{n=7} P_{pA} \text{ had greater tolerance to moon dust (MD) than } P_{p SC_3}$$

Which actually means that, "All seven samples (added together) of Arkansas pecan pie were better than the third piece of South Carolina pecan pie."

This is research. We do not mean to poke fun at the researcher, but the example may not really be so bad. Some strange things have been researched. The text you will be called upon to reproduce will often be written with just such words and symbols.

What about superscripts? These are usually reserved for raising to a power and not to designate a category or a series (as with subscripts). One exception is the prime system. A prime is nothing but an apostrophe. One apostrophe is called "prime," two are called "double prime," three are called "triple prime," and so on. Primes are always written as superscripts and indicate the position of the item in a series of similar items. Thus:

$$P_a{}' + P_a{}'' + P_a{}''' + P_a{}'''' + \ldots.$$

means "the first piece of apple pie added to the second piece of apple pie added to the third piece of apple pie added to the fourth piece of apple pie, and so on."

On the other hand, $P_a{}^3$ is not another way of saying the third piece of apple pie. $P_a{}'''$ was that. $P_a{}^3$ is a piece of apple pie cubed (assuming one can cube apple pie).

If one runs into a problem of differentiating between primes and exponents, the easy way out is to make use of parentheses. For example, the first piece of apple pie cubed is:

$$(P_a{}')^3$$

Summary

1. Refer to Figure 1 when you have a question about the way to write a *decimal*.
2. Listen hard. Do not confuse words like thous*and* and thous*andth*, there is a very great difference between them.
3. Leave plenty of room to write *fractions*. Make sure it is clear where a fraction begins and ends. Make sure it is clear which part is the *numerator* (the part on top) and which part is the *denominator* (the part on the bottom).
4. When you raise A to the *power* 2, you multiply it by itself, $A \times A$; to the power 3, you multiply it by itself again, $A \times A \times A$; and so on. These operations can also be written A^2 or A^3; the ^{2} and the ^{3} are called *exponents* and are written one-half line up. The A is known as a *base*. Refer to Table 1 for additional examples.
5. When an expression is raised to the power 2 it can also be called *squared*, and to the power 3, it can also be called *cubed*.
6. *Taking a root* means finding a number that multiplied times itself will equal another number. So the second (or square) root of 36 is 6; the third (or cube) root of 8 is 2. Taking a root is shown by the use of the root sign, $\sqrt{}$. The fifth root of A is then: $\sqrt[5]{A}$. A root may also be written as a fractional exponent, as: $A^{1/5}$.
7. It is important that you understand the difference between *positive* and *negative exponents*. When an exponent is negative it means that the number represented can be written as the denominator of a fraction whose numerator is 1. Negative exponents are one way of writing decimals. Refer to Table 2 for additional examples.
8. When considered from a particular point of view an exponent is called a *logarithm*. In the expression $A^B = C$, B is the logarithm of C to the base A, and C is the antilogarithm of B to the base A. The abbreviation for logarithm is log: $\log_A C = B$.
9. If there is no base indicated in the expression for a logarithm it is assumed that the base is 10. Another base that is seen frequently is e, the number 2.7183 .... It is also known as the *natural logarithm* and is abbreviated ln, as: $\ln C = B$.
10. Any number that is infinitely large is simply called *infinity* and is represented by the symbol ∞.
11. An *increment* is an increase over what there was at first, and a decrement is a decrease (or a negative increase). Both are designated by the symbol Δ. If you started with $5A$ and added $2A$, the increment in A is said to be 2, or $\Delta A = 2$.
12. The *factorial* symbol is the exclamation point, !, and it means to multiply by themselves all the numbers you can count up to the number before the symbol. So factorial 4 is 4!, and

$$4! = 1 \times 2 \times 3 \times 4 = 24$$

13. The *summation sign,* the Greek letter Σ (sigma) means add all the numbers between the limits that are given, as:

$$\sum_{5}^{7} n = 5 + 6 + 7 = 18 \qquad \text{and} \qquad \sum_{D}^{H} L = D + E + F + G + H$$

Numbers and symbols are added in sequence between the limits, which are written at the top and bottom of the sigma.

14. The *imaginary number* is just that. It is not real: you can still talk about it, however, and the mathematician gives it the symbol i. It means $\sqrt{-1}$.

15. There are a number of important *prefixes* which when added to the front of a word tell you "how much." These prefixes usually have two forms; they may be syllables that are written out or they may be symbols. Thus "one million volts" may be written as "1 megavolt" or as 1 "MV." Refer to Tables 3 and 4 for additional examples.

16. *Subscripts* are a shorthand way to pin something down. You just add a symbol one-half line down for every new object to be described. If you are describing a house (H) as having red paint (P_r) and being set back from the road (SB), it may be done on a very small piece of paper by saying:

$$H_{P_{r_{SB}}}$$

17. *Primes,* typed as apostrophes, indicate the position of an object in a series of similar objects. So H''_{SB} is the second set-back house.

Geometry and Trigonometry

Geometry.   Right this minute you are sitting in a room. Unless it is unusual, it has corners. There are certain distances between these corners. It may be twice as long as it is wide; the ceiling may be eight feet from the floor. When you describe the room this way, you are talking in the language of *geometry.* Geometry is not only the tool of the professional engineer and mathematician; it is also the tool of the plumber, the carpenter, and the seamstress. We do geometry instinctively when we consider how far it is from one place to another, and the shortest way to get there. In other words, geometry is less of an abstraction, less of a mystery, than the other branches of mathematics. What a secretary must realize in reproducing texts dealing with geometrical matters is that her employer is attempting to describe spaces and distances and angles and surfaces and their relationships to each other.

Here is one place where to a great extent you know as much about the subject as your employer. You know as much as he does about whether a room is large or small, whether something is in a straight line or in a curved line, whether an angle is gradual or sharp. But your boss has had one advantage that you may not have had—a course in geometry, which gave him exact words and symbols to use with respect to the distances between things, the angles between things, the curvatures of things, and so on.

All geometry starts with the *point*. A point is the period on your typewriter. What is a point? It is simply a position. It has no length, width, or height. It merely shows a place. It is a *dot*. If the dot were to move, the path it would form becomes another important geometrical concept—the *line*. Lines may or may not be straight. If they are not straight they are either curved or crooked.

Suppose we move a straight line along another straight line. The region covered by the moving line is known as a *plane*. It can be pictured as a flat table top. (Strictly speaking this is only part of a plane, but you don't have to worry about that.) If we say that a plane has certain lines as boundaries, then the region included within these boundaries is known as an *area*. If we use three lines to "outline" our area, as in Figure 3*a*, it is known as a triangle, which means "three angles." The best way to understand what an angle is is to look at a picture of one. (See Figure 3*b*.)

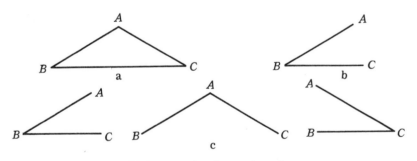

Figure 3. Triangles and angles.

Angles are named by placing letters at the ends of the lines that form them. Thus the angles in triangle *ABC* in Figure 3*a* are angles *ABC*, *BAC*, and *BCA*, as shown in Figure 3*c*. The letter placed in the middle indicates the point at which the two lines meet. This point is known as the angle's *vertex* (the word *apex* is also occasionally used to give the same meaning). An angle may be represented symbolically as, for example, ∠*ABC*.

If two lines that lie in the same plane never meet at a point they are known as *parallel* lines, and when they do meet, forming angles, they are simply *nonparallel*. (If two lines that never meet at a point also don't lie in the same plane, they are known as *skew* lines.) Mathematicians like to say that the universe is so big that eventually even parallel lines creep closer and closer together and meet. In other words, they meet at infinity, just like the rails of a railroad track seem to meet far off in the distance.

Trigonometry. Trigonometry is a special part of geometry, the part that treats angles and triangles. Here too we must become familiar with the words and concepts that are in common use.

Ratios and Angles and Curves. An important idea in trigonometry is that of the *ratio*. A ratio is nothing more than the number of times something is bigger than something else. If we say that Eleanor has had three times as many jobs as Jane, the ratio of jobs between Eleanor and Jane is three to one. This ratio may also be expressed as the fraction 3/1. Or, if we are not comparing Eleanor with Jane, but rather Jane with Eleanor, the ratio may be expressed as 1/3. In the same way, in Figure 4, the diameter of circle Y is twice as long as the diameter of circle X. (The diameter of a circle is the length of a line that goes from any point on the circle to the point directly opposite, and passes through the center of the circle.) Also, in Figure 4, we see that the triangle ABC (in circle X) can be described by ratios. For example, if the distance from A to C is 1 inch, and the distance from B to C is 1/2 inch, then the ratio of side BC to side AC is 1 to 2.

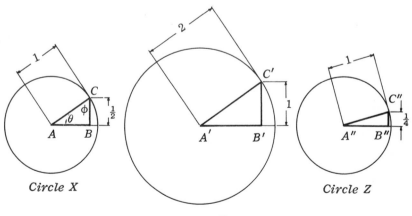

Circle X

Circle Y

Circle Z

Figure 4. Angles and ratios.

Circle Y looks the same as circle X except that everything is bigger—twice as big. Since the diameter of circle Y is twice that of circle X, everything in Y is twice as big too: $A'C'$ is twice as long as AC, $B'C'$ is twice as long as BC, and $A'B'$ is twice as long as AB. But some things are still the same; the angles are still the same.

An angle remains the same (it opens up the same wedge of space) whether the lines that form it are long or short. Thus, in Figure 5, angle QRP is the same angle if we move the point Q to Q' and the point P to P'. It is the ratio of the length of the side that "closes up" an angle to the lengths of the other sides that is important in describing angles, because this ratio doesn't change when the sides of an angle are made longer or shorter.

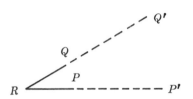

Figure 5. An angle opens up the same width of space whether the lines that form it are long or short.

In Figure 4, the sides that "close up" the angles in circles X, Y, and Z are, respectively, CB, $C'B'$ and $C''B''$. The ratio of side CB to side AC is $1/2$ to 1, and the ratio of side $C'B'$ to side $A'C'$ is 1 to 2. This is the same ratio; in each case the $''AC''$ side is twice the length of the $''CB''$ side. So angle CAB is the same size as angle $C'A'B'$, even though circle Y is twice the size of circle X. (In other words, angle $C'A'B'$ is just angle CAB with sides AC and AB extended.) But in circle Z there is another story. The ratio of $C''B''$ to $A''C''$ is $1/4$ to 1. That is, $A''C''$ is four times as long as $C''B''$. This means that angle $C''A''B''$ is a much sharper angle than CAB or $C'A'B'$. So we see that by describing the relationships (ratios) of the sides of a triangle that contains a certain angle, we are describing the sharpness of that angle.

Sines, Cosines, and Tangents. In trigonometry, these angular ratios have particular names. For example, in circle X, the ratio CB/AC is known as the *sine* of angle BAC, and it is often written as sin BAC. If the ratio is turned upside down to make it AC/CB, then it is known as the *cosecant* of angle BAC, or csc BAC. There are also two other sets of angular ratios that are described similarly. These are the pair *tangent* (tan) and *cotangent* (ctn), and

Table 5.   The Trigonometric Ratios

tangent θ	=	tan θ	=	$\dfrac{CB}{AB}$
cotangent θ	=	ctn θ	=	$\dfrac{AB}{CB}$
sine θ	=	sin θ	=	$\dfrac{CB}{AC}$
cosecant θ	=	csc θ	=	$\dfrac{AC}{CB}$
cosine θ	=	cos θ	=	$\dfrac{AB}{AC}$
secant θ	=	sec θ	=	$\dfrac{AC}{AB}$

right angle

Angle CAB is angle θ

the pair *cosine* (cos) and *secant* (sec). Table 5 shows the specific ratios that these names describe.

Some Greek Angles.   When the mathematician gets tired of naming all three letters of an angle, such as BAC, very often he will use a Greek letter instead. The Greek letter most commonly used to represent angles is theta (θ). Another one often used is phi (ϕ). In Figure 4 angle BAC is θ and angle ACB is ϕ. Some typewriters have the Greek letters on their keyboards, or you may prefer to draw them in neatly. But you may find that a zero, 0, with a hyphen, -, through it, θ, makes a satisfactory theta, and a zero, 0, with a slash, /, through it, $\emptyset$, makes a satisfactory phi.

Writing Trigonometric Expressions.   Trigonometric words and abbreviations are written like the other mathematical shorthands we have met (for example, the log), always keeping in mind that some mathematical operation is being described in a shortened way.   When the word sine or cosine appears, it is just a short way of saying what may be a long ratio.   Instead of saying "the ratio of bc to ac," we can now say "sine."   That is all there is to it.   A trigonometric expression can be treated like any other mathematical expression.   Among other things, it can be raised to a power or be placed under a root sign, as in the following examples:

$$\sin^2 \theta + \cos^4 \phi = x - 3$$

$$\text{ctn}(y^3) - ab = \frac{1}{\sin\phi}$$

$$\cos\left[\frac{2k + \theta}{n}\right] + i\sin\left[\frac{(2k + \theta)}{n}\right]$$

Note that in third expression the angle referred to is the entire term $[(2k + \theta)/n]$.

The ideas you should keep in mind about these trigonometric words are:

1. They refer to angles in triangles; they are a way of describing how big and how sharp these angles are.
2. They are commonly written in abbreviated form as in Table 5.
3. They are used in algebraic expressions to minimize the number of symbols that would otherwise have to be written out.

Some Additional Words. A few words of geometry and trigonometry are of special importance. They are presented below with their definitions.

A *right angle* is an angle such as those on both sides of *GH*, where *GH hits JK* "head on." All right angles are equal to each

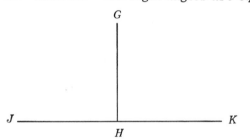

other. In Figure 4, angles *ABC, A'B'C'*, and *A''B''C''* are right angles. A right angle may be shown by the symbol ⊥.

The *hypotenuse* of a right triangle (which is a triangle that contains a right angle) is the side opposite the right angle. In Figure 4, *AC* is the hypotenuse of triangle *ABC; A'C'* is the hypotenuse of triangle *A'B'C'*; and *A''C''* is the hypotenuse of triangle *A''B''C''*.

An important ratio which you must know is that of the perimeter of a circle to its diameter. It is represented by the Greek letter *pi*, π. Its value is always the same, whether the circle is large or small. It equals 3.14159 ... (the numbers go on forever, that is, it is irrational, like *e* is).

A *polygon* is any flat, or plane, figure whose boundaries are straight lines. Thus, a triangle is a polygon with three sides, and a square is a polygon with four sides. A polygon with *n* sides sometimes called an *n*-gon.

Some other key words that are associated with geometry and trigonometry appear over and over again in text relating to these fields. You must be familiar with their spellings and have a rough idea of what they mean. Perhaps the best way to keep them in mind is to put them into groups so that you know whether they refer to lines or angles or circles or curves or solids. This is done in Table 6.

Table 6.   The Words of Geometry and Trigonometry

Name	It Looks Like	Symbol

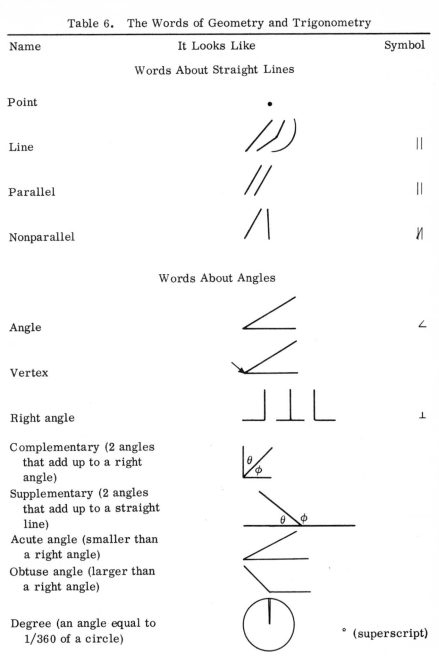

Words About Straight Lines

Point

Line ||

Parallel ||

Nonparallel

Words About Angles

Angle   ∠

Vertex

Right angle   ⊥

Complementary (2 angles
    that add up to a right
    angle)

Supplementary (2 angles
    that add up to a straight
    line)

Acute angle (smaller than
    a right angle)

Obtuse angle (larger than
    a right angle)

Degree (an angle equal to
    1/360 of a circle)   ° (superscript)

Minute (an angle equal to 1/60 of a degree)   ' (superscript)

Second (an angle equal to 1/60 of a minute,
    or 1/360 of a degree)   " (superscript)

Name	It Looks Like	Symbol

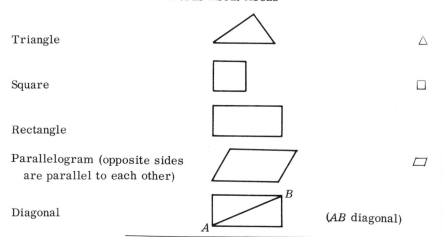

Radian (another kind of angle measure)   (1 radian = 57.3° approx.)

Words of Trigonometry*

Name	It Looks Like	Symbol
Theta (angle designation)	θ	θ
Phi (angle designation)	ϕ	ϕ
Psi (angle designation)	ψ	ψ
hyperbolic sine	$\frac{1}{2}(e^x - e^{-x})$	sinh x (pronounced "cinch x")
hyperbolic cosine	similar to hyperbolic sine†	cosh x (pronounced "cosh x")
hyperbolic tangent	" "	tanh x (pronounced "tanch x")
hyperbolic secant	" "	sech x (pronounced "sech x")
hyperbolic cosecant	" "	csch x (pronounced "cosech x")
hyperbolic cotangent	" "	ctnh x (pronounced "cotanch x")

Words About Areas

Name	It Looks Like	Symbol
Triangle		△
Square		□
Rectangle		
Parallelogram (opposite sides are parallel to each other)		▱
Diagonal		(AB diagonal)

*See Table 5 for definitions of the sine, cosine, tangent, cotangent, secant, and cosecant.

†But not exactly the same.

Name	It Looks Like	Symbol

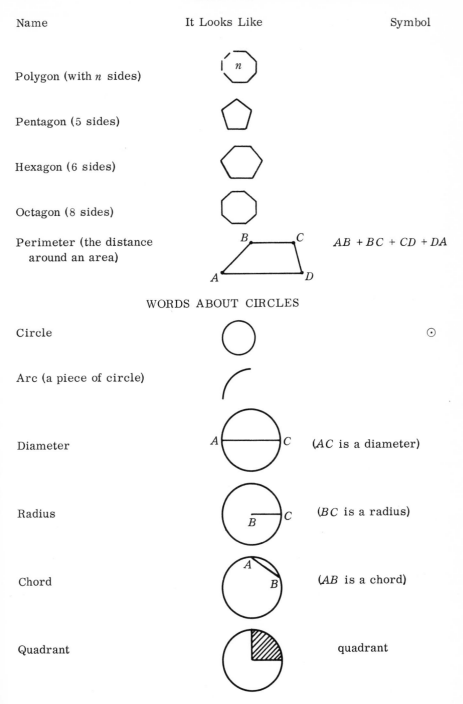

Polygon (with n sides)

Pentagon (5 sides)

Hexagon (6 sides)

Octagon (8 sides)

Perimeter (the distance around an area) $AB + BC + CD + DA$

WORDS ABOUT CIRCLES

Circle   ⊙

Arc (a piece of circle)

Diameter   (AC is a diameter)

Radius   (BC is a radius)

Chord   (AB is a chord)

Quadrant   quadrant

Name	It Looks Like	Symbol

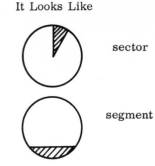

Sector   sector

Segment   segment

Circumference (the distance
around a curved area)

Pi (the ratio of a circle's
circumference to its radius)

Words About Other Curves

Conic section (one of a class of
curves that is related to solid
cones)

Ellipse (a closed conic section)

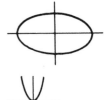

Parabola (an open conic
section)

Hyperbola (an open conic
section with branches)

Catenary (a curve that looks
like a limp clothesline)

Name	It Looks Like	Symbol

Words About Solids

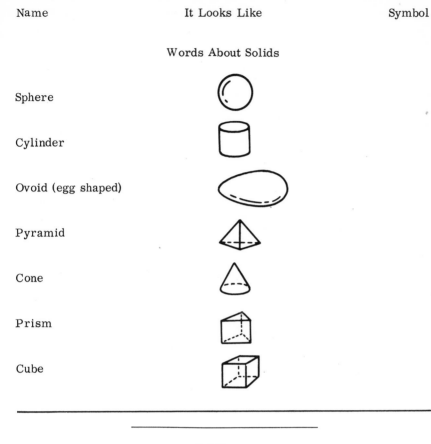

Sphere

Cylinder

Ovoid (egg shaped)

Pyramid

Cone

Prism

Cube

Summary

The best summary of this section is Table 6. Refer to it when necessary.

Algebra

Al Jabr.   My dictionary says that the word *algebra* comes from the Arabic *al jabr*. It also says that algebra is "that branch of mathematics which treats of the relations and properties of numbers by means of letters, signs of operation, and other symbols, including solution of equations...."

Symbols.   The most important thing for you to know about writing and typing algebra is that it uses symbols, just as Webster said. Thus in algebra you do not call a spade a spade. Instead you call a spade an *S*, or you may even call it an *x*.

If we use new symbols for words and concepts it becomes very like a new language; but it is not a difficult new language—not for the secretary anyway. If there is any difficulty, it is the scientist, who thinks in the language of algebra, who has most of the difficulty—you only have to reproduce it. Using x's and y's in typewritten text is not so different from what you have to do all the time. The only trouble is that you have to be neater than when you are simply writing words that flow along in neat uninterrupted lines.

Equations. Another feature of algebra is that it is always making statements in the form of equations. We have already discussed the fact that equations say that "something is something" where the *is* is the equal sign, =. (I refer you to the chapter on chemistry and the section on the chemical equation, p. 11.) Suppose a little boy were to say about his best friend, "Melvin is a rat." Expressed algebraically, it might look like:

$$M = R$$

But the casual reader will not know what $M = R$ means. It could mean "Martha is ravishing." The scientist or engineer avoids such confusion by what he calls "defining terms," a process that usually uses the word *where*. The engineer will say:

$$M = R$$

where

M = Melvin (in boy units)

R = rat (in rat units)

The scientist is saying things carefully and with precise definitions.

This business of *units* is an important but simple concept. The good engineer always states the units to which his numbers and symbols refer. This can best be shown by the example of distance. If we say that San Francisco is at a distance d from Los Angeles, the value of d is different if it is measured in miles or in kilometers. So we must add "where d is in miles" or "where d is in kilometers" or a similar statement. The important thing is that unless the units are stated you cannot set a numerical value for what you are talking about. It is the responsibility of the engineer or scientist to state his units.

Here are some actual algebraic expressions such as you might expect to meet anywhere engineering concepts are written out. An electronics example, making use of much of the material already treated in this chapter, comes from a recent scientific journal:

$$t_\gamma = \frac{1.95 \times 10^{-6}}{V_B^{1/5} \cdot J_c}$$

where
t_γ = rise time of the diode pulse in seconds
V_B = breakdown voltage in volts
J_C = current loading (amperes/cm^2)
(By the way, a whole mathematical statement like t_γ = ... is called a mathematical expression.) This expression is an excellent example of what you may encounter, since here we have:

> raising to a negative power
> raising to a fractional power
> descriptive subscripts
> explanation of units

It is also an example of the kind of inconsistency you will see and which you must get used to. For example, why use, in the same expression, two different symbols, the × and the ·, for multiplication? No very good reason except that it is conventional to use the × in front of 10 to a power; but × may be confused with other symbols of the equation, the V and the J, so it is not used in the denominator. Also, t_γ makes sense for "rise time"; the t stands for time and the γ for rise. In this same way V_B makes sense for "breakdown voltage." But why is the expression t_γ in small letters. No good reason I can think of — just inconsistency. And J_C is even more difficult to understand, with a capital J and small c subscript. It could as easily have been the other way round. The engineer usually has some reason for his preference for certain symbols — perhaps capital T (elsewhere in the text) was reserved for temperature, and R for reverse, and so on. There is even an inconsistency in the description of units where (amperes/cm^2) is in parentheses and volts is not. As always, you must remember — do it as your boss wants it, even if it is inconsistent. Otherwise you will surely introduce confusion!

The Equal Sign and Its Relatives. Do you know how many variations there are on the word "is"? Take the statement, "A Pekinese is a dog." It is not a very exciting statement; but let us mess it up a bit (as a scientist might). He could say that

	the Pekinese *is indeed* a dog
or	*is less of* a dog than the wolfhound
or	the wolfhound *is more of* a dog than the Pekinese
or	the Pekinese *is almost* a dog
or	the Pekinese *is equivalent to* a dog
or	the Pekinese *is similar to* a dog
or	the Pekinese *is not* a dog at all

What we are doing here is playing with nuances; our engineer or scientist is very skilled in nuances, in fact, in some ways, nuances are his business. Table 7 gives some of the nuances of equality. (It is likely that when he dictates statements involving the symbols listed in Table 7 your employer will come to a stop and say something like, "write that last expression as an equation with an 'equal to or greater than' sign;' ".. with a 'similar to' sign;' or "... with a 'greater than' sign.")

Table 7. Equality Nuances

The Statement in Words	May Be Written
1. That *is* that.	this = that
2. This *is indeed* that, in fact *identical.*	this ≡ that
3. This is *more than* that, *bigger than* that.	this > that
4. This is *much bigger* than that.	this ≫ that
5. This is *less than* that, *smaller than* that.	this < that
6. This is *much smaller* than that.	this ≪ that
7. This is either *the same as* that *or*, if anything *bigger*, never smaller.	this ≥ that
8. This is either *the same as* that *or*, if anything *smaller*, never bigger.	this ≤ that
9. This is *similar* to that or *proportional* to that.	this : that or this ~ that or this ≅ that or this ∞ that
10. This is to that as these are to those.	this : that = these : those
11. This *is not* that at all.	this ≠ that

The Parenthesis and Its Family.   The parenthesis has a family with relatives too. You met parentheses previously in the chapter on chemistry (p. 9). Remember there I said that parentheses are used in scientific text to mark off symbols that "go together," that is, behave as though they are simply one symbol. This is still essentially the case in mathematics. Just as in chemistry, the expression denoted by parentheses is *not* (as it is in English) sufficiently unimportant that it can be eliminated without essentially changing the meaning of a sentence.

There is a serious precaution to be observed in your use of parentheses: You must have them encompass the entire expression which they are to include. This means that occasionally the parenthesis signs on your typewriter will not be large enough. For example, if you must put parentheses around a fractional term such as the following:

$$\left(\frac{3 \times d^3}{43.7}\right)$$

you may find that the typewriter symbols do not spread high enough to hold the entire term. Accordingly, you must draw the symbols in neatly with a black ball-point pen.

Parenthetical expressions may have inside of them other parenthetical expressions which may have inside of them still other parenthetical expressions, and so on. As in literary text, this is taken care of by the use of additional symbols, namely,

	brackets	[ ]
and	braces	{ }

The following expression indicates how we use these:

$$\left\{\frac{\left[\dfrac{(4x^2)^3}{3(x-y)}\right]\left[\dfrac{(32d)^{1/4}}{2x^2 - 4xy + y^2}\right]}{2(a-b)}\right\} \cdot \left\{\frac{13^{a/b}}{2xy}\middle/ 3J\right\}$$

The rule is that these symbols encompass each other in this order:

$$\{[(\quad)]\}$$

The Arithmetic of Algebra. You are not a mathematician but you can add, subtract, multiply, and divide. Every scientist-employer expects his secretary to do these things reasonably well. Since you can do arithmetic you are familiar with the symbols: $+$, $-$, $\times$, and $\div$.

Shall We Multiply?   We all know that you can multiply something by something else by use of the symbol $\times$. There is also another way to indicate multiplication in algebraic text, that is by saying nothing. That is, when two numbers or algebraic expressions are simply placed next to each other, with *no* symbol at all between them, that means multiply. For example, "$3C$" means that we have 3 of whatever C represents, or 3 C's. This expands into a general principle in algebra. Whenever two expressions (or three, or four, or any number) are side by side, we infer from this that they are to be multiplied. Thus, in the expression below:

$$3ab(3y^2 - 4x)$$

3, a, b, and $(3y^2 - 4x)$ are multiplied together, and the expression could have been written in the following way:

$$3 \times a \times b \times (3y^2 - 4x)$$

There is still one more way to multiply. This is with a point: a dot placed a half line up between items that are being multiplied. (Remember, we met the point a few pages back.) Thus *"A times B"* which we may write as $A \times B$ or AB may also be written $A \cdot B$. The dot is written above the line so that it will not be confused with a decimal point, and it is used primarily because the letter x occurs so much in mathematical text that it may be confused with the symbol $\times$.

The "Plus-or-Minus." Another symbol you must know is just two of the familiar ones combined. This is $\pm$, which stands "plus-or-minus" he means that there is *range* or *spread* of that much. For example, if you say that your weight varies between 120 and 130 pounds, the spread or range is 10 pounds. Another way to represent this spread is to call it *"± 5 pounds."* In other words, your weight is 125 ± 5 pounds.

Factors and Terms. These are two algebraic words that you *must* comprehend. You must understand them because your employer will use them both in dictation and in ordinary conversation to point out different parts of an algebraic expression. You will not realize what he means unless you have a feeling for these words. *Factors* are merely the items in an algebraic expression that are multiplied together. They may be simple numbers, simple symbols, or complex combinations of numbers and symbols. But the fact is that they are *multiplied* together, and each item which is multiplied by others is a factor of the multiplied product. Thus, in the following expression:

$$3d(2y^2 - 3a)(4b^2)$$

the factors are:

$$3$$

$$d$$

$$(2y^2 - 3a)$$

and $\quad\quad\quad\quad\quad 4b^2$

On the other hand, in any algebraic statement, any piece of the expression which is separated from any other piece by either a *"+"* sign, a *"−"* sign, or a *"±"* sign is a *term*. A term can be either a simple number or any combination of numbers and symbols. The product of many factors may itself be a term; and a factor may be a combination of many terms. Thus, in the following expression:

$$3 \cdot J^3 - 4(x^2 - b^2) + (d^2 + c^3 + 13)(y^5)(c - 3)$$

$$3 \cdot J^3$$

$$4(x^2 - b^2)$$

and $\quad(d^2 + c^2 + 13)(y^5)(c - 3)$

are terms, since they are separated from each other by addition or subtraction signs. Within these terms we find factors. Thus, the term $3 \cdot J^3$ is made up of the two factors:

$$3 \text{ and } J^3$$

The term $4(x^2 - b^2)$ is made up of the two factors:

$$4 \text{ and } (x^2 - b^2)$$

and the term $(d^2 + c^2 + 13)(y^5)(c - 3)$ is made up of the factors

$$(d^2 + c^2 + 13)$$

$$(y^5)$$

$$(c - 3)$$

Now if you examine these factors, you find that some of them are made up of even smaller terms. Thus, the factor $(x^2 - b^2)$ is made up of the terms x^2 and b^2; the factor $(d^2 + c^2 + 13)$ is made up of the terms d^2, c^2, and 13; and the factor $(c - 3)$ is made up of the terms c and 3.

The Function. What is it that the scientist or engineer is trying to say with all these symbols and equations and factors and terms and expressions? He is describing something that is happening or that may happen. The scientist sets up a world of his own with "characters" (the symbols); he puts them into a set of conditions or situations (equations); he makes them interact with each other; and then he sees how the story (the mathematical situation) "comes out." This outcome is known as the "solution." When a scientist works out the solution, he says he is "solving the equations." Generally, when your employer thinks enough of what he has done to ask you to type it up for him it means that he has successfully solved his equations. What you will reproduce for him will be the process he worked through— step by step—in order to arrive at the solution. The final statement will be "the answer!"

The key, both in a story and in algebra, is interaction. Someone or something is making an effect on someone else or on some other thing. If there is a change in "this" it will cause a change in "that." The mathematician says it this way: if "this" changes with "that," then "this" is a function of "that." The function can be described with words (as the storyteller does) or with symbols (in the language of algebra), or with a sketch (like the artist), except that when the scientist sketches he calls the sketch a *graph*. *Two Earthy Functions*.   You perspire freely when the temperature gets warm, you perspire more freely when the temperature gets warmer. In other words, your perspiration is a function of temperature. This fact can be expressed mathematically as

$$P = f(T)$$

where T is the temperature in degrees Fahrenheit, P is the amount you perspire in any units you want, and f simply means that there is a functional relationship between P and T.

The function just described is qualitative. Now let us consider a quantitative functional relationship. Say that John eats twice as much as Mary. The amount of food eaten by John is therefore a function of the amount of food eaten by Mary. If we designate the food eaten by John as F_j and the food eaten by Mary as F_m then

$$F_j = f(F_m)$$
$$F_j = 2F_m$$

This example also illustrates two other ideas you will meet, the *independent* and *dependent* variables. Both the amount eaten by John and the amount eaten by Mary change, or vary. Thus F_j and F_m are called variables. But if John is taking two bites for each one he sees Mary take, the food that John eats always depends on the food that Mary eats. Thus F_m is the independent variable and F_j is the dependent variable.

The Graph.   It may now be desirable to represent the amount of food ingested by John and Mary in pictorial form. This is something that often confuses the secretary and leaves her in a state of bewilderment. It is the question of how something which is represented by F_m's and F_j's can be made into a picture known as a *graph*. Figure 6 is a graph which indicates the increased eating capacity that John has over Mary. You can see that for any point on the line the amount of food taken by John, shown on the vertical line at the left, is twice that taken by Mary, shown on the lowest horizontal line. You can prove this for yourself. In Figure 6, look at point A. If you look at the straight up and down side of the graph, the F_j side, you will note that you read off 2 units, or mouthfuls. The same point read in the left and right direction at the bottom is 1 unit (mouthful) of F_m. Thus, true to the algebraic equations which gave us the function, for point A,

$$F_j = 2F_m$$

John has twice as many mouthfuls as Mary; he has twice as many also for point B—4 for him, 2 for her—and for point C—6 for him and 3 for her. The graph is thus a true picture of the mathematical expression $F_j = 2F_m$.

Here is another algebraic expression involving John and Mary. Say John eats not twice what Mary eats, but rather what she eats *raised to the second power*. In algebra, this is:

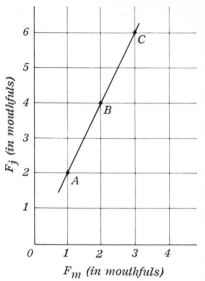

Figure 6. Graph of the food eaten by John as a function of the food eaten by Mary.

$$F_j = F_m{}^2$$

This equation tells you what is happening in a clearer, simpler, and shorter way than can be done in words. It says the number of hamburgers, for example, eaten by John is equal to the number eaten by Mary multiplied by itself,

$$F_m \times F_m$$

or $\qquad F_m{}^2$

or $\qquad F_m$ raised to the second power

This information can now be put into a new graph as shown in Figure 7. You can see it makes a curved line, and the line gets steeper and steeper with every additional hamburger that Mary eats. John's eating rate soon becomes tremendous, because when Mary, having finished

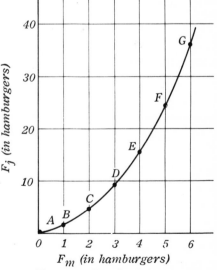

Figure 7. Graph of the number of hamburgers eaten by John as a function of the number of hamburgers eaten by Mary.

her third hamburger, adds 1 more (her fourth) John goes from 9 to 16. He adds 7. When she adds her fifth, he goes from 16 to 25, thus adding the amazing total of 9. So, you see, the curve gets steeper with each additional hamburger that Mary eats.

Drawing A Graph. As a technical secretary you will occasionally be called upon to make graphs. Do not let it throw you. It will not be necessary for you to solve an algebraic expression. Rather you will be given information that will lead you to the knowledge of where to put the dots which must ultimately be connected with a smooth line. This information will usually be given as shown in Table 8. To plot this information as in Figure 7, you run your finger up the vertical line of the graph until you encounter that number; then you go to the right until you come to the number which gives the correct value for the variable F_m. This procedure is just like finding your way in New York City and many other cities of the world that have a regular network of streets. For example, if you wish to find the intersection of Third Avenue and Fifty-seventh Street, you find Third Avenue, which runs vertically, and move up it until you find Fifty-seventh Street, which runs horizontally, and there you are.

Streets and Avenues. The final definitions of this section are of the words *abscissa* and *ordinate.* These are the names that the mathematician gives to a particular "street" and a particular "avenue" that he selects to act as references for all points that are plotted on a graph. All points are then expressed by the number of units they are above or below the abscissa and to the right or left of the ordinate. It is as if, in Manhattan, Forty-second Street and Fifth Avenue were selected as references, and the location of any other point was given by the number of blocks it was above or below Forty-second Street and east or west of Fifth Avenue.

Conventionally, the independent variable is placed on the abscissa and the dependent variable is placed on the ordinate. So in

Table 8. The Relationship $F_j = F_m^2$

F_m (in hamburgers)	F_m^2	F_j (in hamburgers)	Point on Graph
0	0	0	A
1	1	1	B
2	4	4	C
3	9	9	D
4	16	16	E
5	25	25	F
6	36	36	G

the preceding example F_m values were plotted on the abscissa and F_j values were plotted on the ordinate. The abscissa and ordinate are also referred to as the *coordinate axes*. The abscissa is the horizontal axis, and the ordinate is the vertical axis.

Here is what you should keep in mind when you draw a graph. Always be careful to draw straight lines for the ordinate and abscissa. Label the units of the ordinate and the abscissa. Insert numbers on each of these lines either by typing or by using a template (which is described in Part II, p. 188). Find the points to be graphed from the data and connect them with a smooth line, drawn with a black ball-point pen (and possibly with the aid of a French curve, which is described below). Leave indications of the points plotted, either with heavy dots or with small crosses.

The term French curve may sound very outlandish. It is really a very simple tool that can be of great help in drawing curves. You will find as you rotate it around the plotted points that some portion of it will make a smooth curve connecting them. (See Figure 8.) Further discussion of graphs and techniques for dealing with them is given in Part II.

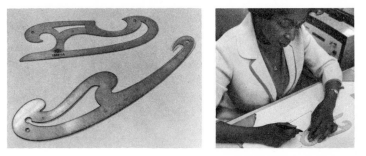

Photographs courtesy of the Raytheon Company.

Figure 8. Some French curves (left) and drawing a graph with them (right).

Vectors. Usually a number does not know where it is going—it just sits there. Take the number 93—by itself it is practically useless. When you apply it to some unit, like dollars, it begins to have some significance. Or it can be applied to 93 pieces of paper or 93 books or 93 hats or 93 anything. And when you talk about 93 miles, there is a chance for an additional meaning to be brought in. For example, if you say that Milwaukee is 93 miles from Chicago, you can add that it is 93 miles north of Chicago. Now the number 93 also begins to have some direction, in this case the direction is north.

It is important in mathematics that when a number has a directional meaning there be a way to indicate this easily to the reader. In printed text the normal practice is to print numbers that have directions associated with them in boldface type. If A were meant to show directionally it would look like this: $\boldsymbol{A}$. But it is no simple matter to show boldface on an ordinary typewriter. Nor is it convenient for the engineer or scientist to do so when he is writing longhand. In typing or in longhand one of several techniques is used: the underline, $\underline{A}$, the overline, $\overline{A}$, or the arrow, $\vec{A}$. The arrow is the most often encountered of the three, and what better way to show direction than to use an arrow? Now in talking about the distance from Milwaukee to Chicago the mathematician will not call it simply d but rather $\vec{d}$. The arrow of course is not pointing north, it just means that this expression is pointing *somewhere*. The actual direction must be stated as "north." Any algebraic term with an arrow over it to indicate a direction is known as a *vector*.

Drawing the Arrow. I have found that the best way to make vector arrows is to go over the text after typing and draw them in with a black ball-point pen as needed. Again I caution you to be neat, and to draw your arrowheads so that they are uniform and small. Some typewriters will have the vectorial arrow on the keyboard, which is a convenience. But since you probably will have to draw arrows, here is how to draw them correctly:

like this $\longrightarrow$
or this $\longrightarrow$
or this $\longrightarrow$
or this $\longrightarrow$

There are many ways to do it. All the above are acceptable, but

this $\longrightarrow$ is awful
and so is this $\frown\!\!\!\rightarrow$
and this $\longrightarrow\!\!\triangleright$ is even worse

Worst of all is a text with an array of nonuniform symbols that are all supposed to mean the same thing. Here is an example of the way it should *not* look:

$$\overrightarrow{AB} + 3X^2 + \overrightarrow{2X} + 3(\overrightarrow{a - b})^{1/2}$$

Here is the way it should look:

$$\vec{AB} + 3X^2 + \vec{2X} + 3(\overrightarrow{a - b})^{1/2}$$

In other words, a mathematical symbol on a typewritten page must look the same every time. Take the letter a. It always looks just like that: a, a, a, a. This is what the reader expects. That is why he will be dismayed by a secretary who types a neat page of text but carelessly draws in lines and symbols.

The "Un-" or "Anti-" Arrow. Now that the scientist has invented a term to show numbers which are going someplace, numbers which have direction, he has gotten himself into the kind of dilemma he is always getting into—namely, he now has to find a way to indicate numbers that may have a direction but which he prefers to treat as though they had no direction. He wants to say, "here is a certain vector, but right now don't think of it as a vector, just think of the number associated with it, its magnitude." You might think that the easiest way to do this is simply to leave out the arrows. That is true, except that when the author presents a text where there are many vectorial arrows, he begins to feel uneasy about terms that don't have arrows over them. He starts to think that the reader might believe that he carelessly left off some arrows. In order to show the reader that he really meant to leave off a given arrow, the scientist adds another symbol to the given expression to show that at that moment he is not thinking of it as vectorial. The symbol used by the scientist is two parallel, vertical straight lines. Now $|\vec{a}|$ is just a number again. It has no direction. The two parallel lines have converted the vector into a simple numerical quantity which is known as the *magnitude* of the vector. This leaves us with just one other kind of number that must be named. If something is not a vector or the magnitude of a vector it is a *scalar*, that is, a quantity with no direction associated with it. We do not employ any symbol to show that a number is a scalar. Anything is a scalar unless we show the vector sign or the magnitude sign.

Gradient, Divergence, and Curl. There is a whole scientific area which is known as vector algebra. The important words used in this algebra, in addition to *vector* and *scalar*, are:

gradient, divergence, and *curl*

Their meanings are quite complex, but as far as you are concerned, they are nothing but kinds of algebraic symbols. Gradient and divergence are often called just "grad" and "div." When used in scientific text these words are placed in front of a mathematical expression to show that a certain kind of vector operation is happening.

In dictation your employer will say "the gradient of x square minus three" or "grad x square minus three," and you will type,

$$\text{grad } (x^2 - 3)$$

If he says "the divergence of V," you will type,

$$\text{div } \vec{V}$$

and if he says "the curl of F," you will type,

$$\text{curl } \vec{F}$$

because the expression after "divergence" or "curl" is always a vector

These words may be placed right inside algebraic expressions. By the way, the *nabla*, ∇, which is a delta written upside down, is often used a symbol for grad. (*Nabla* is the name of an ancient Assyrian harp similar in shape to ∇. It is often called just "del.") The divergence may be represented using the nabla as $\nabla \cdot$ (called "del dot") and the curl may be represented as $\nabla \times$ (called "del cross"). Thus,

$$\text{grad } (x^2 - 3) = \nabla (x^2 - 3)$$

$$\text{div } \vec{V} = \nabla \cdot \vec{V}$$

$$\text{curl } \vec{F} = \nabla \times \vec{F}$$

Some Leftover Words and Concepts. The vocabulary of algebra contains many words. It is not my intention to force upon you the understanding of all of them. On the other hand, a few key ones are important.

Matrices. A matrix is nothing but an array of numbers or symbols arranged in an orderly rectangular pattern. A square matrix, which is often also called a *determinant*, may look as follows:

$$\begin{bmatrix} a_1 & a_2 & a_3 \\ b_1 & b_2 & b_3 \\ c_1 & c_2 & c_3 \end{bmatrix}$$

There are many other kinds of patterns. Probably the easiest thing to do here is merely to advise you to get explicit instructions from your employer when he wishes you to present symbols or numbers in a matrix, since there are always special rules for each case. But in all matrices, all the symbols in a given row (for example a_1, a_2, a_3) must be on the same horizontal line; and the symbols in a column, as

$$\begin{bmatrix} a_1 \\ b_1 \\ c_1 \end{bmatrix}$$

must be in the same vertical line. This may appear evident and not too important. However, if you think about it, you will see that it is very simple to fall into the trap of letting one row or one column slip a little as you type it, and thereby ruin the entire meaning for the scientist.

Words of Order. Very often in speaking about a mathematical statement or expression the scientist will say that "this is a *first-order* (or a *second-order* or a *third-order*) equation." All you need to know is that he is referring to the *highest power* to which any symbol in the expression is raised. Accordingly,

$$x^2 + 2xy + y^2$$

is a *second-order* expression because 2 is the highest power that appears. Second-order expressions are also called *quadratic* expressions. By the same token, the expression

$$y^3 + 3cd + x = \cos \theta$$

is a *third-order* expression.

Summary

1. *Algebra* is a way of talking and thinking and writing which uses *symbols* to stand for quantities and ideas. It is important to identify all symbols that appear with statements like, "Let x equal the velocity." In addition, units may be stated, as "...velocity in miles per hour."

2. Algebraic statements are called *equations*. The *equal sign* =, is one of many kinds of connecting symbols used in equation. Table 7 gives a complete list of these symbols.

3. Parentheses are often used in mathematical expressions. All numbers within a pair of parentheses are treated like one number or symbol. If a parenthetical expression contains other parenthetical expressions, the whole expression is then placed within a pair of *brackets*, [...]. To enclose bracketed terms *braces*, {...}, are used. The squence is:

$$\{[(\ldots)]\}$$

4. In algebra, multiplication is indicated by $\times$ ($A \times B$); or by a dot placed one-half line up ($A \cdot B$); or just by placing the quantities to be multiplied right next to each other (AB).

5. To show a spread or range use the symbol $\pm$, called *plus-or-minus*; so the range 110 to 130 may be shown 120 ± 10.

6. The *factors* in an algebraic expression are the items that are multiplied together. A factor may be anything, a simple number or a complex parenthetical expression.

7. The *terms* in an algebraic expression are the items that are added to or subtracted from one another. A term may also be very simple or very complex.

8. When one thing, A, happens, because another thing, B, happens, the first is said to be a *function* of the second. Symbolically, $A = f(B)$. A is called the **dependent variable** and B is called the **independent variable.**

9. Almost all functions can be represented by pictures known as *graphs,* and almost all graphical pictures can also be expressed mathematically. Figures 6 and 7 are typical graphs.

10. Sometimes a mathematical expression must show a direction as well as a quantity. Then a small arrow is drawn over the expression and it is called a *vector.* For example, $\vec{F}, \vec{d}$. When it is possible to ignore a vector's direction, two parallel, vertical straight lines are used, and an expression such as $|\vec{F}|$ is called the *magnitude* of the vector. In a discussion of vectors a quantity that has no direction associated with it is called a *scalar.*

11. Some important words used in vector algebra are **gradient, divergence,** and **curl,** abbreviated as grad, div, and curl. They may be placed in front of mathematical expressions, as grad A, div A, or curl A.

12. A *matrix* is a rectangular array of symbols or numbers. In typing, you must remember that the correct rows and columns must line up.

13. In a *second-order* expression the highest power is 2. So

$$a^2 + b^2$$

is second order. Similarly, the highest power in a third-order expression is 3, and so on.

Calculus

Introduction. Calculus, like algebra, geometry, and trigonometry, is a technique of mathematics. It is a far more sophisticated one, however, and to the scientist it is more exciting than the others. We can relate the growth of modern scientific thinking to the impact of calculus on the scientific community. For you as a secretary, there is one compensating fact about calculus; you will find it a lot easier to work with than the scientist or engineer does. This is so because the things you do in writing calculus text are almost identical with what you do when you write algebraic material. There are a few more special symbols and a few more rules—and that's it. The next few pages will attempt to give you some insight into the meaning and reasons for these symbols and rules.

The most important operations in calculus are differentiation and integration. The meanings that these words have in mathematics have very little relation to their literary meanings. In mathematics a differential part of something is a very small part—an infinitesimally small part. When you differentiate a mathematical expression you turn it into something that describes how very small parts of the expression behave. When you integrate, you reverse the process, adding up all the small parts to come back to where you started. Like many things in mathematics, it seems to be a pointless circle, an excursion out into a twilight zone, and then a way to come back. But it isn't.

Differentiation.   An exciting, new fact about calculus, in particular about differentiation, is that it will allow us to make a more detailed analysis of John and Mary's hamburger consumption than we were able to do using only algebra. Look at the graph in Figure 7. When Mary is eating 4 hamburgers, and John is eating 16 hamburgers, it may seem that John is eating 4 times as fast as Mary. By the time you have finished reading this section you will have learned that John is not at that point eating 4 times as fast as Mary, he is actually eating 8 times as fast as Mary. How do we determine this? By differentiating.

Differentiation makes it possible to determine how one variable of a function changes when the other variable changes. This is not always a difficult problem. For example, when $F_j = 2F_m$, it is quite clear that whenever F_m increases by 1, F_j increases by 2. In other words, F_j is always changing twice as fast as F_m. There is no need to differentiate to find this out. But for most functions, including $F_j = F_m^2$, the problem is not so easy, because the *rate* at which one variable changes with respect to the other is usually *itself* changing. Fortunately, however, for most functions, even very complicated ones, differentiation makes it possible to determine the desired information.

As a secretary, just what do you have to know about this? Basically, you must know how differentiating a function changes the way that it is written. Consider $F_j = 2F_m$ again. When doing differentiation the scientist or engineer makes a ratio, or fraction, of the two variables he is interested in, and in order to indicate to the reader that he is differentiating, he puts a d in front of each. Thus he starts by writing

$$\frac{dF_j}{dF_m}$$

By making the ratio, he is already comparing John's rate of eating with Mary's. He next goes through a mathematical operation (which I will not attempt to explain) which tells him that in this case the ratio is equal to

$$2F_m$$

Thus he has formed a new equation

$$\frac{dF_j}{dF_m} = 2F_m$$

This new equation is the result of differentiating the first equation. It tells us that at any point John is eating at a rate given by the expression $2F_m$. That is, when Mary is eating her third hamburger $(F_m = 3)$, John is eating 2×3, or 6, times as fast as Mary is; and when Mary is eating her fourth hamburger, John is eating 2×4, or 8, times as fast as she is.

This notation for a differentiated function doesn't spring completely from out of the blue. Do you remember the symbol for an increment, Δ? Well, one way of explaining differentiation is that it is based on a ratio of two increments, where the increments are very, very small. Since Δ is the Greek D, very, very small Δ's are shown as d's.

One other thing of importance, the ratio you end up with after differentiating may not always look as simple as $2F_m$. For example, after differentiating, the result may look like

$$x^3 - \sin y + 9$$

or it may even be a more complicated expression. The answer you get after differentiating has a name. It is known as a *derivative*, because it is what you "derive" from a mathematical statement when you go through the operation of differentiating.

You may ask, "so what?" I can answer only that the mathematician wants to know this. It is often important to him and to most engineers and scientists to know how fast something is changing. He is really not so frantically interested in hamburgers; but he may be interested in knowing at exactly what point a missile changes its speed and direction as a function of the aircraft's motion; or he may want to know the rate at which people spend money in department stores as a function of the tax rate. By differentiating mathematical functions, the mathematician can find out these and similar things. His answers usually end up as expressions containing d's, and start off

$$\frac{dy}{dx} =$$

Of course, it can never be that simple. Derivatives are not always represented as fractions containing d's. Sometimes they are represented by primes,

$$y' \qquad \text{or} \qquad F_j$$

sometimes by dots,

$$\dot{y} \qquad \text{or} \qquad \dot{F}_j$$

and sometimes even with D's,

$$D_x \qquad \text{or} \qquad D_{F_m}$$

(In all of these expressions, y and F_j are considered to be the dependent variables, and x and F_m are the independent variables.) *When You Take Dictation.* When you take dictation it may go like this:

> Boss: In order to determine the rate of change of y with the variable x, differentiate y with respect to x.
> (The secretary feels she can go along with that statement and graciously puts those very words and letters into shorthand just as he said them.)
> Boss: Since y is a function of x where y equals x to the fourth minus three x squared plus forty-two ...
> (Secretary puts down all those words except at the equation, where, realizing that he wants it in equation form, she abandons her shorthand and puts down his shorthand.)
> The dictation pad:.... where $y = x^4 - 3x^2 + 42$ ...
> Boss: The differential expression is as follows: dy over dx equals four x to the third minus six x.
> The dictation pad: ... $\dfrac{dy}{dx} = 4x^3 - 6x$

And so on till the end.

In writing differential fractions, put down $\dfrac{dy}{dx}$, not dy/dx, except when the expression appears inside a sentence. When it appears inside a sentence, you may save the trouble of typing above the line by using the form dy/dx. Otherwise there is nothing to it other than what you already know about algebra. You just keep in mind that your employer is describing how fast something is changing with something else.

Higher Derivatives. When the equation

$$F_j = F_m{}^2$$

was differentiated, the differentiated equation was seen to be

$$\frac{dF_j}{dF_m} = 2F_m$$

Now you may also differentiate this expression. Here you meet a new rule. When you differentiate *a second time,* you write the number 2 into the differential ratio twice, like this:

$$\frac{d^2 F_j}{dF_m{}^2}$$

You put it in like an exponent to the *top* d and like an exponent to the *variable* at the *bottom*. You may also differentiate a third time and a fourth time, and so on. If we change the variables to x and y, just to make it simpler, then the differential ratios look like this:

$$\frac{dy}{dx}$$ is the first derivative

$$\frac{d^2 y}{dx^2}$$ is the second derivative

$$\frac{d^3 y}{dx^3}$$ is the third derivative

$$\frac{d^4 y}{dx^4}$$ is the fourth derivative

and so on.

The Partial Derivative. Sometimes you want to differentiate with respect to only one variable, although many variables may be present. For example, John may not only be eating the number of hamburgers eaten by Mary squared, he may also be drinking one glass of cola for every three that she is drinking (while eating her hamburgers). Then the algebraic expression could include terms for the amount of cola each drinks. They could be called C_j and C_m. Now, here is the point, you can also differentiate the new, more complicated expression as

$$\frac{dF_j}{dC_m}$$

which is the rate of change of John's eating hamburgers relative to Mary's drinking cola, or as

$$\frac{dF_j}{dF_m}$$

which is the original differential relationship, or as

$$\frac{dC_j}{dC_m}$$

which compares the cola drinking only, and completely ignores hamburgers. In other words, the mathematician can compare any variable with any other by just differentiating those variables and ignoring all the others. When the mathematician does this he is differentiating selectively, or partially. He is taking a *partial derivative*. As far as you are concerned, you need to know only one thing. To write a partial derivative, instead of using the ordinary letter d, you use an old-fashioned, round, script ∂. Some technical typewriters have this letter. If you do not have it just write it neatly with a black ball-point pen. A typical equation might then look as follows:

$$\frac{\partial y}{\partial x} = a^2 - 3x + 2ax$$

or, for a double partial differentiation, it might look like this:

$$\frac{\partial^2 y}{\partial x^2} = \frac{1 - 2x + 3a^{3/2}}{2ab}$$

Integration. Integration is simply differentiation in reverse. If we differentiated $F_m{}^2$ to get $2F_m$, then we can integrate $2F_m$ to get $F_m{}^2$. And we show it with an integral sign that looks like a long-waisted capital S:

$$\int$$

So when you hear the words "the integral of two eff sub em," you should write:

$$\int 2F_m$$

Multiple Integrals. There are also double integrals, triple integrals, and so on. To show them, just repeat the integral sign. Thus the double integral of $2F_m$ is

$$\iint 2F_m$$

the triple integral of $2F_m$ is

$$\iiint 2F_m$$

and so on.

Limits. Integration is done between limits. This means that only a small region of the functional relationship may be considered. You can say, for example, in the case of the hamburgers, that you will integrate only in the region between Mary's third and seventh hamburger, that is, from $F_m = 3$ to $F_m = 7$. Then you place the limits of integration at the top and bottom of the integral sign, with the larger number on top. The expression is written as

$$\int_{3}^{7} F_m{}^2$$

which means, the "the integral of $F_m{}^2$ between the limits of Mary's third and seventh hamburger.

The Integral Equation.   Equations containing integrals generally have a certain appearance. There is a common arrangement of symbols that you will see over and over again. Consider the examples

$$\int_{2}^{9} dy = \int (x^2 + b)dx$$

and
$$\int\int 3(a^2 + 2b)dadb = f(ab)$$

What characteristic pattern appears? You see integral signs; you see limits, not all the time, but often; finally, you see differentials: dx, dy, da, and db are all differentials. Integral signs appear at the beginnings of integral expressions and differentials appear at the ends of integral expressions. Figure 9 in Part II (p. 195) reproduces a typical page of typed mathematical text containing integral equations.

Summary

1. Calculus compares things that are varying with each other. The comparisons are usually written as fractions, so that when y is compared with x you will frequently encounter expressions like

$$\frac{dy}{dx}$$

which means that y is being **differentiated** with respect to x.

2. It is possible to take a **second derivative** by putting in 2's like this:

$$\frac{d^2 y}{dx^2}$$

and a *third derivative* looks like this:

$$\frac{d^3 y}{dx^3}$$

and so on.

3. **Partial derivatives**   are similar to ordinary derivatives, but they are written with round script d's, as

$$\frac{\partial y}{\partial x} \quad \text{and} \quad \frac{\partial^2 y}{\partial x^2}$$

They mean to compare two variables ignoring any other variables that may be present (for example z).

4. Integration as a mathematical procedure is just differentiation in reverse. It is shown by the long-waisted S called the integral sign, $\int$. As with the summation sigma, limits can be placed at the bottom and top of the integral sign, as

$$\int_2^8 n\, dy$$

You can integrate the same expression over and over again. You just add integral signs, as

$$\iiint \sin x\, dx dy dz$$

Chapter 3
Physics

Introduction

Chemistry, mathematics, and physics are the three basic physical sciences. Once you are familiar with these three, you will see that most other sciences and engineering disciplines are only variations and combinations of them. Since you have already gone through chemistry and mathematics, the time has come for you to plunge into physics.

What is physics from your point of view? Physics is *almost* everything. It is the discipline which makes a science out of everything around you. Do you feel that something is hard or soft? Do you see that something is red, pink, or blue? Do you sense that something is hot or cold, that something is falling, is moving from left to right, or is at rest, that something is heavy or light? The physicist has taken these observations and applied scientific thinking to them, making them precise with the use of mathematics. Does this take the beauty out of them? The poet may think so, but the physicist thinks that this is in fact the beauty of them.

Some physicists work only in their minds. They write out their speculations about these matters in long mathematical sentences (equations). They are known as *theoretical* physicists. Another group is known as *experimental* physicists, or *applied* physicists. These people spend their time accumulating information (data). Then they recombine these data into new arrangements which may result in blueprints for machinery. Or they may simply arrange the data and feed them to theoretical physicists, who then deal with them in their own speculative way: always asking the question, "what if?"

We will study physics by dividing it into the following broad classifications: mechanics; hydraulics; acoustics; optics; heat and thermodynamics; crystallography and crystal physics; and modern physics. A discussion of electricity and magnetism, another very important branch of physics, will be included in the next chapter, *Electricity and Electronics*.

Mechanics

What Is It? Mechanics is the study of the laws that describe the actions of forces on material bodies. Most of the time, when a force is applied to an object it causes that object to move. Mechanics is the earliest science you meet as a child. Illustrations of the principles of elementary mechanics may be found in any playground. The slide (an *inclined plane*), the seesaw (a *lever*), and the swing (a *pendulum*) are the gadgets with which we first try out the laws of mechanics. As I said in the introduction, the physicist takes things that we feel (and here we are talking about the feeling of motion), and applies precise thinking to them.

When the physicist sees a child on a swing, he sees a pendulum, a weight moving at the end of a rope. To him the rope becomes the radius of a circle, and the weight (the child) moves in a piece of a circle (and you remember from the section on geometry that that is an arc). The swing moves back and forth, over and over again; this repeated movement the physicist calls *periodic*, or *harmonic*. He notices that as the child swings, the speed of movement is greatest at the bottom of the swing and slows down to nothing before changing direction at the end of the swing. He can write a mathematical function to describe the motion, and to tell how the time of each swing depends on the weight of the child, the push the child gives to each swing, and the length of the rope which ties the swing to the crossbar above. It turns out that the mathematical function makes use of the trigonometric sine, and, when plotted graphically, is known as a *sinusoidal* function.

Dependence on a mathematical function may also be observed for the seesaw. In addition, now there is the element of *balance* — there must be another child on the other side of the seesaw. And we can go on again to the other items in the playground. See that child going down the slide? He goes pretty fast, but he would go faster were it not for the *coefficient of friction* of the slide on his bottom.

What about the merry-go-round? It's loaded with physics, what with the *harmonic oscillations* made by its horses, and *centrifugal* force making the full dresses of the little girls stand out and flow prettily. See them as they move around with *angular momentum* in a set *circular locus*, their *angular velocity* going through the states of *acceleration, constant speed,* and *deceleration*. What have I just done? Did I insert words of physics into a playground of children in order to analyze and examine their happy childish play? Yes, that is just what I did. And by so doing, I introduced and to a degree defined:

inclined plane	oscillation	angular velocity
lever	sinusoidal	acceleration
pendulum	coefficient of friction	deceleration
periodic	centrifugal force	circular locus
harmonic	angular momentum	arc

In physics, there are many new words. Not so much new ways of writing formulas or equations or subscripts or super- scripts or symbols—we had most of what we need for these things in the chapters on chemistry and mathematics. No, just words that you should be acquainted with. You should have some idea of what they mean, some idea of how they are used, and you should also know how to spell them. You will find that almost everything you will be asked to reproduce on your type- writer in the field of mechanics will be a combination of these words with the mathematics of the last chapter. Therefore, let me show you what some of these words define.

The Things of Mechanics. First, there are the nouns that de- scribe objects or gadgets, which the physicist might call *sys- tems* or *mechanisms* or *machines*. We have already seen some such words, and we know what they mean. Words of this sort are listed in Table 1. Definitions of the words in this and fol- lowing tables are given in Glossary 7 in Part II.

Mechanics in Action. Mechanical things either move or stand still. If they move, they may move in a variety of ways. They may move in straight lines, curved lines, or circular paths; and they may move in the same pattern over and over again.

The part of mechanics that describes different kinds of movement is called *kinematics*. The part of mechanics that de- scribes "standing still" is called *statics*. The part of mechan- ics that describes the forces that make things move or stand still is called *dynamics*.

Movement. Some words of movement are given in Table 2.

Statics. The key word to remember in statics is *equilibrium*. If something is static, standing still, it is "in equilibrium." This means that the push on that thing from the left is just as much as the push on it from the right—so it does not move either to the left or to the right. In the same way, the push on it from above is just the same as the push on it from below—so it does not move up or down. Are you sitting on a chair right now? That means you are pushing on that chair with your weight; but

Table 1. The Objects of Mechanics

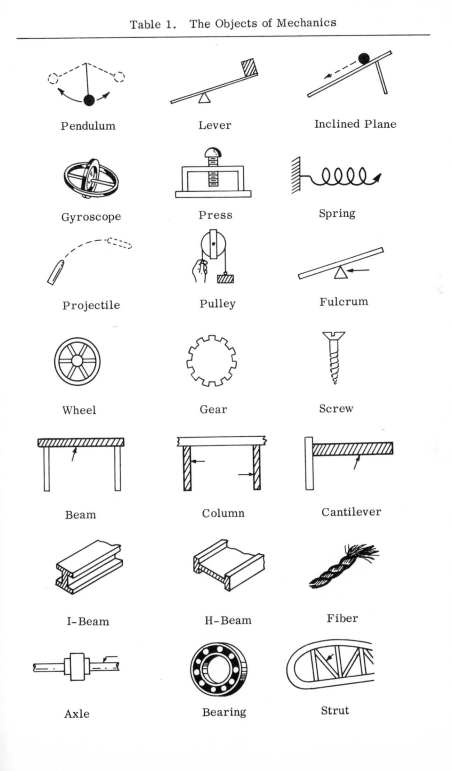

Pendulum   Lever   Inclined Plane

Gyroscope   Press   Spring

Projectile   Pulley   Fulcrum

Wheel   Gear   Screw

Beam   Column   Cantilever

I-Beam   H-Beam   Fiber

Axle   Bearing   Strut

Table 1 (continued)

| Rivet | Bolt | Nut |

Table 2.   Words That Relate to Movement

Straight-Line Movement		Movement in a Curved Path	
velocity	translation	rotation	centripetal
speed	precession	gyration	centrifugal
acceleration	rolling	axis	angular
deceleration	sliding	trajectory	angular velocity
inertia	slipping	angular momentum	

Repeated Movement

periodic	harmonic	phase	steady-state
cyclic	sinusoidal	amplitude	resonance
reiterative	oscillation	frequency	mode

---

the chair is also pushing right back on you. You are not moving up or down, neither is the chair —you are both in equilibrium.

A stone lying in a field is in equilibrium too, because the earth presses back on it with precisely as much force as is exerted by the stone on the earth. This leads us into the terms of statics. Table 3 lists some words on the subject.

Table 3.   The Words of Statics

equilibrium	force of gravity	pressure
constraint	center of gravity	elastic
potential energy	torque	inelastic
inertia	normal force	plastic
moment of inertia	perpendicular force	deformation
tension	stretch	stress
compression	strain	shear
modulus of elasticity	modulus of shear	modulus of compression

Force. We have spoken of movement and of standing still. Things move as a result of the application of forces to them. If the sum of all the forces acting on something is equal to zero, the object is in equilibrium and does not move. But when there is more force in one direction than the others, things start to pop. Things move, roll, slide, fly, collide, shatter, compress, explode. Things become unstatic—in short, dynamic. So this branch of mechanics is called dynamics. There are many kinds of forces. Table 4 lists some of them along with some other words about forces.

Table 4. Some Force Words

gravity	percussion	friction	electrical attraction
impact	collision	torque	heat generated

Coefficients. In physics, a coefficient isn't exactly the same as it was in chemistry, where it told "how many atoms" or "how many molecules." In physics a coefficient is usually something that helps you express one quantity, most often a force, in terms of another quantity.

The *coefficient of friction,* which describes the *force of friction,* is a coefficient you will meet often. Return to the playground and walk over to the slide. You can observe the coefficient of friction operating continuously. A child goes down the slide pulled by the force of gravity, but he goes down at a nice rate—not too fast—because the friction between his trousers and the slide is holding him back. If the slide were to be oiled, the friction would be much less (the coefficient of friction would be much less), and he would fly down the slide like a shot. On the other hand, if he were wearing sandpaper pants, the coefficient of friction would be so high that the frictional force would be greater than the force of gravity—and he would sit there, not moving at all. It is easy to see that the coefficient of friction is an important number. You want the coefficient of friction of your eraser on a piece of paper to be high, and you want the coefficient of friction between your ice skates and the ice to be low. Coefficients of friction are most often shown by the Greek letter μ. Table 5 gives a few other coefficients you may encounter. Each will also usually be represented by a Greek letter, but the Greek letters will not be given here because different people use different letters for the same coefficient.

Table 5. Some Coefficients

Coefficient of:		
restitution	viscosity	surface tension
stiffness	linear expansion	thermal conductivity

An Examination of Force, Energy, and Power. The scientist is sensitive to nuances as was shown in the chapter on mathematics by the many ways he could state an equation. Other important nuances relate to the differences between energy, force, and power. The layman usually uses these words to mean the same thing. When you do things with "vigor," what do you mean—force or energy or power? Webster says vigor is all three—force, energy, and power. But to the physicist, that is ridiculous; force is different from energy, and they are both different from power.

Force tells how much push you give something.

Energy tells how much push you give something over how far a distance.

Power tells how much push you give something over a given distance in a given time interval.

Here is an experiment that will serve as an example, and will illustrate these differences of meaning. Say you weigh 108 pounds. Now, I lift you with 108 pounds of *force*. I carry you to a table 3 feet tall and deposit you there. I have expended 324 foot-pounds (3 ft × 108 lb) of *energy*. Assume that I am physically fit and that I was able to do the whole job in 1 second. I exerted 324 foot-pounds per second of *power*. You see, force, energy, and power are indeed different from each other.

Units. There are two classifications of units in mechanics. One is units of space, mass, and time. The other is units of force, energy, and power. In the experiment above, you weighed 108 *pounds.* That is, the pound was used as the unit of measurement. Your weight could also have been given in terms of a unit called the *gram.* But you must never mix pounds and grams, or any other two units that can be used to measure the same quantity. You use either one unit or the other.

Table 6 summarizes the units you will most commonly meet in mechanics. The units are given in two groups *a* and *b*. The units labeled *a* are in the "pound, foot, second" system of units, also known as the *English system*. The units labeled *b* are in the "centimeter, gram, second," or c.g.s., system of units, which is also called the *metric system* of units.

Table 6.   Units of Mechanics

Some Units of Mass, Space, and Time

Units	Abbreviations
Mass	
a. pound, ounce, ton	lb, oz, t
b. gram, milligram, kilogram	g, mg, kg
Distance	
a. foot, yard, inch, mile	ft, yd, in., mi
b. centimeter, millimeter, meter,	cm, mm, m,
kilometer, micron, Ångstrom	km, μ, Å
Volume	
a. cubic foot, cubic inch, gallon	cu ft, cu in., gal
b. cubic centimeter, liter	cc, l
Time	
a. second, minute, hour, day, week,	sec, min, hr
month, year, decade, century	
b. second, millisecond, microsecond	sec, msec, μsec

Some Units of Force, Energy, and Power

Force	
a. pound	lb
b. dyne	dyn
Energy	
a. foot-pound, inch-pound,	ft-lb, in.-lb,
British Thermal Unit	BTU
b. erg, calorie, joule,	erg, cal, J,
dyne-centimeter	dyn-cm
Power	
a. horsepower	hp
b. watt, kilowatt	W, kW

Summary

1. Mechanics is the study of the laws of motion of material bodies. Motion may be in straight lines, in curved paths, in any combination of these, and repeated (*periodic*) motion. The study of the description of motion is called *kinematics.* The study of the *forces* that cause motion is called *dynamics.* The gadgetry of mechanics is summarized in Table 1. Words relating to movement are summarized in Table 2.

2. *Statics* is the part of mechanics that deals with bodies that are at rest. This means that all the forces trying to move them to and fro or up and down add up to zero. A static body is said to be in *equilibrium*. Words relating to statics are summarized in Table 3.

3. *Coefficients* are factors sometimes used in equations that represent forces. They are multipliers, and are usually represented by Greek letters.

4. To the physicist *force, energy,* and *power* are very different from each other and must not be confused. Force tells how much push you give something; energy is that push for a given distance; and power is that energy for a given time.

5. Always use the correct units and the correct abbreviations for them when expressing measured quantities. There are two basic systems of units used in physics, the English system and the metric system. The most common units encountered in mechanics are summarized in Table 6.

Hydraulics

What Is It? You should know that there is a special kind of mechanics known as *hydraulics*, with a special kind of dynamics called *hydrodynamics*, and a special kind of statics called *hydrostatics*.

Hydraulics is the mechanics of devices using water or other fluids, and hydrostatics and hydrodynamics are the statics and dynamics of systems using water or other fluids. The water-wheel on a river or in a dam is a hydraulic device. So is the water faucet in your sink. Until you turn the faucet, the water is standing still in the pipes, standing statically, that is (or hydro-statically). It is standing in equilibrium, with *pressure* from the city water system pushing from below, and pressure of equal amount pushing back from the closed faucet. When you turn the faucet, the pressure resistance of the closed faucet is removed, there is an unbalance of forces, the static system becomes a dynamic one, and the water flows. When the hydraulic system becomes dynamic, we are talking about hydrodynamics, which is also called fluid *dynamics*.

Table 7 gives a few additional words which apply specifically.

Table 7.   The Words and Concepts of Hydraulics

Fluid	Any liquid or gas.
Pipe	The greatest invention after the wheel and the lever.

Pressure	Force on a unit area. You exert much more pressure when you wear high heels than when you wear flat heels.

Compressible	Can be "squeezed together" into a smaller volume. You can do it with a gas.
Incompressible	It is very difficult to compress a liquid or a solid. They are almost incompressible.
Density	The weight of something per unit volume. It is usually expressed in grams per cubic centimeter (g/cc). A piece of lead is denser than a piece of wood, and water is denser than air.
Wettability	Water will roll off a duck's back without wetting it, and water will wet clean glass but not oily glass.

Capillary action	Water will wet the inside of a small tube and "climb up" it. A drinking straw is a capillary.

Table 7 (continued)

Surface tension

The force that is exerted in fluid surfaces. A soap bubble is held together by surface tension.

Viscous

Gooey. Molasses is viscous, alcohol is not viscous.

Jet

Spouting, spurting out in a stream.

Streamlines

The paths in which a fluid moves around a solid body. A streamlined body is contoured to minimize resistance to the flow of fluids.

Laminar flow

Smooth, orderly, flat flow of a fluid.

Turbulent flow

Swirly, chaotic flow of a fluid.

Vortex

Whirlpool-shaped flow of a fluid, tending to form a cavity in the center.

Table 7 (continued)

Venturi tube

A small tube that is inserted into a large tube to study a fluid that is flowing in the large tube.

Summary

1. *Hydraulics* is the equivalent of mechanics as applied to fluids.
2. *Hydrostatics* is the equivalent of statics as applied to fluids.
3. *Hydrodynamics* is the equivalent of dynamics as applied to fluids. It is also known as fluid dynamics.
4. The field of hydraulics is so similar to that of mechanics that it is only necessary for you to familiarize yourself with a few additional words, as explained in Table 7.

Acoustics

What Is It?   Acoustics is the science of sound. Sounds start somewhere; they are transmitted across distances; finally, they reach your ears, and you hear something. So much in physics is connected with you and your body; you feel movement and temperature in mechanics and heat, you see light in optics, and you hear sounds in acoustics.

The Aud- and the Son- of Acoustics.   The Latin word "to hear" is *audire* ; the first syllable *aud-* is found in many words having to do with acoustics and hearing:

audition	auditor	audible	audio
auditorium	audience	audit	auditory

Another Latin word of importance is *sonus* which means "sound." From this word come the acoustical words

sonorous	song	sonnet
sonority	ultrasonic	resonance

It Is All Done with Vibrations.   There is only one important concept you must understand to be able to deal with the secretarial requirements of acoustics. That is: *the sounds which you hear are the result of things vibrating.* These vibrating things cause the air to vibrate. The vibrating air then hits your ears, like the littlest of winds, and makes your eardrums vibrate.

Some typical vibrating things are the strings of a violin or guitar or bass fiddle, or the membrane of a drum, or the throat of a singer. If you look hard at any of these during a musical performance, you will actually see the vibrations. And what is a vibration? It is something moving back and forth the same way over and over again. You remember in the section on mechanics we discussed the back-and-forth, over-and-over-again motion of the pendulum, and we called this motion periodic, or harmonic, oscillation. That is exactly what sound vibration is too.

In Table 2 of this chapter, these words were introduced: *period*—which tells the time it takes for one oscillation; *amplitude*—which tells the amount of "swing" in each oscillation; *frequency*—which tells how many times the oscillation (or vibration) takes place in any given length of time; *phase*—which describes two or more separate vibrations with reference to whether they are swinging in time with each other or not. Then they may be "in phase," "out of phase," or "somewhat out of phase." When these words are used in acoustics, or specifically in that part of acoustics known as music, they take on meanings that may be very familiar to you, meanings that you never associated with physics.

In music, amplitude becomes *loudness*; frequency becomes *pitch*; period is really part of frequency, so it is related to pitch too; phase relates to whether the instruments are playing together or not. (The Boston Symphony Orchestra will play "in phase," but the Loker Elementary School Philharmonic probably will play "out of phase.")

If sound is composed of vibrations in the air, it is easy to accept the statement that the air is vibrating in *sound waves*. These waves, if they could be seen, would resemble the waves of the ocean at a beach. And if you think about it, those waves too have amplitude (height), frequency, phase, period, and so on. In addition, there are a few other descriptive words that can be used with waves, such as:

wavelength
steady-state
standing waves
node (the part of the wave that is standing still between the peaks)
timbre (the shape of the wave—which allows us to distinguish the different instruments of the orchestra from each other)
cycle (another word for oscillation)

A Short Musical Interlude. Both the musician and physicist (and also the acoustical engineer) use many of the same words. You will find that most of the words say something about the frequency of sound waves (or pitch of musical notes —which is the same thing). Table 8 lists these words, most of which show the relationships of musical notes of one pitch to those of another pitch. These tones are separated from each other by frequency *intervals*. Sometimes they sound well together, they *harmonize,* they are "in phase." Sometimes they sound terrible together, they are *discordant*, or "out of phase."

Table 8. Words About Musical Sound

fundamental	interval	third	frequency
overtone	whole tone	fifth	pitch
octave	half tone	seventh	resonance

ultrasonic (too high a note to hear)

modulation (a wave of one frequency superimposed on a wave of another frequency)

noise (a sound produced by irregular vibrations that don't follow any pattern)

interference (sound waves colliding with each other)

beats (unwanted sounds that may result from interference)

A Unit of Sound. Just as a foot is a fundamental unit of length, so a decibel is a fundamental unit of sound intensity. (It is usually used in its abbreviated form "db," or "dB.") Thus, your employer will often dictate a sentence like, "The received signal was 30 decibels weaker than the transmitted one."

Some Scientific Facts About Hanging Curtains. Sound will often keep rebounding in a room (*echoing*) after the source of sound has stopped producing it. This is known as *reverberation*. I am sure you are familiar with this effect. You will often experience it in a new room before the furniture goes into it. I am sure you know what to do about it too; keep adding furniture and hanging curtains and the reverberation will go away. The acoustic engineer does the same thing in a new theater. Cloth surfaces will *absorb* the sound, keep it from being *reflected* back into the room (reflection is the opposite of absorption). In fact, acoustic engineers have invented a kind of room which has such absorbent surfaces that it is difficult to hear anything at all in it. Such a room is called an *anechoic* room (pronounced an-ek-o-ic). It means, literally, "no echo."

Two additional words used to describe the lessening of sound level are *acoustic impedance* and *attenuation.* When you pass something through an impedance, you impede (lessen, delay) it. When you impede the passage of sound, you make it softer. When you attenuate a sound, you also make it softer. When you add curtains to a room, you are making it more anechoic by adding acoustic impedance, thus causing the sound to be attenuated.

Summary

1. Sound comes to our ears as a result of waves of air which vibrate in repeated (periodic) harmonic motion. The nature of a sound is determined by the characteristics of the sound waves: the *amplitude,* the *phase,* the *frequency.* In this sense, the motion of a sound wave can be compared to the repeated motion of a pendulum.
2. Many words that relate to acoustics, sound, and hearing contain the syllables "aud" and "son."
3. A basic unit relating to the intensity of sound is the decibel (abbreviated db or dB.)
4. Sound can be *reflected* from a surface or *absorbed* by a surface. A reflective surface causes the sound to *echo,* or *reverberate,* even after the source of sound has stopped vibrating. An *absorptive* or *attenuative* surface causes a sound to die out quickly.

Optics

What Is It? Optics is the science of light. Light starts someplace like the sun or an electric light bulb. It moves across space and "shines" on things. Then it reflects off of these things and enters your eyes where it is more or less photographed and transmitted into your brain. When this happens, you see.

Some of the terms of optics and seeing resemble those of acoustics and hearing because *light is a wave phenomenon* similar to sound (and many other things too, such as heat and electricity). Accordingly, it has *frequency, amplitude, period,* and *phase* characteristics. It is a kind of periodic vibration; there are interference and beats and octaves; it even has a similar relationship to the arts. Where acoustics is, in a way, the science of music, optics is, in a way, the science of painting. And if you add solid geometry, it is the science of architecture.

Optics is not completely similar to acoustics, but in some ways, they are very much alike. As an example, differences in the frequencies of sound waves give sounds of different pitch; in the same way, differences in the frequencies of light waves give differences in color. This means that your blue dress is blue because it reflects waves of light that vibrate at a frequency which our eyes recognize as blue. Let the frequency change a little bit and we see red or orange or some other color.

Human ears can hear only sounds in a certain range. When the frequency of sound waves gets too high or too low, our hearing apparatus cannot respond to them, and we do not hear them. Similarly, our eyes can respond only to certain light frequencies; faster or slower frequencies are invisible, or "unseeable." When the vibrations get too fast or slow for your eyes, you might still be able to "see" with the help of a camera. The camera film may be more sensitive than your eyes. So there are cameras that can observe some light waves that humans can't detect — *X-rays* and *ultraviolet rays,* which vibrate too rapidly, and *infrared rays* (which also happen to be heat waves) which vibrate too slowly for your eyes. By the way, all these frequencies of light from the too-fast-to-see to the too-slow-to-see, but including what you do see, make up the light *spectrum.*

What Makes Light Happen?   There are many things that cause light to appear, and in the next few pages, we will discuss some of them.

Incandescence.   When certain things (usually metals) are heated, they begin to glow. At about 900°F (Fahrenheit), we see a dull red glow. At about 1200°F it has turned orange; at about 1800°F, it becomes yellow; at about 3600°F, it is white, and is called *white hot.* Giving off light because of heat is known as incandescence.

The little tungsten metal wire in an electric light bulb is heated by electricity to white incandescence — and it lights a room. The sun is even hotter than the tungsten wire, and as a result, it gives us the incandescent light we call *sunlight.*

Fluorescence.   There are dozens of kinds of light — and there is a word for each kind; sometimes more than one. Consider the word fluorescence. Fluorescent light is light that is given off by a substance only when it is stimulated by some other radiation. An example is a road sign. The light from your headlights hits the sign and it shines back at you, bright and clear. What you see is light *excited,* or caused to appear, because of other light. The thing that has happened is fluorescence, or more exactly, the kind of fluorescence called *photoluminescence.* Photoluminescence means light ("photo-") and glowing ("-luminescence"); that is, "glowing because of being excited by light." The road sign is painted with a fluorescent, or more explicitly, a photoluminescent, material.

The different kinds of fluorescent light are described by words which are made up in the same way; the first part of the word is the name of the "exciter," and the second part is the "glow" part, "-luminescence." Table 9 lists some of these words. All you need to remember is that you must keep them straight when your employer gives them to you; do not confuse one with another, even though they often sound very much alike. There are also many other such words, but this should give you a good idea of what is involved.

Table 9.   The Different Kinds of Fluorescence

Excited by Other Kinds of Wave Radiation	Excited by the Impact of Moving Particles
thermoluminescence	cathodoluminescence
photoluminescence	ionoluminescence
X-ray luminescence	neutronoluminescence
electroluminescence	deuteronoluminescence
radioluminescence	positronoluminescence

Excited by Chemical Changes	Excited by Physical Conditions
chemiluminescence	triboluminescence
bioluminescence	crystalloluminescence
oxyluminescence	baroluminescence
pyroluminescence	sonoluminescence
electrolytic-luminescence	

One place where you may observe fluorescence daily is on the screen of your television set. Here electrons bombard a layer of *cathodo*luminescent material (called a *phosphor*) that is on the inside of the picture tube, and the result is TV. Another place is the aptly named "fluorescent light." Here, electrified gas atoms (ions) strike an *iono*luminescent coating on the inside of a glass tube, and as a result, light is produced.

How Light Travels.   As a secretary dealing with material related to optics there is really only one new group of ideas that you must understand. They concern the way in which light starts someplace, moves across a region or through something, and "shines" on something that either absorbs it or reflects it into space again, so that it reaches your eyes, and you see.

The Beginning and End of the Path.   When something gives off light, we say it *radiates* That is, it gives off *rays* which go off in straight lines in all directions (like the *radii* of a cir-
cle with the source of the light considered to be at the center.) The light is called *radiation,* and what it lands on is said to be *irradiated.*

light bulb

light rays
(like the
radii of
a circle)

When light is coming out of a light source, it is also sometimes said that it is being *emitted.* When light can come out of a light source easily, the light source is said to have a high *emissivity.* If it comes out of the light source less easily, it is said to have a low emissivity.

The same surface can be on the receiving end too, that is, rather than being the source of light, it can be what the light shines on. High-emissivity surfaces *absorb* light easily. Low-emissivity surfaces reflect light easily. So a *mirror* is a low-emissivity surface because it reflects almost everything. What it does not reflect it absorbs. However, a poor mirror may absorb more than it reflects.

When all the light that strikes a surface is completely absorbed, the surface takes on the "color" we know as black, and the object which is black is called by the physicist, logically enough, a *blackbody.* (I put "color" in quotes because black is not really a color —it is the word used to designate "no color." If the light is completely absorbed, then there is no light to be reflected back.)

On the other hand, white is *all* the colors mixed together. Sometimes white light will shine on a surface (sunlight and light from an incandescent or fluorescent bulb are close to white light) and the surface will absorb some of the *wavelengths* of light (some of the colors), and what will hit your eyes will be only that portion of the light that is not absorbed. Another way to say this is that you see the color that is left after the other colors that were in the light rays are absorbed.

The words just discussed, which are mainly concerned with the emission and absorption of light, are summarized in Table 10.

The Transmission of Light.   Light can pass through substances that are *transparent.* Air and glass are transparent. It can also pass through (somewhat) substances that are partially transparent, or *translucent.* Frosted glass is partially transparent.

Table 10. Words Concerning the
Emission and Absorption of Light

radiation	emissivity	white	mirror
irradiation	absorptivity	black	color
light ray	reflection	blackbody	wavelength

Things can be transparent but still have a complex effect on light. You know that when you go swimming objects that are partially in the water and partially out of the water seem to "bend" at the water line. The object is not bending — the light bouncing off it is bending. When light passes from one transparent *medium* to another (what the light passes through is called a medium), it bends. The physicist's word for this bending is *refraction*. Every transparent material refracts, or bends, light through a different distance; the extent of the bending is described by a number called the *index of refraction*.

Figure 1 shows what happens when a light beam (that is, a collection of light rays) passes from one medium into another. The original beam of light, AO, moves through medium 1 and hits medium 2. It hits at the *interface* between the two mediums, which is represented by the line FE. Instead of continuing into medium 2 along the direction of the original beam (also called the *incident* beam), which would be along the line OB, it bends into the line OC. It has been refracted an amount that depends on the *indexes of refraction* of the two mediums. Meanwhile, if we assume that the surface FE is not completely transparent but is also a little like a mirror (you have surely seen reflections in plate glass; their presence shows that not all the light goes through the transparent glass — some is reflected), then the reflected portion of the original beam travels along the line OD.

The interesting thing to notice here is that the angle with which the reflected beam rebounds is exactly equal to the angle with which the incident beam hit the interface. In other words, θ_1 is equal to θ_2. This illustrates a well-known law in optics, that the *angle of incidence equals the angle of reflection*. But you must remember that they are different from the *angle of refraction*. The angle of refraction ϕ is not equal to the angle of incidence because medium 1 has a different index of refraction from medium 2. (Strictly speaking, θ_1, θ_2, and ϕ are not exactly the angles of incidence, reflection, and refraction, but are related to them. But you needn't worry about the exact differences.)

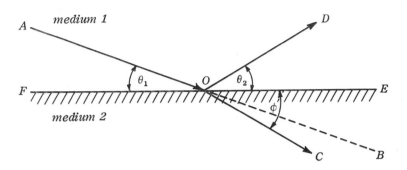

Figure 1. The reflection and refraction of light.

These properties of the angles of incidence, reflection, and refraction are used in the construction and operation of eye-glasses and hundreds of other devices. These valuable gadgets are based upon the *lens*. Figure 2 shows some lenses and what they accomplish. A convex lens looks like two parentheses staring at each other, "()," and a concave lens has the same two parentheses, but back-to-back, ")(." (I remember which is which because if the con*cave* lens were big enough, I could crawl in, as into a cave; while in the case of the con*vex* one, I would just slip off, which would be vexing.)

You can see what the lenses are doing to the light rays as a result of refracting, or bending, them. If an object is placed in front of a convex lens, as in Figure 2a, the light beams bouncing off of it enter the lens, are refracted, and some of them then go through a point called the *focus*, which is a *focal length* away from the lens. If a screen were placed the correct distance from the lens an *image* would be formed on it. The image would be *inverted*, that is, upside down. If the same object were placed in front of a concave lens, as in Figure 2b, its image would be formed on the same side of the lens and would be right side up. A convex lens is also known as a *converging lens* and a concave lens is also known as a *diverging lens*.

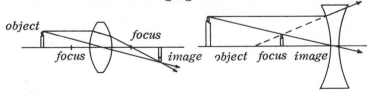

Figure 2. A convex lens (left) and a concave lens (right).

I have described a number of important words used in discussing the transmission of light. They are:

transparent	incidence	focal length
transluscent	reflection	image
refraction	lens	inversion
index of refraction	concave	reduction
light beam	convex	magnification
interface	focus	projection

medium (the plural is mediums or media)

There are many additional words that relate to the transmission of light. Rather than explain them all, they are listed in Table 11 in categories that may be useful.

Table 11. Additional Words Relating to Light

Words Describing Optical Effects

light beam	reflection	diffraction	interference
interface	refraction	polarization	complimentary
incidence	index of refraction	convergence	corpuscle
dispersion	critical angle	divergence	wave

shadow   umbra   penumbra

Words Describing Optical Equipment

lens	stroboscope	spectrograph	microscope
prism	photometer	polarizer	telescope
slit	spectrophotometer	analyzer	cross hair
aperture	interferometer	Nicol prism	binocular
grating	colorimeter	metallograph	sextant

Words Describing Lenses

concave	focus	objective	resolution
convex	focal length	ocular	resolving power
converging	real image	aberration	conjugate
diverging	virtual image	astigmatism	paraxial

Words Describing Quantities of Light

photon   photometry   lumen   lux   candlepower

Some Miscellaneous Optical Words

isotropic	chromatic	transparent	magnification
anisotropic	monochromatic	translucent	reduction
dichroism	spectrum	coherent	inversion

Summary

1. Like sound, light is a *wave* phenomenon and many of the same words, such as amplitude, phase, and frequency, apply.

2. Not all light is visible. When the frequency of the light is very high or very low, the light (such as infrared or ultraviolet or X-ray) cannot be seen by our eyes.

3. Light given off by surfaces which are very hot is called *incandescent* light.

4. Light given off because a material is stimulated by some form of *radiation* is called *fluorescent* light. The process of stimulating the material is called *excitation*. Many different kinds of fluorescence are summarized in Table 9.

5. When light is given off, it is said to be *emitted*. It is emitted in *rays* and is also called *radiation*. Surfaces that emit light easily are called high-*emissivity* surfaces. High-emissivity surfaces also *absorb* light easily. The best absorbers are called *blackbodies*. If a material is a poor emitter or absorber, it is a good reflector. A mirror is a good reflector.

6. When light can pass through some material, that material is called a *transparent medium*.. When light passes from one transparent medium to another, the light rays are bent. The *index of refraction* of a medium describes the extent to which it bends light rays.

7. *Lenses* are made of transparent materials and make use of refraction either to *reduce* or to *magnify* an *image*. A concave lens, ")(", gives a different image from a convex one, "()".

8. Words relating to light are summarized in Tables 10 and 11.

Heat and Thermodynamics

What Is It?   Heat is what you have when you are not cold. In other words, it is the absence of cold. To the physicist, heat is a form of energy. It moves in waves like light; it can be absorbed and reflected like light; it is radiated like light. In fact, heat and light are practically the same thing; heat is infrared radiation—that is, radiation of a lower frequency than visible light.

Words Containing "Thermo-."   The prefix *thermo-* is used a great deal in the discussion of heat. It comes from the Greek, *thermē*, which means heat.

Thermodynamics is the science of heat.

Thermal is an adjective that means pertaining to heat.

Thermometer means, literally, a measurer of heat—but that is not really what it is. A thermometer does not measure heat, it measures *temperature*, and temperature is different from heat. Temperature increases as the result of adding heat. Temperature is a manifestation of heat.

A *thermocouple* is another kind of thermometer. It is made of two pieces of metal (a couple) in which an electrical voltage is generated as a result of heat. The higher the temperature, the higher the voltage.

Thermos bottle. You know what that is.

Thermostat. On the wall, in your oven, in your car.

And other words like:

thermion	thermovoltaic	isothermal
thermionic	thermopile	exothermal
thermochemistry	thermoelectric	exothermic
thermotherapy	thermogenesis	endothermic

The Transmission of Heat.   Heat can be transferred from one place to another by three mechanisms: *radiation, conduction,* and *convection.* Heat can be radiated like light. That is, it can be emitted from a heat source the way that light is emitted from a light source. And it is emitted more easily from a high-emissivity surface than from a low-emissivity surface. Just as with light, it is also absorbed more easily by a high-emissivity surface than by a low-emissivity surface. And it is absorbed more easily by a black surface than by a reflective surface. That is why you should avoid wearing dark clothing in the summer. You can feel the radiation of heat. Just put your hand near a hot surface, like the heating elements of a stove; near, but not touching! Feel the heat? That is radiation, the first means of transferring heat.

The second mechanism for the transfer of heat is conduction. Again, I am sure that this is very familiar to you, but you may never have thought about it in this way. Return to the stove. The kettle is on. The heat enters the kettle through its bottom and raises the temperature of the bottom of the kettle. That tells us how the bottom of the kettle gets hot, but why is the handle of the kettle hot too, or at least warm? That is because of conduction! The heat is *conducted* from the bottom of the kettle, up the walls of the kettle, and finally out along the handle. In other words, the heat moves in the path just described through the solid material of the kettle. The movement of heat through solids is known as conduction. Heat moves more easily through solid materials of high *thermal conductivity* than through materials of low thermal conductivity. All metals, particularly copper, have high thermal conductivities, and most nonmetals have low thermal conductivities. That is why the bottom of the kettle is often made of copper and the handle of wood or plastic.

The third way for heat to be transferred, by *convection,* means that it is moved around by air currents. A hot surface conducts heat into the air around it; the air gets hot, and since "heat rises," the hot air moves up and makes a "hot wind." That is why baseboard heating is a good way to heat a room; the air just keeps being heated and rising: in other words, it circulates and makes the room uniformly warm.

The Generation of Heat.   Heat can be created by:

chemical reactions (burning wood is a chemical reaction)
electric current (like the hot coils in your toaster)
mechanically (by friction—like Boy Scouts rubbing sticks)
atomic reactions (like the atom bomb)
and several other ways.

When a chemical reaction produces heat as burning does, it is called *exothermic*. Some chemical reactions, on the other hand, require that heat be pumped into them in order that they "go." These are called *endothermic* reactions.

All reactions or activities that involve a change of energy (like chemical reactions, atomic reactions, electrical heating, or mechanical effects) may be described precisely in mathematical form. The scientist and engineer have broken down heat changes into a number of constituents. They are:

the change in heat content, ΔH, also called enthalpy,
the change in free energy, ΔF, called free energy,
the change in entropy, ΔS, called entropy.

These are very important words and symbols, and you will meet them over and over again in thermodynamics.

A few other thermodynamic terms you will encounter are:

fugacity	equilibrium constant	phase rule	dew point
activity	ideal gas	latent heat	adiabatic

Units.   There is very little more to say about heat and thermodynamics, except for a few words about measuring quantities of heat and quantities of temperature. Remember that heat is a form of energy, so some of the units for measuring energy, already discussed in the section on mechanics, apply here too. These are:

calories (cal)
British Thermal Unit (B.T.U.)
joule

Calories can be measured with a device called a *calorimeter*.

Measuring temperature is perhaps a little more complicated than you may think. It is always measured in *degrees,* and the small "°" written as a superscript is always used. But, and this is something that you must remember, there are several different sizes of degrees, and they may start at different zeros. For example, it takes 1.8 *Fahrenheit* (F) degrees to make 1 *centi-grade* (C) degree; this means that a degree C is bigger than a degree F. Furthermore, zero degrees centigrade (0°C) is the same as 32 degrees Fahrenheit (32°F). The different scales used to measure temperature, and their abbreviations, are listed in Table 12.

Table 12.   The Different Temperature Scales

Scale	Symbol
degrees Baumé	°B
degrees centigrade (or Celsius)	°C
degrees Fahrenheit	°F
degrees Kelvin (or absolute)	°K
degrees Rankine	°R
degrees Réaumur	°Ré

Summary

1. The study of heat is called **thermodynamics**. Like sound and light, heat is a kind of wave. Heat may be thought of as *infrared* light.
2. Heat can transmitted by three means: **radiation, conduction,** and **convection.** Heat radiation moves across space like light radiation; heat moves through solid materials by conduction; heat moves through gases by convection, or winds.
3. Materials that transmit heat easily are said to have high **thermal conductivity**.
4. Heat is described mathematically by the concepts of: **enthalpy**, ΔH; *free energy*, ΔF; and *entropy*, ΔS.
5. The different scales for measuring temperature are: degrees Baumé. °B; degrees centigrade (or degrees Celsius), °C; degrees Fahrenheit, °F; degrees Rankine, °R; degrees Réaumur, °Ré.

Crystallography and Crystal Physics

Amorphous and Crystalline.   Let me start by making a catege-gorical statement—and in so doing, divide the world up into two categories. The *crystallographer* (or crystal chemist or crystal physicist) divides the world into *amorphous* and *crystalline*—then he proceeds to ignore the amorphous and to give his life to the study of the crystalline.

Anything *amorphous* is made up of atoms that are jumbled together in a random way; anything *crystalline* is made up of atoms (it could even be the same atom) arranged in regular, neat, re-peating, periodic, and orderly patterns. Any liquid or fluid or gelatin is amorphous. Most minerals, all metals, and certain chemicals are crystalline.

What makes a material crystalline or amorphous anyway? You can provide the best answer yourself by borrowing some marbles from your small brother. Place these into a glass container, perhaps a milk bottle, and shake them gently. Now hold the jar up and look at the marbles from below. If the marbles were the right size and you shook them well enough, you will see that they will appear to be arranged in regular patterns. You can find triangles, squares, and hexagons, as illustrated in Figure 3. Since the marbles are trying to get into some regular pattern, they are becoming non-amorphous, that is, they are becoming crystalline. At this point,

Figure 3. The regular arrangement of marbles in a bottle is similar to the arrangement of atoms in a crystal.

it is not hard to imagine that the marbles represent atoms, which may also be considered to be round. It is also not hard to imagine that during the course of the formation of the world these atoms have been shaken up a good deal, and have settled out as crystals. Look at a diamond or at a grain of rock salt; they are both composed of crystals. On their faces you find the same shapes again: triangles, squares, hexagons.

Isotropic, Anisotropic, and Cleavage.   Sometimes a crystal is *isotropic*. That means it is *symmetrical*. It does not change from one direction to another. The cube in Figure 4a is isotropic; but the elongated rectangular solid in Figure 4b is *anisotropic* ("not isotropic"). Up at its square ends, the atoms are packed quite densely, but along its length, there is a much greater separation between atoms. One anisotropic crystal with which you may be familiar is *mica*. This mineral is notable because it can be peeled in sheets. The fact is, it is so anisotropic (that is, in one direction the atoms are so far apart) that it takes almost no force at all to rupture the weak bonds that hold the crystal together in that direction. On the other hand, in the direction along the sheets that peel off,

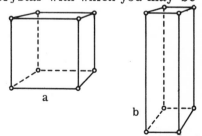

Figure 4. Isotropic (a) and anisotropic (b) arrangements of atoms.

the material is quite strong. Thus, if a crystal is anisotropic, its *physical properties* are also anisotropic. That is, it will be stronger in one direction than in others; it will have different electrical and thermal conductivities in different directions; it will expand and contract with temperature to a different extent in different directions; and so on.

We have just discussed the fact that there is an "easy" direc--tion to peel or separate sheets of mica from each other. The fact is that in all crystals there are some planes running parallel to layers of atoms along which it is easier to cut than other planes. Such planes of easy separation are known as *cleavage* planes. A diamond cutter is a man who can turn a diamond around and around, catching different light reflections, and noticing different planes on the diamond's surface. He soon recognizes where the cleavage planes are. Then, if he wants to break the diamond in two, he strikes it with a sharp, chisel-like hammer—and it separates into two pieces along a flat plane. The diamond cutter does not cut, he cleaves.

The Different Shapes of Crystals. Since atoms arrange themselves in different patterns, we should not be surprised that these patterns persist to large size materials. Even though a diamond weighing one carat contains approximately one thousand million billion atoms of carbon, we know that all these atoms arrange themselves in groups of five. So a one-carat diamond contains two-hundred million billion such groups. These groups of atoms just add onto each other until the whole diamond is similar in shape to the original group of five atoms—only bigger. Then the diamond cutter cleaves it into attractive shapes, and each one resembles the original group of five atoms.

The Unit Cell. A basic group of atoms (such as the five atoms of a diamond shown in Figure 5) which is duplicated billions of times to make a final crystal structure, is known as the unit cell of a crystal. There are many forms of crystals. Each different form must have a different cell. If two crystals both have unit cells with the same shape, the crystals must have the same shape. The science of the study of crystal shape is known as *cyrstal morphoiogy*. Morphology

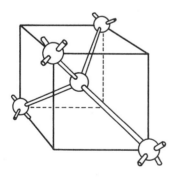

Figure 5. The diamond unit cell.

comes from the Greek *morphē* which means shape; therefore, amorphous materials are correctly named, "a-morphous," no shape.

Measuring and Describing Crystal Shapes. The crystallographer can study a mineral just by observing its geometry. He can study its angles and measure them with an instrument called a *goniometer*. A goniometer measures "gonies," and "goni" means angle.

If the mineral has been around in the world for some billions of years, and most have, the corners may be knocked off, and the mineral may just look like a formless "hunk of rock." The trained scientist can strike at the rock, as a diamond cutter might at a diamond. In so doing, he would get it to start cleaving, and thus reveal its basic crystal planes.

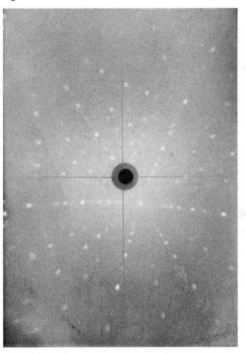

If the crystal physicist wants a more detailed look into the insides of the crystal, he can "see" with X rays. X rays are a kind of light. Their wavelengths are such that they can sneak inside the rows of a crystal's atoms, and come out as strong beams between the rows. This is similar to what you might observe when you drive past a corn field; at certain angles, certain rows and spaces between rows stand out. As a result, you might say to yourself (if you wanted to) something like, "Goodness gracious, these rows of corn are certainly laid out in equally-spaced, periodic patterns of rows of corn!"

Figure 6. A Laue picture of a crystal.

In the same way, the scientist with the "seeing-eye" of an X-ray camera can recognize different atomic-row arrangements. The procedure is called X-ray diffraction and is generally done by a method named after its inventor, Laue (said to rhyme with "Howie"). So, when your boss speaks of "Laue cameras" and "Laue pictures" he is only looking deep inside a crystal, and measuring angles. Figure 6 is a typical Laue picture.

Pointing to a face. This brings us to the next problem. If the scientist has measured the angles and faces, or sides, of some crystals, and wants to describe them in written form (the form you will reproduce), how does he do it? There is a way that is ingenious and simple. I shall not attempt to explain it completely, but just tell you enough so that you will know what the system is. Crystal morphology (shape) and particular planes within a crystal are described by using *Miller indices*. Miller, noting that solids take up three dimensions (left–right, back–forth, and up–down), decided that three numbers should be enough to describe and point out any face of any crystal. The Miller indices are the three numbers. They are generally written in parentheses as three single-digit numbers. The following are typical Miller-index designations:

(001)
(111)
(021)
(010)
(123)

Figure 7 shows how the Miller indices "point out" and name different crystal faces.

Occasionally, Miller indices are written with one or more of the digits overlined:

(1̄1̄0)
(1̄20)

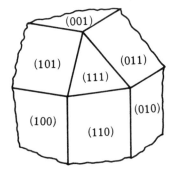

Figure 7. Naming crystal faces with Miller indices.

or with the parentheses replaced by brackets or braces:

{111}
{103}
[111]

These all mean something special to a crystallographer (edges or zones instead of faces), so write them *exactly* as he wants them.
The Thirty-two Crystal Classes. One of the most interesting facts to the crystallographer is that, in a three-dimensional world, there are only thirty-two possible combinations of crystal shapes. These are known as the *crystal classes* or *crystal habits*. The most important words you will encounter if you work for a crystallographer are listed in Table 13. Some examples of a few different kinds of crystals are shown in Figure 8. Figure 12 in

Part II reproduces a typical typed page of crystal physics text.

Table 13. Some Important Words of Crystallography

Cubic	Orthorhombic	Isometric	Domatic
Tetragonal	Monoclinic	Asymmetric	Prismatic
Hexagonal	Triclinic	Pinacoidal	Pyramidal
Rhombic	Trigonal	Sphenoidal	Dipyramidal

Photograph courtesy of the Raytheon Company.

Figure 8. A few different types of crystals that are commonly encountered.

It's Almost Like Being Alive. Of all inanimate things, crystals are the most like living organisms. They are *born*, they may be *seeded*; within the limits of their forms, they may have endless variety; they have *twins*; they may be coarse and rough on the outside and beautiful and regular on the inside; they may be nearly perfect or imperfect—and they *grow*.

Crystals start their growth on a seed, or nucleus. Once they are *nucleated,* they keep adding one unit cell of atoms onto another until the crystal becomes big enough to be seen. If a *crystal imperfection* occurs during growth, the crystal may change its direction of growing, and then change back again. The band of crystal of different direction, or *orientation,* is then called a *twin band* (see Figure 9), and the crystal is said to have *twinned* or to have undergone *twinning.*

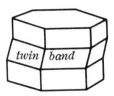

Figure 9. A twin band in a crystal.

Summary

1. When the atoms that make up a solid are arranged in a regular, repeatable pattern, the solid is a **crystal.** If this is not the case the material is **amorphous.**
2. When the physical properties of a crystal are different in different directions, the crystal is **anisotropic.** This occurs because the crystal's atoms are spaced differently in different directions. A crystal whose properties are the same in all directions is *isotropic.* Anisotropic crystals may be split easily along the directions of large spacings of atoms. Isotropic crystals may also be split, but not quite as easily. This splitting is known as **cleavage.**
3. The shape of any piece of crystalline material is a repeat of the arrangement of the atoms in one molecule of the material. The arrangement which is repeated is called a **unit cell.**
4. The study of crystal shape is called **crystal morphology.** There are only thirty-two crystal shapes (or **habits** or **classes**) that are possible in a three-dimensional world. Table 13 lists some words used to describe these shapes.
5. It is possible to label and identify the different sides, or *faces,* of a crystal with three numbers called **Miller** *indices.*
6. Crystals are **seeded,** or **nucleated,** and **grow** by adding atoms onto the central nucleus.

Modern Physics

What Is It? Physics has its "classic" and its "jazz." Everything discussed thus far in this chapter was known before 1900, and is known as *classical* physics. Everything that has been learned only since then, although very jazzy in nature, is not known as jazz, but as *modern* physics. Modern physics concerns itself primarily with the study of the structure of matter. So, this section discusses the particles that are smaller than atoms; that is, the *constituents* of atoms.

The Structure of the Atom. Once atoms are divided into their constituents, they lose their identities as particular elements. These constituents of atoms are known as *subatomic particles*. For our purposes, we can consider all atoms to be made up of only three basic particles, combined in different ways. We will now look into how these combinations are built up.

The Three Fundamental Particles. Some of the most modern physics indeed (as distinct from merely just plain modern physics) tells us that the *electron*, the *proton* and the *neutron*, are themselves made up of even smaller, more "fundamental" particles. Let us not worry ourselves about these. Let us just agree that the fundamental particles are:

> the electron
> the proton
and   the neutron

Let's Mix Up Some Atoms. Here is how you make atoms. Protons — which have a positive static electrical charge (remember, we discussed static electricity in the chapter on chemistry) are combined with electrons — which have a negative charge. Each positive charge is *balanced* by one negative charge, so there must be one electron in each atom for each proton. In the meantime, neutrons may be added as well; they have no charge, so they do not need to be balanced. They should be thought of as being associated with the protons in a sort of proton-neutron "clump." This clump takes up a position in the center of the atom and is called the *nucleus*; the electrons "hover" around the nucleus.

How Electrons Arrange Themselves Around a Nucleus. The "hovering" of electrons around the nucleus is a most intriguing subject because it follows such a regular pattern. It is convenient to think of this hovering as planetary; that is, as similar to the way the planets move around the sun. First there is the nucleus, then the electrons orbiting around it, like Mercury, Venus, Earth, Mars, Saturn, and the others orbit around the sun. All that you need to be careful about here is to remember that the electrons move around the nucleus in *set* orbits, and that only so many electrons can fit in any one orbit. When an orbit is *filled*, the next atom is made by adding the next new electron to the next orbit. These orbits are also called *shells*, and the shells are designated, from the nucleus out, as follows: $1s$, $2s$, $2p$, $3s$, $3p$, $3d$, $4s$, $4p$, $4d$, $5s$, $5p$, $5d$, $6s$, etc. These shells may also be labeled with capital letters starting with K. They are then, K, L, M, N, O, P, etc.

More Atom Building. If there are only a few protons, neutrons, and electrons in an atom, it is a light material. Hydrogen, the lightest material we know, has one proton, one electron, and no neutrons. Lead, one of the heaviest materials we know, has 82 protons, 122 neutrons, and 82 electrons. The weight of a neutron is almost the same as that of a proton, while an electron weighs almost nothing. So, for the lead atom, we can add 82 to 122 and get 204: an atom of lead weighs about 204 times what an atom of hydrogen weighs.

Try a few more. Aluminum has 13 protons, 14 neutrons, and (to balance the protons), it has 13 electrons; it has 27 particles in its nucleus (13 plus 14) that weigh about the same as the one particle in a hydrogen atom, so an aluminum atom is about 27 times as heavy as a hydrogen atom. Carbon has 6 protons, 6 neutrons, and 6 electrons. Copper has 29 protons, 34 neutrons, and 29 electrons. Gold has 79 protons, 118 neutrons, and 79 electrons — which makes it almost as heavy as lead.

The number of protons *or* the number of electrons (it is the same number) is called the *atomic number* of the atom, and it is given the symbol Z. There are as many atomic numbers as there are kinds of atoms, in other words, about one hundred. They start at number one and they go by number up to over one hundred. Another number of importance in atomic theory is the *mass number*, *A*. It is the sum of the neutrons and protons in any atom. Table 14 gives the atomic numbers and mass numbers of a few elements. The table has only six elements in it. We could have gone on to list all the elements with their atomic numbers and mass numbers, but these few should give you the idea.

That is how it is done; that is how you make a universe. Just add proton-electron pairs. Every time you add a proton and an electron, you have made a new atomic number and a new atom. Do it a hundred times, meanwhile maneuvering a bit with neutrons, and that is it.

Isotopes. Up to now, I have been guilty of an oversimplification. I have talked about neutrons as though there were always only one set amount of them for each element. This is not quite true. Actually, while the number of protons and electrons for any element never varies, the number of neutrons in an element may vary. There is a form of hydrogen, for example, which has one neutron. Remember we gave hydrogen in Table 14 as a material with mass number 1, that is, with no neutrons. But the fact is that about one hydrogen atom in 5,000 does have a neutron, and so has mass number 2. That form of hydrogen is known as *deuter-ium*. Deuterium is twice as heavy as ordinary hydrogen, and water made with deuterium is called *heavy water*.

It turns out that most elements are not changed chemically if the number of neutrons they contain is changed slightly. These different forms of the same element are called *isotopes*. Isotopes of an element have the same atomic number, but have different mass numbers. If all the different isotopes are included, Table 14 becomes Table 15. You can see from Table 15 that gold has only one form, or isotope, but that lead has four. An element may have even more isotopes than any of these elements has. New isotopes are constantly being discovered.

There are several ways of writing isotopes. They are always shown by giving the name of the element with the mass number following. But, for example, uranium with mass number 235 may be written as U-235 or U^{235}, or U_{235}. Use the one your employer prefers. The symbol all in one line (U-235) is usually used in text, and the form with the mass number as a superscript (U^{235}), in equations. The third way, U_{235}, creeps in occasionally in accordance with no particular rule.

Radioactivity. Some isotopes have the property of *disintegrating*. If integrate means to add together, then disintegrate means to split asunder. In other words, some isotopes are unstable. Now, in the chapter on chemistry we said that even if atoms went through many chemical changes and combinations they still remained the same atoms. This *is* true in chemistry. But under certain extraordinary conditions, for example in an exploding atomic bomb, atoms of an element *do* disintegrate to form new elements. And even under ordinary conditions, certain rare elements disintegrate spontaneously. Uranium, for example, even when left alone, will break up to give other elements, which also break up, until the original uranium has become lead.

The material that breaks up (or perhaps breaks down is a better description) in this manner is called *radioactive*. The words *radium* and *radioactive* both contain the prefix "radi-," which we already know has something to do with rays and radiation. Let us now consider just which rays are involved.

Some New Rays. Sometimes, when one isotope breaks up into another isotope, or even becomes another element, the protons and neutrons do not come out even. As a result, there may be a few particles left over. These particles are not welcome in the parental atomic home, so thay depart in the form of *rays*.

Table 14. Atomic Numbers and Mass Numbers*

Element	Atomic Number, Z	Mass Number, A	It Looks Like This
hydrogen	1	1	
carbon	6	12	
aluminum	13	27	

copper	29	63	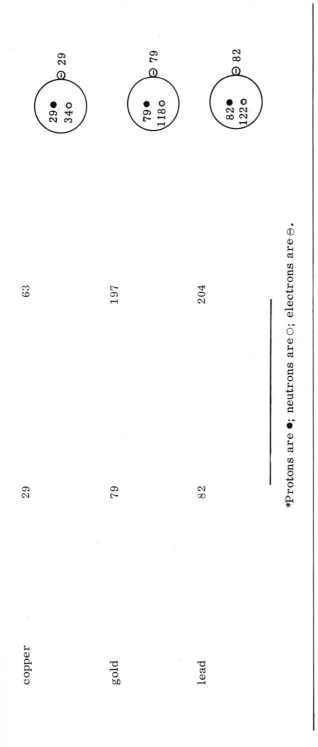
gold	79	197	
lead	82	204	

*Protons are ●; neutrons are ○; electrons are ⊝.

Table 15.   The Isotopes of Some Common Elements

Element	Atomic Number, Z	Mass Number, A
hydrogen	1	1
		2
carbon	6	12
		13
aluminum	13	27
copper	29	63
		65
gold	79	197
lead	82	204
		206
		207
		208

Electrons that are free to leave a nucleus are known as *beta particles*. They go into the outside world, attached to nothing, and are also called *beta rays*. Beta rays are also written with the Greek β , as "β rays."

An *alpha particle* is the odd combination of two protons and two neutrons. Since the protons have a positive charge and the neutrons have no charge, this particle is positively charged. And these alpha particles go off as alpha rays (α rays).

Finally some rays that come out of a nucleus are made up of energy like light. They are called gamma rays (γ rays). They penetrate heavy metals even better than X rays do.

Some New Chemistry—Radiochemistry.   Some elements are quite stable and need help in order to disintegrate. This help is given by *bombarding* their nuclei with neutrons or other subatomic particles. These particles can combine with the elements that are being bombarded to form new isotopes or elements which could otherwise not form because some particles were missing.

It is possible to look at the situation as though it were a kind of chemical reaction. The difference is that where in a chemical reaction atoms react together to form chemical compounds, in a nuclear reaction the reacting takes place between certain particles and the nuclei of certain elements. The results are new isotopes, new elements, and new particles. The field which studies these reactions is a combination of physics and chemistry and is called *radiochemistry*.

The equations of radiochemistry look a great deal like chemical equations. You use the abbreviations for the chemical elements just as you learned them in the chapter on chemistry, but you must also include (as superscripts) the mass numbers of the particular isotopes that are involved. The particles that are being used to bombard the elements are shown by the abbreviations α for alpha particle, β for beta particle, γ for gamma ray, and n for neutron.

A typical reaction is the one where uranium-238 changes as a result of being bombarded with neutrons into uranium-239. This, in turn, changes further into neptunium-239 and beta rays, then into plutonium-239 and beta rays, and finally into uranium-235 and alpha rays. The equations used to show this sequence of reactions are usually written in one of two forms. The bombarding and emanating particles (anything given off in a radiochemical reaction is said to be an *emanation*) may be treated in the same way as the elements, for example,

$$U^{238} + n \rightarrow U^{239} \rightarrow Np^{239} + \beta$$

$$Np^{239} \rightarrow Pu^{239} + \beta$$

$$Pu^{239} \rightarrow U^{235} + \alpha$$

Alternatively, the abbreviations for the bombarding particles may be placed in parentheses after the element on which they are acting, and the emanations may be written over the reaction arrows, as

$$U^{238}(n) \rightarrow U^{239} \xrightarrow{\beta} Np^{239} \xrightarrow{\beta} Pu^{239} \xrightarrow{\alpha} U^{235}$$

Similar equations may be written for all other radiochemical reactions. This type of reaction, where an element dissociates as a result of bombardment, is known as *fission,* and such elements are said to be *fissionable,* or *fissile.*

You may be interested to know that the person who worked out most of the fundamental concepts of radiochemistry was a woman, Madame Curie. She was also the first person who ever won two Nobel Prizes, one in chemistry and one in physics.

Half-life. Radioactive dissociations do not go on indefinitely. There comes a time when all of the emanations slow down and stop. Physicists usually cannot wait for all of the emanations to stop in order to measure them. That may take many years. So they have invented a concept that tells them how long something will remain radioactive: the *half-life.* Half-lives are often relatively simple to measure in short periods in time. The knowledge of how fast a nuclear reaction is happening is of great importance to the nuclear scientist—and the half-life tells him.

For example, in an atomic bomb, the reaction takes place very quickly.

Half-lives may be written right into radiochemical reactions. For example, the preceding reaction can be rewritten as follows to include the half-life of each new product of the reaction:

$$U^{239} \xrightarrow{\text{23 min}} Np^{239} + \beta$$

$$Np^{239} \xrightarrow{\text{2.3 days}} Pu^{239} + \beta$$

$$Pu^{239} \xrightarrow{\text{24,000 yr}} U^{235} + \alpha$$

or $\quad U^{239} \xrightarrow[\text{23 min}]{\beta} Np^{239} \xrightarrow[\text{2.3 days}]{\beta} Pu^{239} \xrightarrow[\text{24,000 yr}]{\alpha} U^{235}$

Words. Some of the words you will meet if you work with an atomic physicist or a radiochemist or a nuclear engineer are given in Table 16.

The Bomb. We should say a word about why nuclear reactions liberate so much energy. In a nuclear reaction material (mass) can become energy. This idea, more than any other, is what separates modern physics from classical physics. Before 1900, mass was one thing and energy was something else. One would act on the other — mass could be moved or heated with energy — but the idea of creating energy by making mass disappear — never. However, Einstein's theory of relativity predicted that energy could be created out of mass, and the testing explosions that started at Alamogordo, New Mexico in 1945 have shown that he was right.

What is the reason for this? In some nuclear reactions, the equations do not exactly balance. Sometimes it becomes evident that there are fewer subatomic particles at the end than there were at the beginning. Where has that mass gone? It has changed into energy, and that energy was the big boom, the explosion. The explosion can be very great because there is a great quantity of energy stored in the mass of even a single atom.

You must not blame Einstein for what happened. He was only scribbling with pencil and paper and writing out some interesting things about atoms. The results of his speculations were completely unexpected to him.

Quantum Physics — Step by Step. The idea of the *quantum* (plural, *quanta)* is one of the most complicated and most important for the physicist, but one of the easiest for you. It is easy for you because with what you have already learned in chemistry, mathematics, and physics you are really qualified to take dictation and

Table 16. Words About Atomic Reactions

The Word	Which Means
Reactor	Where the nuclear reaction takes place.
Atomic pile	The part of a reactor that contains the reacting isotopes.
Cyclotron	A device to produce beams of sub-atomic particles to be used in bombardment.
Accelerator	Similar to a cyclotron.
Moderator	The material in a reactor that slows down and controls the speed of the bombarding particles.
Breeding	Building up to an explosion.
Cross section	A description of how well a material will slow down (or moderate) a bombarding particle.
Mother isotope	The original isotope before it dissociates into new isotopes.
Daughter isotope	The "new" isotope into which the "mother" has dissociated.
Curie (abbreviated cu or Cu or Ci)	A measure of the amount of radioactivity.
Millicurie (abbreviated mcu or mCu or mCi)	A thousandth of a curie.
Tracer	A radioactive isotope that is mixed in very small quantities with other, nonradioactive, isotopes of the same element. The movements of the radioactive material can now be "traced."
Geiger counter	A device which measures the quantity of radiation coming from a radioactive material. The greater the number of "counts" the greater the radiation.

type material on this subject. However, you should have an idea of what the concept of the quantum is.

The concept of the quantum is related to atoms and things that happen to atoms. It is primarily concerned with the fact that when atoms absorb or give out energy, this energy is absorbed or emitted *in steps*, and not continuously. (You are familiar with the idea of something absorbing or emitting energy. We discussed this in the sections on acoustics, optics, and heat.) Energy seems to be continuous — objects appear to heat smoothly, not in jerky steps; light and sound seem to get louder and softer smoothly, not in jerky steps, But the fact is that these things *are* happening in steps. The steps are just too small for us to see or feel; our senses are too coarse. It's like walking upstairs. You walk up one step at a time. If a staircase has twelve steps, you go up in twelve different stages, or levels. You can be on the fifth step or on the sixth step, but never on the "five-and-a-halfth" step because there is no "five-and-a-halfth" step. It is as though five-and-a-half were forbidden.

In physics, it is not steps of a stairway we talk about but *levels* of energy. There are *allowed* energy levels and *forbidden* energy levels, and the energy needed to move from one level to another comes in fixed, distinct, set amounts (the physicist likes to refer to them as *discrete* amounts — and you must be sure to spell it just like that: *"-ete"*), the quanta. (And you should always remember that when the physicist talks about changing energy levels he is just talking about absorbing and emitting energy.) Sometimes there are groups of levels. These are called *energy bands*. One band is separated from its neighbor by a forbidden region called an *energy gap*.

In this field, you will encounter the names of several men over and over again: Planck, the discoverer of *Planck's constant, h;* Boltzmann, the discoverer of *Boltzmann's constant, k;* Pauli, the inventor of the *Pauli exclusion principle;* Fermi, who found a particular energy level called the *Fermi level;* Heisenberg, who invented the *Heisenberg uncertainty principle,* also known as the *principle of indeterminacy;* and many more.

Some typical typewritten pages dealing with quantum physics and other branches of modern physics are to be found in Figures 9, 10, and 11 of Part II (pp. 195–197).

Probability. Are you surprised to find probability in a discussion of physics? This is not the probability of collecting data, it is the science of educated guessing. Are there any reasons a physicist would ever have to guess? Yes, basically there are two reasons. First of all, a physicist can never really get down inside an atom. Atoms are too small. Even light waves are too big to use to see what is going on down there. So physicists can only know in a general way how groups of atoms and groups of particles that are smaller than atoms are acting. From this information they can determine the probability that a certain atom or a certain particle will act in a given way. The rules of probability that the physicist uses to study these objects are known as *quantum mechanics*.

But even, theoretically, if a physicist could know how each atom acted (and under certain conditions he can act as if he did — but let's not try to explain why, or things will become even more complicated than they now are), there are so many atoms and molecules in even what seems to be a small object that there would be no practical way for him to add up all of the effects on all of the atoms. He would again have to resort to probability, this time by using *statistical mechanics*.

Some of the statistical systems used in physics are named after their inventors. You should recognize:

Boltzmann, Bose-Einstein, and Fermi-Dirac

One word of caution: do not let the above discussion lead you to believe that the physicist is never completely sure of his information. His rules of probability have brought him the right answers so many times that, as far as he is concerned, they are right.

Solid-State Physics. This branch of modern physics brings together most of the other topics we have discussed in this chapter: the wave phenomena of acoustics, optics, and heat, crystallography, atomic structure, quantum mechanics, and statistical mechanics. Add to these electricity and electronics, which we will study in the next chapter, and you begin to see how this field represents a wonderful synthesis and a remarkable reward. It is a reward for all of the theoretical work done by thousands of physicists over the years, because it has resulted in new and marvelous practical gadgets like the *transistor*, which we all now use as a matter of course in our portable radios and dictaphones.

In this section I will introduce only one new idea that is important in solid-state physics. We will treat the subject in greater detail in the next chapter.

Electrons That Are "Loose."   You know from your everyday experience that electricity flows in a wire similarly to the way that water flows in a pipe. The wire is known as a *conductor of electricity* just as a pipe is a conductor of water. Not every material is a conductor of electricity; for example, wood and plastic and glass are not electrical conductors. A nonconductor is also called an *insulator*.

What is it that is flowing in a stream, or *current*, of electricity? The answer is *electrons*, the same electrons that hover and orbit in atomic shells. In good conductors like copper and other metals the electrons of the outer atomic shell of each atom are held in that shell so loosely that they can move around. They can move from their own atoms to neighboring atoms — and the spaces they leave are filled by still other electrons from still other atoms — and so on.

In an insulator, the electrons are associated with atoms that hold onto all of their electrons very tightly. Then there are no electrons to break loose and flow. Since there is no flow of electrons, there is no electric current — and the material is then recognized by us as an insulator.

Transistors are made of materials that are in between conductors and insulators. They are called *semiconductors*. A semiconductor is a crystalline material, usually consisting of one of the two elements silicon or germanium. As its name implies, a semiconductor cannot make up its mind as to whether it wants to be a metallic conductor like copper, or a nonmetallic nonconductor like glass. It starts out like an insulator: all its electrons are tightly bound and used up just forming the atomic structure and holding the crystal together. What makes a semiconductor different is that *impurities* can be added to it. These impurities dissolve into the semiconductor *crystal lattice,* or *crystal structure,* and each impurity atom contributes one leftover, or free or loose, electron to the crystal structure. *That* electron will conduct current. Since the impurity *gave* an electron, it is known as a *donor* impurity. Now, as more impurities are added to the crystal (they are melted in as the crystal is grown), it becomes a better conductor of electricity. But the conduction is never as good as that of ordinary metals, where *every* atom has a loose electron. Here, only the impurity atoms have loose electrons. On the other hand, the material is not a nonconductor either, it conducts somewhat. It is just what its name implies, a *semi*conductor. It is this fact, that the amount of conductivity in a semiconductor can be controlled, that has made possible the development of the transistor.

Actually, there are two types of impurities: the donor impurities just mentioned and *acceptor* impurities. An acceptor impurity mixes into the crystal lattice, just as a donor does, but

instead of contributing an extra electron, it has one less electron than each of the surrounding crystal atoms has. Strangely
enough, this "place" where there is no electron (known, logically enough, as a *hole)* behaves like a kind of free electron, and
as the holes move around (which they do) they cause a result
called *hole conduction,* which is a kind of electrical conduction
just like electron conduction.

A Matter of Life and Death. The holes and electrons move about
within the crystal lattice — but they are in constant danger for
their lives. The electron has a negative static electrical charge,
and if it moves past a place in the crystal which is particularly
positive in static charge, it will "fall in," and join up negative
with positive (remember, in the chapter on chemistry, we talked
about this). If it joins up, it stops being loose or free. A hole
behaves like a positively charged electron, and when it passes a
negative place in the crystal, it can join up with it and likewise
be nullified. In either case, we say that the *carrier of electricity*
has "died" because it fell into an electrical *trap.* If there are
many such traps, the semiconducting crystal is said to be a
low-lifetime material; if there are few such traps, it is called a
high-lifetime material.

There is also another kind of trap where electrons and holes
can be killed. They can be moving in the regular spaces between atoms that one would expect to find in a crystal and *meet
each other.* Then the electron will fall into the hole by a process
called *recombination.* Then there isn't any hole, because it has
been filled by an electron, and there isn't any free electron, because it has been tied up in the hole. For all practical purposes,
they have canceled each other out.

Summary

1. Modern physics deals with physics as it has been investigated since
   1900. It is concerned primarily with the study of the basic structure of matter.

2. The atom may be considered to be made up of three basic **subatomic**
   particles: the **proton,** the **neutron,** and the **electron.** Protons and
   neutrons together make up the atomic **nucleus,** which contains almost all of the weight of an atom. Electrons hover about the atomic
   nucleus.

3. Protons carry one positive electrical charge each, and electrons
   carry one negative electrical charge each. An atom is **electrically
   neutral,** so it has the same number of protons as electrons. The
   number of protons or electrons in an atom is its **atomic number.**

Since there are about one hundred different kinds of atoms (different chemical elements) atomic numbers range from one to about one hundred.

4. The number of protons and neutrons in an atom is its *mass number.* The number of neutrons in an atom with a certain fixed number of protons may vary. The forms of a chemical element that differ because the number of neutrons in the nucleus differs are called *isotopes.*

5. The electrons that hover about a nucleus are always in prescribed paths, or *orbits* or *shells.* The various shells are referred to by different combinations of numbers and letters, as: $1s$, $2s$, $2p$, $3d$, or K, L, M, and others.

6. Some elements are basically *unstable.* They are said to be *radioactive,* and they *decay* into other elements or into other isotopes by *emitting* particles or rays known as *emanations.* The most commonly encountered emanations are alpha particles (or α particles or α rays), beta particles (or β particles or β rays), and gamma rays (or γ rays). Some stable elements can be made to decay by *bombarding* them with subatomic particles. The *half-life* of a decaying atom is a measure of how long it will continue to give off emanations (all emanations stop eventually). The study of all forms or radioactivity is called *radiochemistry.*

7. It is possible to write *radiochemical equations* that are similar to ordinary chemical equations. The same abbreviations are used for the chemical elements, but the mass numbers of the particular isotopes involved are also included. Thus, when uranium-239 emits a beta particle and becomes neptunium-239, the reaction may be represented as

$$U^{239} \rightarrow Np^{239} + \beta$$

or
$$U^{239} \xrightarrow{\beta} Np^{239}$$

The half-life of the original element is often shown as

$$U^{239} \xrightarrow{23 \text{ min}} Np^{239} + \beta$$

$$U^{239} \xrightarrow[23 \text{ min}]{\beta} Np^{239}$$

8. The *theory of relativity* led to the concept that the mass of subatomic particles could be converted into energy. The amount of energy that can be obtained from even one atom is tremendous. It is this conversion that produces the enormous energy of an atomic explosion.

9. *Quantum physics* deals with the absorption and emission of energy. It is a fundamental result of modern physics that energy is not absorbed and emitted continuously but in set, discrete amounts called *quanta.*

10. *Probability* enters physics through *quantum mechanics,* which deals
    with what happens inside an atom, and through *statistical mechanics,*
    which deals with what happens to large groups of atoms.

11. *Solid-state physics* deals with the relationships of crystal structure
    and atomic structure to electrical behavior. A *semiconductor* is a
    crystalline material that conducts electricity only when *impurities*
    are added to it. There are *donor* impurities and *acceptor* impuri-
    ties, and a semiconductor may exhibit *electron conduction* or *hole
    conduction.* Electrons and holes may be "killed" by falling into
    traps in the material. A semiconductor with few traps is known as
    a *high-lifetime* material, and one with many traps is a *low-lifetime*
    material.

Chapter 4
Electricity and Electronics

Introduction

Electricity should be familiar to you by now. In the chapter on chemistry, the section on electrochemistry taught you that chemical ions have electrical charges which are either positive or negative. This, in turn, introduced the battery. You learned about static electricity, and how it causes objects to cling to each other or repel each other. This led to ionic bonds which are electrical in nature and hold some chemical compounds together. In the chapter on mathematics, you learned of prefixes such as kilo-, milli-, and micro-, which can be applied to electrical units such as volts and amperes (among others), to make them larger or smaller. In the chapter on physics, particularly in the section on solid-state physics, there was a good deal of fundamental information on the electron, how it moves — to make an electric current — and how the materials it moves in may then be considered to be conductors, semiconductors, or insulators. You should glance at these sections again — especially the one on electrochemistry and the one on solid-state physics — for a quick introduction to what you will meet here. Then proceed with this chapter.

Electrons in Circuits

Electrons Everywhere. This section is an adventure story that starts with the electron, follows the electron around wherever it goes, and ends with the electron. Electrons in crystals, electrons in chemical solutions, electrons in the middle of the air, electrons in vacuum, electrons in conductors, resistors, semiconductors, capacitors, vacuum tubes, transistors, rectifiers, thyratrons, transformers, motors, switches, relays, oscillators, amplifiers, generators, inductors, coils, dynamos, spark plugs, radios, television sets, dictaphones, computers, light bulbs, photocells, phonographs, and many others.

Electrons are very nervous and jumpy. You can no more make one stand still than you can make a seven-year-old boy stand still. An electron wants to move around all the time. It moves quickly and it moves slowly. As it moves, it makes lights go on, engines run, phonographs play, and egg beaters beat eggs. It makes more remarkable inventions work than Edison ever dreamt about, and it solves more mathematical problems (of certain sorts) than the wisest mathematician could take on in a million years. An electron is always having adventures, and always comes out of an adventure completely unchanged and ready for the next one.

As I explained in the section on solid-state physics, an *electric current* is nothing more than the movement of a stream of electrons. We can make such a stream move in many kinds of gadgets. A system through which electrons move is called a *circuit*. Basically, *electronics* is the study of the movements of electric currents through electric circuits.

Let me repeat what an electron is. First, and most important, an electron is a *subatomic particle*. It is one of the constituents of matter, one of the constituents of the atom (the others, remember, are the proton and the neutron). An electron hovers around the nucleus of an atom (and the nucleus is made up of a cluster of all the protons and neutrons of that atom). The protons have a positive, or plus, electrical charge, and the electrons have a negative, or minus, electrical charge. There is always the same number of electrons as protons in an atom, so the electrical charges balance each other, one plus for each minus.

When many atoms get together they form a material substance. This substance may be crystalline or amorphous (for an explanation of these terms see the section on crystallography and crystal physics in the chapter on physics). In any material, but more usually in one that is composed of crystals (as any metal is), the electrons which hover around the nucleus in the outermost orbits, or shells, are not held very tightly, and they can move from one atom to another. These "loose" electrons are "available." When there are a lot of them in a material it is a conductor; when there are none, the material is an insulator; when there are only a few, the material is a semiconductor.

Attraction and Repulsion. Here are some things that can be done with electrons. We know that electrons carry a negative charge. Since opposites attract, if the negative electricity sees some positive electricity in the neighborhood, it will be attracted by it and move toward it. We know already that this movement of electrons is called an electric current. The important fact now is that it is the presence of positive charge that makes the electrons move.

The Battery. One way to expose electrons to positive electricity is to attach a conductor (which is full of
"loose" electrons) to a battery. In
the chapter on chemistry, in the section on electrochemistry, you learned
that a battery is a device that "makes
electricity chemically." It has a way
of making positive chemical ions con-
gregate at one side of it and negative
chemical ions pile up at the other side.
These two sides are *contacts,* or *terminals,* or *connections,* or *electrodes*

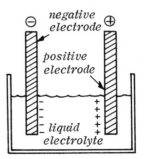

Figure 1. The battery.

(in electronics these words all have the same meaning), and there
is a positive electrode and a negative electrode. (See Figure 1.)

Voltage—and Pull. If a typical conductor of electricity such as
a copper wire is attached to the positive end of a battery, as in
Figure 2, there is a "rush" of free electrons through the conductor to the positive electrode of the battery. If it is a strong
battery it will gather in a greater number of loose electrons than
if it is a weak battery. This electrical pulling "force" is called
voltage, named after the Italian Count Allesandro Volta, who was
a contemporary of another great experimenter in electricity, Ben-
jamin Franklin. Voltage "pulls" electrons. When you pull a
weight with a rope you are pulling with a mechanical force; when
you pull electrons with positive electricity you are pulling with
an electrical force. (See Figure 2.) While a mechanical force
can pull any object, an electrical force can only pull something
that is charged electrically.

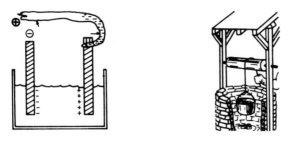

Figure 2. The pos-
itive terminal of a 10-
volt battery pulls
electrons out of a con-
ducting wire with 10
volts of "electrical
force." You pull a
bucket that weighs 10
pounds out of a well
with 10 pounds of me-
chanical force.

Connection—Extension. In Figure 2, something interesting has
happened at the battery when the conducting wire is attached at
the positive electrode. Because electrons are pulled toward the

positive electrode of the battery, the rest of the wire, all the way to the end, now behaves as though it is as positive as the battery electrode was at the point of attachment. Since the end of the wire has been robbed of some of its electrons, it has less negative electrical charge in it then it had previously. That makes it positive. (Some people say that if you are not with me you are against me; in the same way, in a conductor, if you are *less negative* if follows that you are *more positive.*) The end of the wire has thus become an *extension* of the terminal of the battery.

When an electrician attaches a wire to an electrode that has voltage on it, the wire is said to become "live." The live voltage has been brought to a new place, the end of the wire. If anyone then touches the wire he will "feel" the voltage: he will get an electric *shock.*

In the same way, you can attach the conducting wire to the other side of the battery, the negative side, as in Figure 3. Then the negative voltage at the negative terminal of the battery will "push" the loose electrons in the conductor away from the battery, as far as they can go into the wire. This happens because similar charges repel each other. Then the end of the wire will take on the same negative electrical charge that the battery terminal had before the wire was attached. Again, the conducting wire added to a battery terminal has acted as an extension of the terminal.

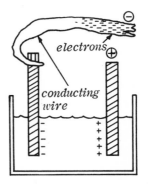

Figure 3. A conducting wire attached to the negative terminal of a battery.

Potential — Sitting There, Waiting. If you put your fingers where they do not belong, namely, at a point where there is voltage, you will get a shock. In other words, the voltage at the end of a battery terminal (or at the end of a wire connected to it) is "sitting there" in readiness to be used. But until you touch it it is not being used — it is *potential!*

Potential is an important word to the electrical engineer. It is his way of saying "static," not moving — but ready to move. When it does move, it becomes "dynamic." In fact, electricity, just like mechanics and hydraulics, can be divided into statics and dynamics: *electrostatics* and *electrodynamics.* Coming back to the word *potential*, the electrical engineer will often say things like, "a point has a potential of 200 volts." What he means is that there is a voltage ready to act at that point, potentially ready. When it acts, it will move electrons through wires, over distances. Now remember, motion is caused by force, and force acting over distance is energy. So potential is ready to exert *potential energy*. Once the energy is set free to act it becomes *kinetic*, dynamic or active, energy. You should be aware that your boss will often use the word "potential" as a noun, to mean "voltage," poised and ready to leap.

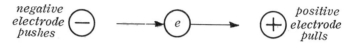

negative electrode pushes
positive electrode pulls

the net result is motion to the right

Figure 4. When one electrode pushes an electron and the other pulls it, the net result is motion.

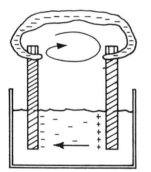

Figure 5. When a conducting wire is connected to both electrodes of a battery an electric current results.

What Is a Circuit? There is one more thing we can do with a wire and a battery. We can attach *both* ends of the wire to the battery, one for each terminal. What happens now? If the positive electrode of the battery is pulling the electrons *in* and the negative electrode of the battery is pushing them *out* from the other end, then the push and the pull are both in the same direction and the net result is motion. We see how the "push" adds to the "pull" on one electron, in Figure 4. Figure 5 shows the total effect when the wire is attached to both terminals of the battery. As the positive terminal pulls and the negative terminal pushes, the electrons move through the wire, go inside the battery (where they keep moving), and then go back out of the negative terminal and into the conductor again.

When connected in this way, the electrons just go round and round. This is the opposite of electrons piling up in the wire as in Figures 2 and 3. That was static, this is dynamic. This keeps happening! As long as the connection holds and as long as the battery lasts, the electrons move as an electric current, round and round and round and round again, always in the same path. This path has a name that is most important—it is a *circuit* (which means a path that ends up where it started). The electrical engineer who specializes in circuits calls himself a *circuit engineer* and the work he is doing is *circuitry*.

The Loop Circuit.   Different circuits have different names. The short little loop which connects the terminals in Figure 5 is called just that, a *loop*. It is so easy for electrons to travel in a loop that they may go in so much of a rush that the wire of the loop burns up. When a circuit burns up we say that it is a *short circuit* or a *short*. If a wire falls across two points in an electrical appliance that are not usually connected together, there may be a rush of current through the short circuit (or short cut); overheating and melting of the wire *(burnout)* is the result. (You must certainly at one time or another have been told by a repairman that your toaster or broiler or radio didn't work because it had a "short.")

On the other hand, a circuit can be very complicated with all kinds of long *parallel* or *series* paths and branches and loops and alternate paths; it may then be called a *network*. Sometimes even networks have networks; such a system may be called a *mesh*. But most circuits are just called *circuits*.

Putting a Circuit to Work.   As electrons move from one terminal of a battery (or other source of electrons, your wall outlet is one) through a conducting wire, and back into the terminal at the other end, over and over again, as they pass certain points they may make certain useful things happen. What can the electrons do "in passing"? Well, as they move through a toaster they heat up the wires in the toaster — and they make toast; after they have completed this task, they just go back to the place they started, so that they can keep going round and round some more. In fact, if you do not eventually "open," or make a break in, the circuit (or if the toaster doesn't turn itself off) the toast burns. In the same way, other circuits create heat for electric blankets and electric stoves. Electrons can also move through an electric motor and cause a shaft to turn around — and so you have electric fans, electric subway trains, electric elevators, electric mixers, electric washing machines, and all kinds of electric appliances run by motors.

Electrons also can move through radio tubes and transistors. As they move through these elements they are "bunched up" and then spread out thin — that is, they move as waves. The results are sounds out of radios and pictures out of television. These motions of electrons are very complex, far more complex than any motion in an electric blanket or in a toaster. But, no matter how complicated the job they do, the electrons in your radio or television set are still going round and round — in circuits.

I always compare electrical circuits to toy electric trains. The trains too run on a kind of circuit. But now the circuit is a train track, not a conducting wire. As long as a train keeps running on a piece of track it just goes round and round. In Figure 6 I have pictured the simplest train circuit, one loop. It looks

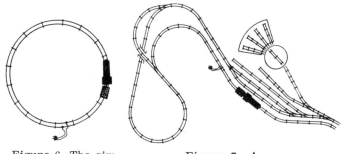

Figure 6. The sim-
plest train circuit.

Figure 7. A com-
plicated train circuit.

like the electrical loop in Figure 5. On the other hand, it is possible to buy and set up the most complicated kind of track system, which may look like Figure 7. As the train passes certain spots in this complex system it makes drawbridges go up and down, lights and signal bells go on and off, safety barriers go across the road, and so on. Things are also done to the train as it moves past certain places on the track. It may be made to slow down or speed up. It may be made to blow whistles or put on lights. Most interesting of all, the train may be asked to "make a choice"; should it go down the left set of track or the right set of track. That is, should it *switch* its direction?

As electrons move in circuits they also get certain jobs done — they toast bread and run radios. They also have things done to them — they go into an amplifier circuit at low potential and come out at high potential. Electrons can "switch" too — with an electric switch.

Just as Figure 7 is a diagram of a complicated train circuit, so Figure 8 is a diagram of a complicated electric circuit. The electrons flow through all the gadgets represented by all those wriggley symbols, round and round. This is a radio circuit. That is, after the electrons have gone through the whole circuit, the net result is that the *loudspeaker* on your radio starts to vibrate and produce the sounds that you think of when you think about a radio.

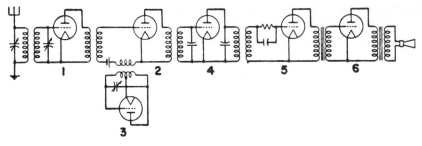

Figure 8. A complicated electric circuit.

Sometimes the circuit engineer does not want to bother showing all of the elements in a circuit diagram. He just wants the reader to know what each part of the circuit is doing. Then he merely represents each part of the circuit with a block which has the name of that part, or *stage,* written inside of it. Another engineer, who understands all about this, can then fill in the elements which will do the jobs indicated. The *block diagram* for Figure 8 is shown in Figure 9.

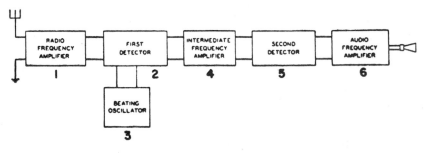

Figure 9. The block diagram for Figure 8.

The Many Varieties of Circuits.   As you might expect, certain combinations of circuit components are more common than others, and have come to be known by characteristic names — names that either describe something that the circuits do or immortalize the names of the circuits' inventors. Table 1 lists the names of some circuits that you are sure to meet if you work in the electronics industry. Read the list, word by word. Then when your employer uses one of these words, you will have seen it before. This is what is important to you as a secretary. Oh yes, one more thing, this list could not possibly include every circuit. In fact, your boss is always inventing new ones — so do not be surprised at the outlandish, but descriptive, names he may give them.

Table 1.   Some Words About Circuits

push–pull	oscillator	binary
flip–flop	amplifier	phase shifter
doubler	discriminator	tuned
integrator	detector	feedback
differentiator	inverter	regenerative
trigger	switching	degenerative
cathode follower	multiplying	demodulator
limiting	dividing	blocking oscillator
chopping	resonant	relation oscillator
clipping	tank	avalanche
clamping	filter	multivibrator
cascade	mixer	trippler
squaring	modulator	gating
delta	comparator	regulating
star	generating	stabilization
delta–star	saw-tooth generator	wye
counting	sweep	delta–wye
scaler	filter	delta–zig-zag
decade	limiter	series
delay	rectifying	parallel
remote cutoff	memory	synchronizing (synch)
bridge	accumulator	transmission line
delay line	screen	direct-coupled
network	equivalent	stagger-tuned
loop	adding	video amplifier
storage	superheterodyne	audio amplifier
Hartley	Armstrong	Miller
Colpitts	Eccles-Jordan	Franklin

Summary

1. Electrons traveling through a conducting wire form an *electric current*. They move because *voltage* from a battery or a wall outlet has been applied to the ends of the wire. If you touch a point where there is voltage you will get a *shock*.
2. Electrons travel only in continuous paths that end up where they start. These continuous paths are called *circuits*. A circuit can be very simple like a *loop*, or very complex like a *network* or a *mesh*. *Circuitry* is the science of connecting sources of voltage and networks of wires to form useful circuits.
3. If there is a *break* in a circuit (an *open circuit*), there is *potential* (another word for voltage) at the point of the break, but no current flows.

4. The most important fact about a circuit is that when current flows, useful results may be obtained. Some of these results are seen in the electrical appliances we use daily—radios, light bulbs, motors, and so on.

5. Many different types of circuits exist and are in common use. Each circuit performs a job that is in some way different from all others. Table 1 lists some of the words associated with different types of circuits. Read this table carefully and become familiar with these words.

Ohm's Law

Rigorous Thinking.   Enter the physicist. What does he do? He looks at something that happens and applies rigorous thinking to it. Remember what he did in the playground in the last chapter, with his analyses of the swing, the slide, the seesaw, and the merry-go-round? Well, now he is up to the same tricks with the movements of electrons. It is as though he were to ask himself, "How many rigorous, analytical things can I say about the movements of electrons?" Then he proceeds to say them. What he says your boss will say too. As a result, you will have to take it in dictation and type it.

An Electrical Quartet.   Some words that you will encounter over and over again in material dealing with electricity are derived from the names of four physicists who contributed to the study of various aspects of electricity.

The *coulomb*, named after the Frenchman Charles Augustin de Coulomb (1736-1806), is a specific number of electrons, actually, it is quite a few billion electrons. An *abcoulomb* is ten coulombs.

An *ohm* is a measure of the *resistance* that something offers to the flow of electric current. It is named after the German physicist Georg Simon Ohm (1787-1854). You will get an idea of what is meant by electrical resistance if you think about cars moving on a crowded highway. Cars can flow faster on a highway with four lanes than on one with only one lane. The four-lane road offers less "resistance" than the one-lane road does. Similarly, an electric current flows more easily through a wide wire than through a narrow one. The unit of resistance is named after Ohm because he did much of the fundamental experimental work that led to the understanding of the concept.

As it turns out, the opposite (or inverse, as the physicist would say) of resistance also is a concept with physical significance. It is called *conductance* and is measured in *mhos* (that's right, *mho* is *ohm* spelled backwards—it is pronounced to rhyme with the name Joe). Mathematically,

$$x \text{ ohm} = \frac{1}{x} \text{ mhos}$$

So, for example, anything that has 0.1 mhos of conductance has 10 ohms of resistance.

An *ampere* is a unit for current flow. When 1 coulomb of electrons flows past a point in 1 second, you have an electric current of 1 ampere. The ampere is named after André Marie Ampère, who was a French physicist (1775-1836).

From the last section, you may remember the *volt* (named after the Italian count Alessandro Volta, 1745-1827). There we said that it is used to measure the amount of "voltage" in a battery. Voltage is also known as *electromotive force* or *emf* or *EMF* or *e.m.f.*, so these are also given in volts.

The Law. This international quartet of physicists is bound together by a law which is named after Ohm: *Ohm's law.* It says that

A coulomb per second—that is, an ampere—will flow through a conducting wire of resistance of one ohm, when pushed with a force of one volt.

Then, if there are 2 volts, there will be 2 amperes, and if there are 3 volts there will be 3 "amps," and so on. In the same way, if there are 2 ohms there will be twice the resistance that there was to start with and the flow will be half what it was at first, or half an ampere. Ohm's law can be expressed as the simplest of equations, but one which your employer will use over and over again. It looks like this:

$$V = IR$$

where V = voltage in volts
I = electrical current in amperes
R = resistance in ohms

You see, if you multiply the number of amperes by the number of ohms, you get the number of volts. So if you plug your toaster into the electrical socket in your home, and the toaster has ten ohms of resistance and the amount of current "drawn," or pulled from the socket is eleven amperes, then you know that everything is all right: 10×11 is 110, and 110 volts is a voltage that can be provided in the electric outlets in your home.

Summary

1. There are four words that occur over and over again in discussions of electricity. A *coulomb* is a unit that represents a certain number of electrons. An *ohm* is a unit that describes the resistance to current flow offered by a conductor. An *ampere* is a unit that describes the rate of flow of electrons. A *volt* measures *electromotive force* (or *emf*, or *EMF*, or *e.m.f.*) which is equivalent to voltage.
2. *Ohm's Law*:

$$V = IR$$

relates ohms (R), amperes (I), and volts (V). If two are known, the equation lets you determine the third.

Electrical Waves

Wave and No Wave—Alternating and Direct Current. Electricity is a wave phenomenon. But it does not need to be all the time. Electricity from a battery is not a wave. It flows out of the battery in a simple, straightforward surge or flow—in a *direct current*. But most of our electricity comes out of our wall plugs, and is *not* direct current. It is *alternating current*. And alternating current alternates in waves.

What is alternating current? A current alternates when the voltage supplying it is alternating. This means that the voltage keeps changing from plus to minus, back to plus again, and so on. These changes from plus to minus and back are known as changes of *polarity*.

It is as though the battery pictured in Figures 1, 2, 3, and 5 were to keep changing its mind about which terminal should be the positive terminal and which one should be the negative terminal, and was changing its mind very quickly, and regularly. Remember the word for regular, repeated changes of direction —like those of the pendulum: *periodic*. So each periodic change of polarity may be called a *cycle*, or an *oscillation*, and the time of each cycle may be called a *period*. These are the familiar words of waves; the same words you met in acoustics, mechanics, optics, and heat. Do the terms *amplitude, wavelength, phase, frequency*, and the others apply here too? Indeed they do. The universe keeps repeating the same patterns over and over again.

Waterwheels and Generators. But there is still one very important question to be answered: Who ever heard of a battery that keeps changing its terminals from plus to minus and minus to plus? There is no such battery; but there is something else: the *dynamo* or *generator*. A dynamo or generator is another way of making electricity—and a much more convenient way when you want to make large quantities of electricity.

Figure 10. A waterwheel.

I shall not try to give a detailed and complete explanation of how a generator works, but you should know roughly what one does. Let me start by pointing out that most of the machines invented by man go round and round. That is why the wheel is considered the greatest of our inventions. It is so much a part of so many things. Probably one of the oldest ways to get wheels to go round and round is by using water power. Figure 10 shows how a waterwheel, that is, a wheel driven by water power, works. No matter how large a waterwheel is (and some that are used in modern power stations are truly enormous), it always works in a similar way.

A waterwheel may be attached to a loop of wire (or, if it is a large wheel, to many loops of wire). If the loops are arranged so that as they turn they move past a magnet, an electric current is set up in the wire. (You've certainly seen a magnet at one time or another, but, as usual, the physicist's definition of a magnet is more precise than the one that you would offhandedly give. It will be given in the next section.)

A generator ordinarily produces alternating current. The current is carried from it by electrical contacts called *brushes*. If direct current is desired, it can be obtained from the same generator by inserting a *commutator*.

Table 2.   Words About Motors and Generators

Types		Parts	
motor	alternator	stator	brush
generator	converter	rotor	commutator
dynamo	selsyn motor	armature	magnetic pole
	synchronous motor		

Motors — Backward Generators.   This brings us to electric *motors*. Motors are everywhere. Most ordinary American homes contain dozens of motors: in refrigerators, electric fans, electric mixers, hair dryers, phonograph turntables, can openers, washing machines, and so on. What is a motor? It is a generator or dynamo that works backwards. If we turn a wheel (with water power) we can get electricity out; in the same way if electricity is put *into* a wheel, it turns. And that is what all motors do. They turn round and round and do useful work as a result of our feeding electricity to them.   Table 2 brings together some important motor and generator words.

Rectification.   Electrical engineers and physicists make good use of both direct current and alternating current. There are special uses for each one and the engineer uses the one he needs for a particular job. He has invented many ways to make one out of the other.   For example, your automobile has a battery and that gives direct current — but your car radio may not want direct current. So your car may have an *alternator* or a *converter* or a *vibrator,* any one of which can convert direct current into alternating current. What if the engineer has alternating current and he wants to convert it into direct current? He may use a *rectifier,* which may be part of a *power supply.* ("Rect-" means "right" and "-fier" is from a Latin word meaning "to make," so to rectify is to "make right.")

Leading and Lagging.   We even have devices (circuits) that can make alternating waves alternate "too late" or "too soon" when compared with other electrical waves. From what you already know about waves, these waves are then "out of phase" or, like some music, out of tune. Sometimes an engineer wants waves to be out of phase on purpose. He then uses a *phase changing* circuit or network, or a *delay line,* in order to make the waves *lead* or *lag.*

How Fast?   So far I have talked about alternating current, but I have said nothing about how fast it may alternate. The fact is that the frequency of alternation can be so fast that no river turning a waterwheel can ever cause electrical oscillations even one-billionth the speed of the ones used in the most modern electrical systems. How an engineer achieves these frequencies is not important to you as a secretary, but what he names them is.

Please believe me when I say that it is good to make electrical waves that alternate at faster and faster frequencies. (The higher the frequencies the greater the number of television stations you can have, for example.) But engineers never predicted how high the frequencies would actually become as new equipment was invented and developed.   That is how they got into trouble with names.   They ran out of names for the different classifications of high frequencies, and the frequency ranges they did name, they named badly.   You will understand what I mean when I tell you the names.

Start with *audio frequency* (af), which simply means a frequency that our ears can hear.   The next faster set of frequencies (those used in radio) was called the *radio frequencies* (rf), and took care of all the electronic needs of the world until World War II.   During the war, in order to add stations and increase communications, another set of frequency bands, called the *high frequencies* (hf) was added.   The next extension of frequency (always to faster rates of vibration, remember) was called *very-high frequency* (vhf).   Then, along came television and the next higher set of frequencies, which were named *ultra-high frequencies* (uhf).

What should the next names be?   "Super-ultra-high frequency" or "really high frequency" or "very-ultra-high frequency indeed" or "I-really-mean-it-this-time high frequency"?   Engineers seem to have solved the dilemma in a convenient, if unpoetic, way.   They have gone to letters.   Names of the various frequency ranges or *bands* are shown in Table 3.

Table 3.   The Frequency Bands

audio frequency	radio frequency	high frequency
very-high frequency		ultra-high frequency
S band X band K band	Ku band L band	

The Shortest Lengths.   As frequencies become higher, many more waves are crowded into a given time interval (like a second).   In fact, kilocycle waves (rf) vibrate on the order of thousands of times in a second; megacycle waves (vhf) vibrate millions of times per second; and gigacycle waves (X band and up) vibrate billions of times in a second.   If the number of vibrations in one second is high, then the time for one wave to pass is very short.   So *shortwave* radio works on waves of short wavelength, which is just another way of saying "very-high frequency."

All electrical waves have wavelengths that are measurable; the longest ones (shortest frequency) are *meter waves* and we go right through the metric system of length measurement to *centimeter waves, millimeter waves,* and *micron waves.*   Frequencies that are in the higher ranges are known as *microwave* fre-

Table 4.   Words About Electrical Waves

Wave Words

wave	bandwidth	cross talk
cycle	selectivity	discharge
period	eddy current	band
oscillation	arc (or spark)	square wave
wavelength	mean free path	sawtooth wave
amplitude	transient	leading edge
sinusoidal	time constant	trailing edge
root-mean-square (rms)	heterodyne	tuning
phase	superheterodyne	side band
lag	Doppler	noise
lead	pulse	signal-to-noise ratio
delay	pulsewidth	intermediate frequency
frequency	synchronism	video frequency
carrier wave	interference	microwave
carrier frequency	harmonic	microwave components
signal	pip	microwave plumbing
signal envelope	readout	meter waves
locking frequency	scan	centimeter waves
sum frequency	lobe	millimeter waves
difference frequency	side-lobe	micron waves
alternating current	channel	shortwave
direct current		longwave

Voltage Words	Units	Circuit Words
charge	ampere	rectifier
polarity	coulomb	power supply
potential	volt	delay line
equipotential	ohm	alternator
dipole	mho	vibrator
field	erg	waveguide
flux	joule	amplifer
corona	watt	switch
lines of force	watt-hour	
	kilowatt-hour	
	horsepower	
	kilovolt-ampere	

quencies, to show that the wavelengths associated with them are very small. Engineers who work with waves of these frequencies are called microwave engineers. The electrical components that can handle these frequencies are called microwave components, the circuits are called microwave circuits, and the whole field is called microwave engineering. Table 4 lists some of the words that pertain to the wave nature of electricity.

Summary

1. An *alternating current* moves first in one direction and then the opposite way. It is produced by a source of voltage which changes its *polarity,* that is, which switches from positive to negative and then back over and over again.
2. Since an alternating voltage switches its direction in a regular, repeated pattern, it is a *wave* phenomenon, and has such wave properties as frequency, period, wavelength, amplitude, and phase. Words about electrical waves are summarized in Table 4.
3. *Generators,* in which mechanical power, usually water power, turns wheels which are connected to loops of wires, are sources of alternating current.
4. *Motors* work like generators in reverse. Instead of turning wheels producing alternating current, alternating current is used to make wheels turn.
5. Alternating current may be turned into *direct current* in a *rectifier,* and direct current may be turned into alternating current in a *converter* or *alternator.*
6. The phase of an alternating current wave may be made to *lag* or *lead* another wave.
7. Electrical waves are grouped into *frequency bands.* The names of these bands are given in Table 3.

Magnetism

What Is It?   *Magnetism* is attraction. We have already met attraction in electricity, *static electricity.* That was the attraction (or pull) of positive electrical charge for negative electrical charge. Magnetism is also an attraction of opposites. But there are several differences. In order to feel magnetic pull you have to be magnetic too. It is like belonging to a snobbish and exclusive club —if you are not born with certain qualities you can't get into the club.

Some minerals are magnetic. *Lodestone* was known to people of ancient times. Its modern, more descriptive name, is *magnetite.* Magnetite is mined out of the ground and put into blast furnaces together with a few other ingredients and comes out as iron. Iron is the metal from which steel is made. All three, magnetite, iron, and steel are magnetic. These three are a family that can get into the magnetic fraternity, which is limited mainly to iron, nickel, cobalt, many of the alloys of iron, nickel, and cobalt, and to certain minerals, like magnetite (which contain iron). There is also a group of artificial, synthetic magnetic materials whose names you should recognize, the *ferrites*.

So, to summarize, 99% of all the magnetic materials known are in the following list:

iron or steel
nickel
cobalt
alloys of iron, nickel, or cobalt
Alnico (the trade name of an alloy which is derived from what it
    contains, aluminum, nickel and cobalt)
magnetite
the ferrites

The prefix "ferro-" means "pertaining to iron." Since iron is the best of the magnetic materials (the most magnetic), the word *ferromagnetic* means very magnetic. When a material is weakly magnetic it is given the name *paramagnetic*. Everything else is out of the club and is called *nonmagnetic,* or *diamagnetic.*

You must also know that objects that are not magnetic but that bear an electric charge may be affected by magnets. Consider an electron. A magnet will not attract an electron, but it *will* divert it. What it does is move it around without actually pulling it over. The way it does this is described by the *left-hand rule.* This is one of the oddest rules in all science (it is matched only by the *right-hand rule*). It instructs the scientist to spread the thumb and first two fingers of his left hand so that they all point in different directions, as shown in Figure 11. You can do it too. The rule says that when an electron is moving as an electric current in the direction of the forefinger and the magnetism is in the direction of the middle finger then the electron will get a push in the direction of the thumb! So you see the electron gets a push from a magnet but in an unexpected direction. Some day your employer will be dictating to you when suddenly he

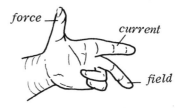

Figure 11. The left-hand rule.

will whip out his left hand and look intensely at his thumb and first two fingers. Do not begin to worry about his sanity. He is just deciding which way the magnetism will push a stream of electrons. (If you are wondering about the right-hand rule, it gives him the same information for particles that have positive charges.)

How Does It Work?   How does a magnet work? A magnet works like tadpoles look. A tadpole has two ends and the important thing about a tadpole is that one end is a head and the other end is a tail; the two ends of magnet are its north pole and south pole. Now any object that is one way at one end and the opposite way at the other end is known as a *dipole*, from "di-pole," which means "two ends" (since the dictionary says that a pole is an end, or extremity). So a magnet is a dipole, and opposite poles attract each other while similar poles repel each other.

You already know that all the atoms that make up materials contain electrical charges. Magnetic materials, in addition, contain magnetic dipoles. You also know from the section on crystallography in the chapter on physics, that in crystalline materials atoms "line up" in regular arrays, or patterns. How are these facts related? Sometimes little crystals (*crystallites*) are magnetized like dipoles. Groups of these little crystals are then called *magnetic domains*.

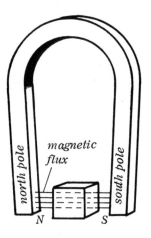

It is possible to have a material made up of magnetic domains but the material may still not be magnetic —it may only be *magnetizable*. If all the domains are pointing every which way, they tend to cancel each other out. Instead of working together like the forces working on the electron in Figure 4, they may be working in opposition to each other. In order for the material to become magnetic, all of the domains must be made to point in the same direction. How do you make magnetic domains in a magnetizable material all point in the same direction? You place the material in a region between two magnetic poles as in Figure 12. The region between the poles is a very magnetic place. Such a place is known as a *magnetic field*, and we say that the field is full of a *flux* of (imaginary) *lines of*

Figure 12. Magnetizing a magnetizable material.

magnetic force. The magnetic lines of force of the magnetic field cause all the domains that are pointing the wrong way to rotate around just enough so that they are all pointing in the right way. It is just like a military organization. When the order is given to salute the flag, all the soldiers turn in their tracks and face the flag and salute. Similarly, all the magnetic domains turn and point so that the north poles of the little domain magnets are all pointing at the south pole of the magnetic field imposed from outside. (That makes all the south poles of the little domains point toward the north pole of the imposed magnet too.) But, unlike the soldiers, who turn away from the flag when the order is withdrawn, when the big magnet is taken away, the domains remain pointing all the same way. The act of putting a potentially magnetic material into a magnetic field is called *magnetization.* Now the piece that was treated in this way has become a magnet itself and it can magnetize other objects (provided, of course, that they too belong to the club of materials that can be magnetized).

Why is the material now a magnet? Remember, each little domain was a magnet to begin with. Making tham all point the same way has caused them all to reinforce each other. Before, some of them were canceling each other out; now they are all acting together.

Clicking Noises.   You might be interested to know that the rotation of the little domains can actually be detected with a loudspeaker. If you turn the wire from the loudspeaker around a piece of metal as it is being magnetized it is possible to "pick up" the sound of the domains rotating —as each one flips into position it makes a little clicking noise. I have heard it; it sounds like the popping of the smallest popcorn. This effect was named after the first man to define it; it is known as the *Barkhausen effect.*

Magnetization and Demagnetization.   Will a magnet stay a magnet? If so, how long? The answer depends on the material. Some materials stay magnetic for years, for lifetimes. These are sometimes called *permanent magnets.* But very little done in this world by men lasts forever. Usually magnets gradually lose their magnetic qualities. Little by little, the magnetic domains discover that the magnet that lined them all up (magnetized them) has been taken away, then they slowly begin to revert to their previous unmagnetized state, canceling out each other's magnetism. The magnet *demagnetizes.*

When physicists talk about magnetic materials they seem to

Table 5.   Words That Describe Magnetic Qualities

	Symbol	Unit
susceptibility	χ, k	
reluctance	ν, Z	gilbert per maxwell
coercivity		oersted
retentivity		gauss
magnetic field intensity	H	oersted
magnetic flux	ϕ	maxwell, weber
magnetic flux density	B	gauss
permeability	μ	gauss per oersted
magnetomotive force	F	gilbert
permeance	P	maxwell per gilbert

attribute almost human qualities to them. A material is said to have a certain *susceptibility* to being magnetized, and a magnetic *retentivity* after the field that was used to magnetize it is removed. It may also be said to possess an amount of *coercivity* and a magnetic *reluctance.* These qualities of magnets (along with some others), the units in which they are measured, and the symbols used to represent them are given in Table 5.

A Sextet This Time.   Gilbert, Maxwell, Weber, Oersted, Gauss, and Barkhausen all were physicists. Their discoveries, or the units in which their discoveries are measured, were all named after them. The important words that pertain to magnets and magnetism are given in Table 6.

Table 6.   Other Important Words of Magnetism

magnetic	Alnico	magnetic field	dipole
nonmagnetic	magnetite	magnetic flux	north pole
ferromagnetic	lodestone	lines of force	south pole
paramagnetic	ferrite	domain	demagnetize
diamagnetic	magnetic core	permanent magnet	hysteresis

Summary

1. *Magnetism* is an attraction. Only certain materials are attracted magnetically. They are known as *ferromagnetic* and *paramagnetic* materials. All other materials are *nonmagnetic*, or *diamagnetic.*
2. Although materials that are charged electrically are not necessarily attracted by magnets, they are always diverted by magnets. The way that an object with negative charge is diverted is given by the *left-*

hand rule; the effect on a positive charge is given by the *right-hand rule.*

3. A material is magnetic when it is made up of crystallites (little crystals) that are themselves magnetic. These crystallites are called magnetic domains. A crystallite is magnetic if it is a *magnetic dipole*, that is, if it has a *north pole* at one end and a *south pole* at the other end.

4. A *magnetizable* material may be magnetized if it is placed in a magnetic region (a *magnetic field*). This causes all the magnetic domains that it contains to line up and reinforce each other.

5. Words like *susceptibility, retentivity, reluctance* , and *coercivity* describe the magnetization of a magnet. These and other words that pertain to magnets are listed in Tables 5 and 6.

Components

I have said a good deal about the physics of electricity in the last four sections, mostly about how electrons move as a result of being pushed around by electric and magnetic forces. The next three sections deal with the devices that the electrons move in. These can be divided into "passive" components, such as resistors and capacitors, which we will describe in this section, and "active" components, such as radio tubes and solid-state devices, which we will go into in the next two sections.

Some Word Variations. Look again at the circuit diagram in Figure 8. It is reasonable to guess that like so much else that looks complicated it is a kind of shorthand. That is all it is. You know all about secretarial shorthand. Is the shorthand of the electrical engineer more difficult? No, it is easier. It is easier because there are fewer symbols and because they stand for whole words instead of just parts of words. The words that the symbols represent are the names of the building blocks of circuits. These building blocks can be called building blocks, ingredients, parts, constituents, elements, or components of electrical circuits. *Component* is the word conventionally used by electrical engineers. Figure 8 is full of components; the shorthand of the circuit diagram makes them look like this.

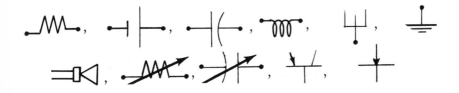

This section will discuss these symbols from the point of view of the secretary, emphasizing the words you will meet in discussions of components. Start with the word *resistor*, and consider some variations on it. A resistor is a gadget that offers *resistance* (or clogging, like a clogged drain) to the flow of electrons (current). The amount of resistance it has may be large or small, but whatever its size it is measured in *ohms*. We say, "A resistor has a thousand ohms of resistance." If you work for an electrical engineer, you will often meet statements similar to that one.

An engineer may want a certain amount of resistance at a certain point in a circuit he is building. He can buy a little cylindrical device with a wire sticking out of each end as shown in

Figure 13. A resistor.

Figure 13. That is a resistor. When he buys a resistor he picks out one with just as many ohms as he wants. A resistor can have one ohm of resistance or ten million ohms of resistance (also called ten megohms). In this country so many television sets, computers, radios, and other electronic machines are built that we use up millions of resistors every day!

Anything that has resistance also is *resistive* and has *resistivity*. The suffix "-ivity" means that a unit amount of a quality (in this case, resistance) is being described. For example, the resistance of a cube of copper that is one centimeter long on each side is at the same time the resistivity of the copper. From our discussion of Ohm's law you remember that we can talk about *conductance* (measured in mhos). So, in the same way, we can form the nouns *conductor* and *conductivity* and the adjective *conductive*.

A resistor and its resistance also can be represented by the abbreviation R (sometimes also r, but R is preferred). The number of ohms in a circuit is usually represented by the Greek letter capital omega, Ω so the sentence several paragraphs back ("A resistor has a thousand ohms of resistance.") may be written,

"A resistor R has 1,000 Ω of resistance."

or

$$R = 1,000 \ \Omega$$

both of which have the same meaning as the original sentence. Resistivity is designated by the Greek letter rho, ρ.

The names of other components and units can be made into electrical terms in similar ways, by adding a few prefix or suffix syllables. We can make adjective with "-ives" and "ics," like this:

resistive   ohmic

conductive   voltaic

and nouns with "-ances," "-ages," and "-ivities," like this:

resistance   voltage

amperage   conductivity

Most of these terms can be represented by abbreviations (usually English or Greek letters). Some examples of letter abbreviations are:

Voltage is often referred to as "V" or "v"

millivolts are "mV" or "mv"

microvolts are "μV" or "μv"

kilovolts are "KV" or "kv"

megavolts are "MV" or "Mv"

amperage is "A" or "a"

milliamperes are "mA" or "ma"

microamperes are "μA" or "μa"

ohms are Ω

kiloohms are kΩ

microohms are $\mu\Omega$

Measurement — with Meters. All electrical units are measured with meters. A *meter*, if you look it up in the dictionary, turns out to be a "a measurer." Every quality has its own meter. There are

ohmmeter   ammeter   voltmeter

not to mention the

millivoltmeter   microvoltmeter   microammeter

which measure only the smallest quantities of volts or amperes. On the other hand there is the

megohmmeter

which measures millions of ohms. Figure 14 gives you an idea of what some meters look like.

A meter is shown with the symbol —◯— or this one —①— .

A voltmeter is —Ⓥ— and an ammeter is —Ⓐ— . Some words about meters that you may encounter are:

wattmeter	galvanometer	electrometer
watt-hour meter	d'Arsonval meter	damping meter
potentiometer	dynamometer	power-factor meter

The Other Components. Two other types of circuit components that you will encounter almost as frequently as resistors are *capacitors* and *inductors*. As a resistor has resistance, a capacitor has *capacitive reactance* (symbol X_c) and an inductor has *inductive reactance* (symbol X_L). Resistances and reactances are often grouped together as *inductances* (Z). Table 7 summarizes what has been said about resistors, capacitors, and inductors, and treats other components in the same way. In this table "associated words" are just that. They are words that mean either the same thing as the named word, almost the same thing, or the opposite. Words derived from the named word either in meaning or in appearance are also given. The part of speech is shown in some cases. The expressions in parentheses following the associated words have the following meanings:

> (*syn*) means synonym
> (*d*) means derived from this one in meaning
> (*opp*) means opposite in meaning
> (*adj*) means adjective
> (*v*) means verb

Table 7 is the sort of table you should read as though it were text. It is there to study in order to get a feeling for the kinds of components that make up a circuit (and their symbols). After

Photographs courtesy of Simpson Electric Company, Inc.

Figure 14. Some typical meters.

you have read the table look back at Figure 8, a typical circuit. It is just like a jigsaw puzzle made up of all the components of Table 7. You should now recognize most of them. After you have become familiar with the table, you should know the names of the components and that most of them have some kind of symbol associated with them. In addition, they may have abbreviations, and what they do may be measured in some electrical units. You shoud know that most of the components have alternate names and also have other words that "go with them." Finally, you should know that each one of them does something to electrons as they flow in electric currents. They push and pull the electrons; they speed them up or they slow them down; they bunch them or they spread them apart; or they make them stand still.

You do not need to know exactly what each component does to electric current—leave that to your boss. But you should know that it does something. Then the combination of what many components do together in a circuit is something good and useful.

Refrain. How circuits are made out of components, how electrons behave in circuits (as shown by Ohm's law), and what circuits accomplish is worth saying one more time.

Remember, as the electronics engineer adds components to a circuit he is building, and joins them together with connecting wire, and finally applies a source of voltage, he is making electrons perform a different kind of "trick" at each component. Finally, the circuit is placed into a piece of equipment like the electric typewriter, the dictaphone, or the desk calculator in your office.

Then you press a button and *connect* a complicated electrical circuit to a place where there are a lot of "loose" electrons (the battery or the wall plug). The electrons come rushing in and do the job you ask of them. If you use an electric typewriter and type 60 words a minute and each word has an average of 6 letters, then each time you press a key (6 × 60, or 360 times a minute) you are really closing a connection to the source of electrons and allowing them to rush into the circuits to do your bidding.

Summary

1. The building blocks of circuits are called circuit *components*.
2. The names of the different components serve as root words for other

Table 7. Circuit Components and Associated Words

Name	Associated Words	Abbreviation	Circuit Symbol	Unit	Symbol for Unit	Measured by	What It Is What It Does
resistor	resistance (d) resistivity (d) resistive (adj) shunt (syn) conductance (opp) ohmic (adj)	R, r	●〜〜〜●	ohm mho (opp)	Ω	ohmmeter	Impedes the flow of electric current.
capacitor	capacity (d) capacitance (d) capacitive (adj) condenser (syn) filter capacitor (d)	C, c	●⊣⊢● or ⊣⊢	farad, micro-farad, micro-micro-farad	F μF $\mu\mu$F	capacitance meter	Stores voltage.
coil	toroid (syn) choke (syn) inductor (syn) inductance (d) inductive (adj) induction (d) induce (v) self-induction (d) filter coil (d)	L, l	●〰〰●	henry	H	induction meter	Stores magnetic energy.
transformer	turns turns-ratio transform (v) step-down transformer (d)	Xfmr					Makes voltages and currents increase or decrease.

term	abbr.	symbol	definition
step-up transformer (*d*) core			
battery	batt		Generates electrical energy chemically.
cell			
terminal			
positive charge			
negative charge			
potential			
voltage			
	volt		
	V		
	voltmeter		
switch	sw		Opens and closes a circuit. When it is "open," no current flows, when it is "thrown" or "closed," current flows.
relay (*syn*)			
open circuit			
closed circuit			
single pole single throw	SPST		
single pole double throw	SPDT		
double pole single throw	DPST		
double pole double throw	DPDT		
antenna	ant		"Picks up" electrical energy "out of the air."
ground	gnd		A place in the circuit where the voltage is zero.
loudspeaker	spkr		Converts electrical energy into sound.

words that describe features of the components. For example, *re-sistance* is the root for: *resistivity,* *resistive,* and *resistor.*

3. Most components also may be represented by a symbol. There are also usually abbreviations for the electrical quality of a component and the units used to measure it. (So resistance is R and the number of ohms of resistance is Ω .)
4. The capacity of an electrical component is measured with an electrical *meter.* There is a different meter for every kind of component. For example, the number of ohms of resistance of a resistor is measured with an *ohmmeter.*
5. Table 7 lists the common circuit components, derived words, abbreviations, symbols, and definitions. You should understand this table. While you do not need to know what each component does, you should know that each one does something useful by modifying the way that electric current flows through it.
6. The end results of the combination of many circuits (each made up of many components) are the modern electrical devices that we see around us everywhere; the radio, the TV set, the dictaphone, the electric typewriter, and so on.

Radio Tubes

Amplification.   A *radio tube* is a circuit component just the way a resistor is. I have put it into a section by itself because it has some special meanings and some special words that belong to it alone. A radio tube is different from most other components because a tube *does* something. On the other hand a resistor just "resists." There is a real difference. That is why resistors are called "passive" components and tubes are called "active" components.

What does it do? It does many wonderful things. The most important thing it does is *amplify.* That word comes from the Latin, and means to make big, to enlarge, to increase, to magnify, to augment. Amplification enables a man to address vast throngs through a microphone and they hear him adequately even if they are far away. Amplifying thousands of times is child's play for a radio tube. A radio tube (or several radio tubes) can even amplify something billions of times! How this is accomplished is shown in Figure 15.

There are three tubes in the figure. Each one can amplify a thousand times whatever is put into it (called the *input*). Whatever goes into tube 1 comes out a thousand times stronger than it went in. Now the *output* of tube 1 is at the same time the *input* of tube 2. Therefore, since the same amplification takes place

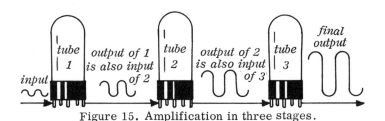

Figure 15. Amplification in three stages.

in tube 2, the output of tube 2 is also a thousand times stronger than *its* input. This means that by the time it emerges from tube 2 what went into tube 1 has been multiplied by a thousand *twice*. Since 1000×1000 is $1,000,000$, or 10^6, what comes out of the combination of tubes 1 and 2 is a million times stronger than what went into tube 1. But here there are three tubes, and tube 3 will amplify the million-times-amplified original input a thousand times more. A million multiplied by a thousand is a billion! By using three tubes something has been amplified a billion times. This power enables you to listen to your radio or phonograph or watch and listen to moving pictures or your television set.

This Is How Your Radio Works.   In today's world we are all living in the middle of a lot of electrical and magnetic (or electromagnetic) waves sent out from radio and television stations many miles away. These waves are constantly bombarding buildings, trees, mountains, and people. Yet, no electrical shock is felt. The reason is that the voltage of these waves is so weak it can't be felt. The battery in a flashlight has $1\frac{1}{2}$ volts and that can't be felt, so it follows that billionths of a volt can't be felt. Still, the volts are there, *radiating* from the "sending" *antenna* of a *radio station* to the "receiving" antenna of a *radio set.* People are not sensitive to these electrical waves but an antenna is sensitive to them. It will "pick them up" (even if they are so small that they must be measured in micromicrovolts), and it will lead them to the radio-tube amplifiers. After three *stages* of amplification, as shown in Figure 15, what is put out (the output) is now a fairly large voltage. It is large enough so that when it is fed into a loudspeaker (a device that converts electrical waves into sound waves) sounds are heard.

Now you know why your radio set has more than one tube in it and why a ten-tube set can pick up stations that are farther away than a five-tube set can. The ten-tube set has more *stages of amplification,* so it can pick up weaker signals. Instead of amplifying only a billion times it may amplify a billion times a billion times. As you may know, it is possible to make sets so "powerful" that they can pick up programs, or *signals,* from overseas stations, and indeed from the other side of the world.

No Amplification Without Modulation.   A tube amplifies by the principle of *modulating* a powerful stream. You will understand what it means to modulate a stream if you think about a reservoir of water backed up behind a dam. Imagine that the dam has a gate which can be lowered or raised by a man just pulling on a rope and pulley system, as shown in Figure 16. If he lowers the gate, with millions of gallons of water pressing on it, he can make an enormous waterfall—all by himself. If he lowers the gate just a little bit, he makes a smaller waterfall. In any case, if he wants to stop the waterfall, he can just raise the gate, and everything dries up again. The important thing to realize is that *one* man can *control* the flow of millions of pounds of water just by moving a gate that weighs, let us say, only one hundred pounds! The great flow of water moves in proportion to the movement of the gate. If he lifts the gate so that it is half-closed, the flow of water is cut down to half; if he lifts the gate so that it is one-quarter closed, the flow of water is cut down by one-quarter. In other words, a few foot-pounds of work by the man is amplified into millions of foot-pounds of work by the water. This is mechanical and hydraulic amplification.

Figure 16. Manipulating the gate at the dam.

In a similar way, a radio tube, using modulation, will perform electrical amplification. In a radio tube, instead of a flow of water, there is a flow of electrons, a current flow that is proceeding from one electrode in the tube to the other. In moving through this path, the stream of electrons goes through a gate which works just like the gate at the dam. But this gate is electrical. If the gate has a negative voltage on it, it will repel the electrons. If the gate is positive, the electrons will be attracted to it and will go right through. Negative voltage on the electrical gate is like having the gate of the dam up, and positive voltage is like having the gate down. An in-between amount of negative voltage is like having the gate on the dam part-way open. We see that the streams of electrons will be "modulated" by the electrical gate in proportion to the amount of voltage placed on it. Furthermore, just like the gate in the dam, it takes very little energy on the electrical gate to make a large difference in the flow of the stream.

Now, if the tiny voltage that the receiving antenna of a radio obtains from the air is placed on the gate of a radio tube, it will be a modulator and it will be amplified. That is how your radio works.

The Structure of a Radio Tube. Figure 17 shows the structure of a radio tube, also called a *vacuum tube* or an *electron tube*. The British call it a *valve*. A radio tube is a glass *bulb* which has been *evacuated*, Any such evacuated chamber is said to contain a *vacuum* (which is the same as saying that it contains nothing). In making a radio tube, all the air is sucked out of the bulb through a glass pipe, just as you suck a drink out of a glass through a drinking straw. Then, as I have said, when there is neither air nor anything else left in the bulb, that absence of everything is known as a vacuum.

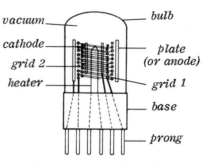

Figure 17. A radio tube.

Inside of the bulb of Figure 17 are electrical *terminals*; another word for these is *electrodes*. They are all electrodes, but in addition each part has a special name and duty. The center electrode is the *cathode*. When it is red hot, electrons boil out of it like steam boils out of a kettle. It is heated by a little wire inside of it called the *heater*. You may have looked into a radio set or a TV set and seen the red-hot heaters and cathodes. Remember the "loose" electrons in conductors that move between atoms (we discussed them at the beginning of the chapter). Well, between atoms, there are no atoms. Between atoms there is a vacuum just as in the bulb of a vacuum tube. When the cathode gets hot the electrons feel just as much at home outside of the cathode as inside — so they boil off.

When a positive voltage is put on the outside electrode, called the *plate* (another name is *anode*), the electrons, being negative, are attracted to the plate, and they move across the vacuum toward the plate in a stream. This stream is just like the water stream I talked about when I explained amplification.

Table 8.   Some Words About Radio Tubes

The Tube and Its Parts

radio tube	electrode	shield
electron tube	cathode	filament
vacuum tube	grid	heater
valve	plate	deflection plate
diode	anode	focus electrode
triode	screen grid	getter
tetrode	supressor grid	filamentary cathode
pentode	control grid	oxide-coated cathode
	thoriated-tungsten cathode	

Different Kinds of Tubes

receiving tube	gas tube	beam-power tube
transmitting tube	magnetron	mercury-arc tube
power tube	klystron	cold-cathode tube
cathode-ray tube	amplitron	traveling-wave tube
thyratron	phototube	backward wave oscillator
ignitron	flash tube	dynode

Some Commercial Tube Numbers
(usually a combination of capital letters
and numbers, sometimes numbers alone)

6L6	12V4	5686
6AG7	6SN7	7077

(and thousands more)

Some Other Words About Tubes

amplification	admittance	electron emission
rectification	cascade	photoelectric emission
switching	degeneration	secondary emission
modulation	signal	thermionic emission
inversion	microwave	interelectrode capacity
primary emission	quiescent state	class A operation
field emission	stage	class B operation
transconductance	regenerative	class AB operation
input	phase-inverter	class C operation
output	arc	amplification factor
input impedance	conversion	dynamic characteristic
output impedance	deflection	frequency response
clipping	bleeder	harmonic distortion
glow discharge	ionization	equivalent circuit
avalanche	crossed field	inverse peak-voltage
space charge	neutralization	mutual conductance

(continued)

Table 8 (continued)

Some Other Words About Tubes (continued)

resistance	grounded grid	relaxation
grid leak	linear	electron ballistics
distortion	nonlinear	frequency modulation
plasma	mixing	amplitude modulation
work function	large-signal	static deflection
dissipation	small-signal	amplification factor
bias	narrow-band	variable mu
self-bias	broad-band	remote cutoff
feedback	grid bias	saturation
voltage gain	low-level	resonance
current gain	stabilization	suppression

The third, or middle, electrode is the gate that does the modulating. It has holes in it to let some of the electrons through, so many holes that it seems to be a mesh or a *grid*. In fact, this gate electrode is called the *grid*. Some tubes have more than one grid.

There you have it. The electrons move from the cathode to the anode in a continuous stream. They move through the holes in the grid where they can be modulated, or controlled, or regulated. A little voltage signal on the grid becomes a big signal by the time it gets to the plate. That is amplification.

Name-odes and Symbol-odes. The symbol for a radio tube (or electron tube, or vacuum tube, or valve) is shown in Figure 18. A little signal enters the grid making it move up and down (electrically) like the gate of the dam, making the main streams of electrons move the same way, only more so to give amplification.

Since the tube contains three major parts, the cathode, the anode, and the grid (the heater doesn't count because it doesn't

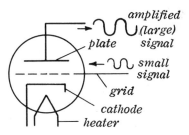

Figure 18. Amplification in a radio tube.

participate in amplification), it is known as a *triode*. This means (I suppose) three "-odes." Sometimes the grid is left out; then the tube is known as a *diode*. It is also possible to have tubes with two grids (called grid 1 and grid 2); then the tube is a *tetrode*. There are also *pentodes,* and so on.

The suffix "-ode" means "path" or "way." Then in a diode the electrons can go two ways, in a triode three ways, and so on. That seems to make sense. So an electrode is a path for electrons. Where do *cathode* and *anode* come from? Well, *cath-* means up (or positive). I guess that means that in a tube the river of electrons is going upstream.

The time has come to summarize the radio-tube words. Table 8 does this both for the words you have already met and also for some you have not met.

Summary

1. A *radio tube* (also called *vacuum tube, electron tube,* or *valve*) is an *active* circuit component. That is, it does something as an electric current flows through it.
2. The most important action performed by a radio tube is the *amplification,* or enlarging, of weak *electric signals* into strong ones. A tube amplifies by *modulating,* that is, by using a small change in one signal to produce a large change in another signal.
3. Amplification is usually accomplished in *stages.* That is, a weak signal is fed into one tube, the amplified signal produced by that tube is then fed into a second tube, where it is amplified further, and so on.
4. The basic components of a radio tube are the cathode (which emits electrons), the heater (which heats the cathode), the *plate* or *anode* (which receives the electrons), and the *grid* (which does the modulating).
5. Table 8 lists words that pertain to radio tubes.

Transistors and Other Solid-State Devices

Transistors.   A transistor is another "active" electronic component. It does almost all the things a radio tube does. It is constructed on the principles of solid-state physics which were discussed in the last chapter (p. 129). These principles are very complicated (or, as the physicist says, "very sophisticated") so we will not discuss them. All you need to know is that in a transistor electrons move through the vacuum between the atoms of a semiconducting material just as electrons move through the vacuum of a radio tube. Then the same things happen, and amplification is again the most important.

The Parts of a Transistor.   Just as there is a cathode to emit electrons in a radio tube, there is a part of a transistor that emits electrons. It is called the *emitter.* The electrons then

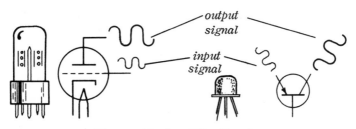

Figure 19. Amplification in
a radio tube and in a transistor.

travel through a modulating region in the transistor, however it
is not the grid but rather the *base*. And the part of a transistor
similar to the plate in a radio tube is called the *collector*. Such
a transistor, with three basic parts, like the three-part radio
tube, is a triode. There are also semiconductor diodes and tetrodes. The symbol for a transistor diode is $+$ and for a transistor triode is Y. Figure 19 shows a transistor triode and a
radio-tube triode. Even though the transistor is much smaller
it is doing just as good a job of amplifying as is the tube.

Some Like It Cold. The transistor was invented in 1948, and
won the Nobel Price for its inventors, William B. Shockley, John
Bardeen, and Walter H. Brattain of the Bell Telephone Laboratories. Their work was not merely a study in theoretical physics. It was the beginning of a product that in less than two de-
cades has built a tremendous new industry in the United States,
not to mention the rest of the world. It is estimated that hundreds of thousands of people work on transistor manufacture and
application in the United States today.

What is remarkable about a transistor? Most important, it
has no heater. The emitter of a transistor gives off electrons at
ordinary room temperatures, whereas the cathode of a radio
tube must be heated to red heat before it emits electrons. The
little wire heater in a tube may burn out and you may have to
throw it away and get a replacement. In a transistor there is no
heater —it can literally last forever. Furthermore, there is no
waiting for heaters to warm up. Your transistor radio works
instantly.

A transistor is also very tiny, much much smaller then any
radio tube. This is very important. In the 1940's, a person who
was hard of hearing had to carry a hearing aid (made with radio
tubes) that was the size of a cigar box. Now, with transistors,
the hearing aid is so small that many times you never even

Table 9. Words Concerning Transistors and Other Semiconductor Devices

Different Kinds of Semiconductor Devices

transistor	alloy transistor
diode	silicon transistor
triode	germanium transistor
tetrode	*NPN* transistor
pentode	*PNP* transistor
junction transistor	microwave diode
point-contact transistor	post alloy diffused transistor (PADT)
power transistor	surface barrier transistor (SBT)
high-frequency transistor	surface alloy diffused transistor (SADT)
rectifier	silicon-controlled rectifier (SCR)
zener diode	field-effect transistor (FET)
reference diode	trinistor
power rectifier	binistor
varactor	varistor
variable reactance diode	MOS transistor
mesa transistor	avalanche transistor
planar transistor	avalanche diode
controlled rectifier	tunnel diode
gold-bonded diode	step-recovery diode
diffused diode	Read diode
passivated transistor	PIN diode

Parts of Semiconductor Devices

emitter	package	alloyed region
base	encapsulation ⁾	graded base
collector	N-doped region	junction
space-charge region	P-doped region	ohmic region
gate	intrinsic region	impurity gradient
transition region	diffused region	chip

Electrical Effects in Transistors

amplification	zener voltage
rectification	reference voltage
switching	saturation current (I_S or I_{sat})
modulation	large-signal operation
avalanche	small-signal operation
space charge	skin effect
electron conduction	common base circuit
hole conduction	common emitter circuit
ionization	lifetime (τ)
resistance	mobility (μ)

(continued)

Table 9 (continued)

Electrical Effects in Transistors (continued)

inductance	resistivity (ρ, rho)
capacitance	emission efficiency (γ, gamma)
time constant	basewidth
input	built-in field
output	voltage gradient
bias	saturation voltage (V_{sat})
dissipation	amplification factor (β, beta)
cutoff current (I_{co})	junction capacitance

avalanche voltage

Commercial Numbers of Semiconductor Devices

All diodes start with "1N-":

1N82   1N789   1N21   1N1734   1N341A

(and thousands more)

All triodes start with "2N-":

2N89   2N169   2N679   2N1142   2N4521

(and thousands more)

All tetrodes start with "3N-":

3N79   3N1891   3N2017

(and thousands more)

---

know it is there. It may be hidden in the frame of a pair of eyeglasses or even inside the ear!

You do not have to be a scientist or engineer to realize how remarkable all this is. But the radio tube has not been killed by the transistor. It still can do enough things better than the transistor that millions of radio tubes are used every year. For example, no transistor has yet been made that can handle as much power as the radio tubes that are used in television stations or in many high-power military installations. And even though we hear every year that our television sets will be "transistorized," it has not yet happened to any significant degree.

Just about all of the words that you need to know about transistors and other semiconductor devices are summarized in Table 9.

Integrated Circuits.   One of the most fascinating aspects of the electronics industry in general, and of the semiconductor industry in particular, is the constant obsolescence of everything. Nothing lasts. Transistors are developed and put on the market and six months later new and better ones appear and many of the old ones disappear. The new ones are always better, capable of

Figure 20. The miniaturization of transistors.

doing more remarkable things, and almost always less expensive.

Think Small.   Perhaps the most interesting new feature of the new transistors is their way of getting smaller and smaller. They are getting so small now that it is often almost impossible to see them. Some are so small that they must be constructed under microscopes with the finest tweezers or *micromanipulators*. The manual delicacy and dexterity of the ordinary production worker in a transistor factory can be compared with that of an eye surgeon. Figure 19 compares a transistor with a radio tube. (Keep in mind that they both do the same job.) Figure 20 shows how transistors themselves have become smaller in the last ten years or so. As a component becomes smaller and as it works on less and less power the final electronic system in which it is used becomes smaller. When these systems are smaller it is possible to pack more of them into constricted spaces. One result it that now both military aircraft and commercial aircraft can carry fantastic quantities of electronic gear for radar, communication, and other purposes.

Miniaturization.   The process of making components smaller is called miniaturization, and it keeps many thousands of research and development engineers and their assistants working in this country. Some people feel that they are beyond mere miniaturization; they claim they are doing *microminiaturization*. When I was a boy I was advised, "think big." Today's solid-state physicist would tell a boy, "think small." There is still one other term used for this miniaturization: *molecular engineering* —as though the engineer has stopped working with things and is now working with the molecules that make up things —and that is pretty tiny!

The miniaturizer does not stop with the transistor. He tries to make every component in a circuit small. This means resistors, inductors, capacitors, magnets, transistors, diodes, even the connection wires between the components are smaller than ever before. Back in the Middle Ages theologians used to argue about how many angels could dance on the head of a pin. I do not know whether that argument was ever resolved, but I do know

Photograph courtesy of Sylvania Electric Products, Inc.

This is the actual size → ▪ of a Sylvania logic block.

Figure 21. The head of a pin.

that the head of a pin is comparatively very large, probably sixty-thousandths of an inch across (which is almost a sixteenth of an inch across). In recent years people have put a whole stage of transistor amplification in such a space, with plenty of room left over for their trademark (see Figure 21). They have put one transistor, two capacitors, five resistors, and all the required connected wire for a circuit into such an area.

When components of many different kinds are so small and are put together in such a small space it is necessary that they all be built at once by the same procedure. Usually this is a kind of photographic process, and the components are "printed" just as a photograph may be printed. In this case the components of the circuit are not built as discrete (separate) parts; they are built as a whole, and are said to be *integrated*. Such circuits are made by techniques that have the following names:

photodeposition	integrated-circuity techniques
photolithography	microcircuit techniques
vapor deposition	thin-film techniques
epitaxy	thick-film techniques

and a few others, some of which will be invented during the time it will take for this book to go to press.

Summary

1. A *transistor* is an active circuit component that performs many of the functions that a radio tube performs. It is constructed on the principles of solid-state physics, and so is often called a *solid-state device*.
2. The important parts of a transistor perform the same functions that the important parts of a radio tube do, but these parts have different names. In a transistor, the source of electrons is called the *emitter*; the modulator is called the *base*; and the collector of electrons is called simply the *collector*.
3. Transistors are superior to radio tubes for many applications because they are much smaller, work on less power, and can work at ordinary temperatures (radio tubes must have heaters).
4. Words concerning transistors and other semiconductor devices are summarized in Table 9.
5. An *integrated circuit* is made up of all of the conventional electrical components, including transistors, resistors, and capacitors. However, all of these components are built at once in one manufacturing process which is similar to printing. Integrated circuits are therefore also known as *printed circuits*.
6. Integrated circuits can be made so small that one can fit on the head of a pin with room left over. Nevertheless, they can perform all of the jobs that ordinary-size circuits can perform. The process of making components smaller is known as *miniaturization* or *microminiaturization* or *molecular engineering*.

Transducers

There are all kinds of "-duce." For example: *in-, de-, pro-, tra-, con-, ad-, trans-*. -Ducing means "leading"; so *transducing* means "leading across." A transducer leads something across something else. What does that mean in electronics? In electronics, a transducer is an electrical component that takes something that happens optically or acoustically or mechanically or thermally and changes it into something electrical.

Table 10. Transducers

Name	Type of Energy Change	Name of the Phenomenon	Used In
phonograph crystal	pressure to electricity	piezoelectricity	phonographs
thermocouple	temperature to electricity	Seebeck effect	temperature measurement
thermoelectric cell	electricity to heat	Peltier effect	energy conversion
solar cell	light to electricity	photoelectricity	energy conversion
photocell	light to electricity	photoelectricity	light measurement
phototube	light to electricity	photoelectricity	light measurement
strain gauge	stretch to electricity	change of resistivity	strain measurement
humidity indicator	moisture to electric current	electrochemical conduction	humidity measurement
microphone	sound to electricity	electromagnetism	public address, radio
pH meter	acid level to electric current	electrochemical conduction	chemistry
antenna	electromagnetic waves to electric current	induction	television, radio, radar
acoustic transducer	magnetic vibrations to acoustic vibrations	magnetostriction	sonar

It can also work the other way. It can also change some electrical action into another form of energy. That is where the "leading across" happens. It is the leading of one form of energy "across" into another form of energy.

In a way an electric motor is a form of transducer. It takes electricity and changes it into movement (mechanical energy). A loudspeaker is another form of transducer. It takes electricity and changes it into sound (acoustical energy). Table 10 lists the more common transducers that are of importance to the electronics engineer. You can see from the table that transducers can do many of the things that human sense organs do. A photocell "sees" light as our eyes do; a microphone "hears" as our ears do; both a phonograph crystal and a strain gauge "feel"; and so on. Since these transducers "sense" things, they are also called *sensors*.

Summary

1. In electronics, a *transducer* is a component that changes electrical energy into another form of energy, or vice versa.
2. Table 10 lists the most common transducers.

Electronic Systems

What Is a System?   I have described how adventurous, wandering electrons are made to dance around in circuits by the actions of voltage and magnetism. I then described the various components the electrons move in: the passive components like resistors and capacitors and the active components like radio tubes and transistors. Now it only remains to talk of collections of circuits, which are called *systems*.

One circuit is never enough to accomplish all the electron must do. In the amplification of a weak signal shown in Figure 15, one stage of amplification was not enough so three were used. The three circuits then became a system. The radio diagram shown in Figure 8 shows another assemblage of circuits, and the final system is the radio. Another system seen every day is the television set. A television set as it is made today is a system that contains about eighteen different circuits. Some of the circuits amplify, some rectify, some detect, some discriminate, and some do some of the other things listed in Table 1 of this chapter.

Surveillance—Some Systems. You have heard of *radar*. It is a system used for military purposes and also for such commercial purposes as the control of aircraft landings at airports. Some radar sets contain as many as 300 separate circuits (again, most are listed in Table 1). Radar is a system that "sees" objects far away, and tells you how far away they are. It sends out a radio wave which may hit an object, for example, an airplane or a missile. The wave is reflected and "bounces" back and is received by the radar set and amplified. The equipment is capable of "understanding," from the direction from which the signal came and the time it took to get back, just where the reflecting object is. The radar set acts like three other systems put together: a *transmitter* which sends the signal out; a *receiver* which accepts and amplifies the signal that is bounced back; and a *display system* which shows on a television screen just where the screen.

Sonar is just like radar, except that it uses sound (acoustic) waves instead of radio (electromagnetic) waves. These sound waves are sent out and received through water. Sonar is used to find submarines and is one of the most important tools of the Navy. Fishermen also can use it to find schools of fish.

Radar and sonar are ways to make our eyes and ears see and hear over longer distances than would otherwise be possible. They are called systems of *surveillance,* from the French word that means "watching over," or "observing."

Some Communication Systems. Another job electronic systems do is help people communicate with one another. You already know about radio and television, which are certainly communication systems. So is the *telephone*. The science of the telephone is called *telephony;* and there is the *telegram (telegraphy)*. All are electronic communications systems.

Telemetry. Telemetry is the communication of information that takes place not between people but between a person and a thing. You know the expression, "talking to him is like talking to the wall." Well, telemetry "talks" to the wall. Or, more accurately, the wall "talks back." Electrical instruments (which are electrical systems), working through transducers, or sensors, may send information — if anyone wants to know—about the color of the wall, the temperature of the wall, the stiffness of the wall, or similar things. That is telemetry.

Perhaps the most exciting thing that happened in telemetry in recent years was the Venus Probe. This was a satellite that flew close to the planet Venus after a trip of several months and actually "probed" Venus and sent back information about what it was like. It measured and then *telemetered* back the information it got. And it did this with no person on the sending end, only transducers in electronic telemetering equipment. Even more recent was the flight of an unmanned vehicle to Mars which sent back (telemetered) photographs of craters on that planet. It will be a number of years before we can hope to send men to the planets; until we do this information telemetered back from them is our best way of finding out about them.

Computation.   Electronic *computers* are the most complex electronic systems ever made. The biggest ones use *millions* of components in *millions* of circuits. What do computers try to do? Only the same things we do in our heads. A computer can do arithmetic and algebra and calculus. But so can we. The computer is no smarter than we are. But it *is* much faster, and in a few minutes can do certain computations that it would take the most brilliant mathematicians years to do. Why? Because the electrons in the computer can move very fast, while whatever it is that is moving in our brains moves much more slowly.

Since we have designed computers to do what our brains do, they have many of the qualities that people have. For example, a computer has a *memory* (so it can file information). But computers also have human failings; they can seem to get nervous, they can have the equivalent of nervous breakdowns, and they can even occasionally make mistakes.

If we *program* a computer correctly, it will give correct answers; if we program it incorrectly, it will give wrong answers. Programming a computer means "feeding" it the problem that it must solve. The people who feed a computer are called *programmers*.

How can a collection of vacuum tubes, transistors, resistors, capacitors, integrated circuits, and other components handle information? They can handle information by breaking the information down into its smallest pieces. What is the smallest piece of information that can be handled electronically? The *bit*. So when you hear a scientist or engineer talking about a "bit," you should realize what he means.

When computers first became available, they were the tools, if not the toys, of mathematicians. Now people have become so used to having them and using them that almost every kind of engineer and scientist has some reason to employ a computer. When your employer sends problems to a computer, you may never get involved, since the computer itself is generally located in a "computer center." On the other hand, to a steadily increasing degree, computers are being brought into engineering offices and scientific laboratories, so that you will probably find yourself someday working with computer instructions, writing computer language, and diagraming computer programs — all as part of your regular secretarial assignments. This means that we must provide you with some additional details about this field.

In the first place, you are really more familiar with computer devices than you think. The speedometer in your automobile is a kind of adding machine, adding a mile for every so-many turns of the car wheels. The desk calculator, which is undoubtedly sitting in your office, is also a simple computer. Computers like the speedometer and the desk calculator are based on the arithmetical process of addition, and are called *digital computers*. (Even when the desk calculator multiplies, it is adding. When it multiplies 347×598, it is actually adding 347 to itself 598 times.) Of course digital computers can become very large and complex, far exceeding the size and complexity of a desk calculator.

The other major type of computer is known as an *analogue computer*. The name is descriptive of what it does; it makes a calculation based on an analogy with a *model*. The analogy is always electrical because the computer consists of a system of electrical devices which can only perform a function when fed electricity. So, if we want to add two numbers in an analogue computer, we represent the two numbers with two voltages of corresponding sizes. We feed the two voltages simultaneously into the input of a vacuum tube or transistor, and the output of the device is then the result of both of the voltages. In other words, the output is the result of the sum of them. To subtract, we make one of the voltages negative and the other one positive, and the output is the result of the difference — subtraction. In the same way, we can simulate all of the other mathematical operations discussed in the chapter on mathematics: differentiation, integration, taking trigonometric functions, and so on.

What should you as a secretary know to be able to cope with material concerning computer operations? Most important, you should know that a computer must be instructed in a language that it can understand. The programmer writes directions to the computer in this language and the computer answers with text typed in the same language on long sheets of paper. Very often, the words look like English words — but not always; more often, the words look like what they are — a code. A code is a type of language, and it must possess an important quality that all languages possess. That is, it must be possible to translate it back into our native tongue so that it makes sense. Actually, you give instructions to a machine in a special code more often than you think. Consider your typewriter. It may have a key that says "M.R." and another that says "T.S." In typewriter language that means "margin release" and "tab set." When you press either of those keys, you are instructing your typewriter. You are telling it either to release the margin or to set the tab. If I were to write you a note telling you to

  a. Type three lines of text
  b. T.S. at the two-inch point
  c. M.R. at the bottom of the page, and type into margin

I would be giving you a *program* for your typewriter that used words in typewriter language, T.S. and M.R. This is exactly what is done with a computer. In fact, there is a very good reason why it is so similar: to talk to a computer, you use a typewriter.

There are a number of different computer languages. One of the most common is FORTRAN, which stands for "FORmula TRANslation." Your employer will usually employ only one language and it may or may not be FORTRAN. What you will see will be a host of code terms that will not seem to make much sense. Letters will stand for numbers; symbols such as apostrophes and dollar signs will stand for specific instructions (that have nothing to do with apostrophes or dollars); capital letters will make up whole words; and so on. Generally, there will be a "Summary of Operations" that will translate the symbols you will be working with. Table 11 is typical of such a summary. Other mathematical operations describing functions (remember them from the mathematics chapter?) may look like Table 12. Then a set of instructions—a program—may look like Table 13. What do *you* do? You simply type it carefully and without mistakes.

Very often the program must be further clarified; it must say more than just what can be described in a table. In that case, "pictures" must be used. A program will then often have some of the features of a diagram. That is, there will be a mixture of drawings and typewritten, or neatly handwritten, material on the same page. A typical segment of such a program is shown in Figure 22. You can draw these diagrams with the aid of templates that are illustrated in Part II (p. 188). Figure 14 in Part II shows a typical page of text such as you might be called on to prepare if your employer deals with computer matters.

Finally, we must list some words. I believe we meet more odd and unfamiliar words in dealing with computers than in any other scientific field—and most of these words are not in computer language, but in the English language. Consider, for example, words like mnemonic, tetrad, radix, and augend. Then, there

Table 11.   A Typical Summary of Operations*

Operation	Code
Set location	*
Enter word and advance location counter	□
Set location to register A	'
Step location	$
Start compute at location	J
Enter subroutine at location	•
Fill from photoreader	F
Verify from photoreader	V
Stop fill or verify and return to keyboard	/
Stop fill or verify and return to keyboard BP 4 SET	≢
Set indirect address tag	I
Set relative forward	+&
Set relative backward	—
Start typeout octal format, BP 2 RESET	T
Start typeout absolute instruction format, BP 2 SET, BP 4 RESET	T
Start typeout relative instruction format, BP 2 SET, BP 4 SET	T
Start punch octal format, BP 2 RESET	P

*Table courtesy of the Raytheon Company.

Table 12.   A Typical Function Code*

Function		Name	Function Code	
			Octal	Mnemonic
u	→ v	Transfer	400	TRAT.
u	→ v	Transfer Complement	313	TRAC.
u·v	→ v	AND	011	ANDT.
$\overline{u \cdot v}$	→ v	NAND	311	NAND.
u + v	→ v	OR	322	OR.
$\overline{u + v}$	→ v	NOR	022	NOR.
u ⊕ v	→ v	EXCLUSIVE OR	351	XOR.
$\overline{u \oplus v}$	→ v	COINCIDENCE	051	COIN.
u Σ 1	→ v	COUNT (Increment)	163	INC.
u Σ − 1	→ v	DECREMENT	253	DEC.
u(2)s complement)	→ v	TWO's COMPLEMENT	153	2CMP.
u Σ v	→ v	ADD	251	ADD.
−u Σ v	→ v	SUBTRACT I	252	SUB1.
u Σ − v	→ v	SUBTRACT II	261	SUB2.

(continued)

Table 12.* (continued)

All Zeros	→ v	CLEAR	000	CLR.
All One's	→ v	SET	003	SET.
Timing: 1				

Registers Affected: A, B, Q, R, P, C, E, or X (Destination Register)

*Table courtesy of the Raytheon Company.

Table 13.   A Typical Short Fortran Program

C = A+B	or C = (A**2)+(B**2.)
C = A−B	C = SQRTF ((A**2.)+(B**2.))
C = A/B	or C = ((A**2.)+(B**2.))**.5
C = (A*A)+(B*B)	X = A+(B*C)/D+F**3.

Table 14.   Some Computer Words

analogue	retrieval	tetrad	adder
digital	bit	Boolean	iteration
model	binary	Venn	divisor
linear	encoding	minterm	sort
nonlinear	storage	Mach	mnemonic
nomograph	alphanumeric	radix	AND
program	6-tuples	addend	NAND
summer	4-tuples	augend	OR
memory	serial	multiplicand	NOR

Computer Names

AD-2-24PB   TR-20   PACE TR-48   EASE   ENIAC
CI-170   ORDVAC   DYSTAC   REAC   HYPAC-1

are also the purely "computer words," which, by the way, will probably be in all the unabridged dictionaries in the 1970's. Words like "NAND," "NOR," "MACH," and "tuple" are "computer words." Different computers also have names which the computer expert uses as ordinary words. But computer names always sound futuristic and surrealistic, they always seem to use only capital letters, and they have a weird quality of being just

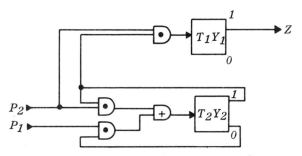

Figure 22. Part of a computer-program diagram.

barely pronounceable. In addition, after you have said them, they make absolutely no sense, since they come from no known roots and seem to have no inherent meaning. They are acronyms, that is, words made up from the first letters of a number of words. So, we have "ENIAC," "ORDVAC," "DYSTAC," and so on. A number of words you will encounter in computer work are given in Table 14. The meanings of these words are given in simplified form in Glossary 7 of Part II.

Control, Guidance, and Automation.   When a transducer-sensor is tied into a machine to telemeter, or *feed back,* how the machine is operating, and then to send that knowledge in the form of bits into a programmed operator, the computer has enough information to "decide" how to run or control the machine. In the same way, a computer can steer, or *guide,* a missile. This is *automation.* That is, by use of mechanical mechanisms tied to electronic systems, some of the jobs once done only by people are done without them.

They Can't Do Everything.   Electronic systems can perform the following functions:

> surveillance
> communication
> telemetry
> computation
> control
> guidance

and also some others. In fact they can do almost everything the brain can do—but they were always "told" in the first instance. And they can't make jokes or coffee or the office more attractive. So they will never replace the secretary. I speak as one who has worked closely with electronic systems and secretaries.

Summary

1. An *electronic system* is a collection of circuits that is put together in order to perform a particular task.

2. Some of the most important tasks performed by electronic systems are in fields known as *surveillance, communication, telemetry, computation*, and *control* and *guidance*.

3. The most important surveillance systems are *radar* and *sonar*.

4. Important communication systems are *radio, television, telephony*, and *telegraphy*.

5. Telemetry is communication between an inanimate object and people. Electronic circuits *telemeter* information from the inanimate object to the people on the receiving end.

6. Electronic *computers* are the largest electronic systems that have ever been made. There are *analogue computers* and *digital computers*. A computer must always be *programmed*, that is, it must always be told what to do. A computer must be given information in small pieces called *bits*.

7. Many electronic systems are now used to control and guide operations that used to be performed only by people. This replacement of people by machines is known as automation.

Part II

Techniques for the Technical Secretary
and
Glossaries of Technical Terms

Techniques for
the Technical Secretary

Part II of this book stresses secretarial techniques and word references. It is hoped that Part II will become a handy quick reference to supplement an ordinary dictionary, and, as such, it will fulfill a separate function from Part I. Part II consists of a broad range of source material, which has been arranged to provide information in a form convenient for a secretary to use. This material is intended to give the guidance a secretary may need in order to write equations, words, and parts of words, and to draw tables, graphs, and simple sketches.

Part II is itself in two parts. The first portion deals primarily with techniques for handling problems of typing, drafting, sketching, and graphing. A generous number of examples is provided. The second portion of Part II consists of seven glossaries of technical words, parts of words, abbreviations, and necessary foreign alphabets. It may be considered a secretary's technical dictionary.

The Secretary As Draftsman. As a technical secretary you are not expected to become a real draftsman, but you should be capable of dealing with simple drawings, charts, graphs, and tables, all of which require the use of rudimentary drafting tools. I recommend that you have your employer acquire the following tools for you:

a compass
a set of templates similar to those shown in Figure 1a
some plastic rulers
a 45°, 45°, 90° triangle
a 30°, 60°, 90° triangle
a small drafting board just big enough for an $8\frac{1}{2} \times 11$ sheet of paper
one or two French curves
a black felt-tip pen with a sharp point

Figure 1b shows these items.

You will find that you will need almost no training to use these materials. The drafting board is the only item whose use

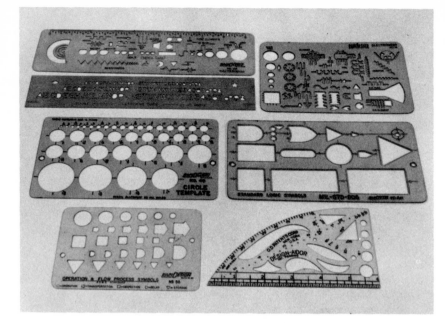

Figure 1. Some templates (a, above) and some other drafting tools (b, below). *Photographs courtesy of the Raytheon Company.*

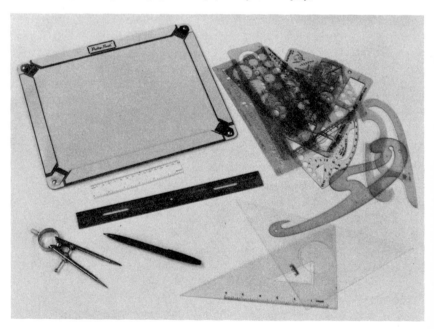

Photograph courtesy of the Raytheon Company.

Figure 2. Using a triangle.

is not self-evident, and all that you need to know about the drafting board is that the left edge and the bottom edge are both
slightly raised to allow the triangles to ride along them. As a
triangle moves along one of these edges, one of its sides must
be up against the edge. This leaves the other two sides available
for drawing straight lines. With these two triangles it is therefore possible to draw lines in the following directions anywhere
on the paper

      straight up and down
      straight across
      at angles of 30°, 45°, or 60° with the edges of the board

Figure 2 shows how this is done. When you want very bold black
lines (or letters) it is often a good idea to use one of the felt-tip
pens, if you take care to select one with a sharp tip.

    You can use any of the edges of the triangles to draw parallel
lines. *Cross hatching*, as shown below,

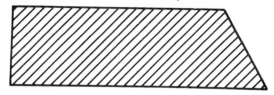

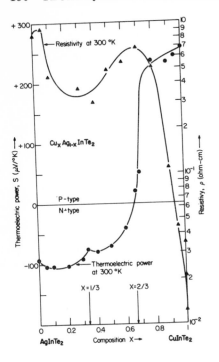

Figure 3. A well-drawn graph.

Photograph courtesy of the Raytheon Company.

Figure 4. Using a template.

TABLE I

Validity of Mooser-Pearson's
Criterion for the Semiconductivity of Compounds

Solid	Compound	n_{el}	n_{an}	b_{an}	b_{cat}	$\dfrac{n_{el}}{n_{an}} + b_{an} - b_{cat}$
Ge	$A^{IV} A^{IV}$	4	1	4	0	8
GaAs	$A^{III} B^{V}$	8	1	0	0	8
ZnSe	$A^{II} B^{VI}$	8	1	0	0	8
CuBr	$A^{I} B^{VII}$	8	1	0	0	8
CuGaSe$_2$	$A^{I} B^{III} C_2^{VI}$	16	2	0	0	8
ZnGeAs$_2$	$A^{II} B^{IV} C_2^{V}$	16	2	0	0	8
ZnGa$_2$Se$_4$	$A^{II} B_2^{III} C_4^{VI}$	32	4	0	0	8

Figure 5. A well-made table.

is easily done simply by moving one of the triangles in little displacements and drawing a line with each movement.

Your best guide for drawing sketches or graphs or the lines that separate rows and columns in tables is common sense. Center the material logically on the paper, draw neat lines, and be consistent. Do not make the same kind of line darker on one side of a sketch than on the other side. Make a pattern or symbol the same size every time it appears.

You will often find that a sketch requires arrows and captions. Practice making arrows so that they always come out looking neat and consistent. (See the section *Drawing the Arrow* in the chapter on mathematics, p. 76, for some hints on how to do this.) As for captions and symbols, they may be typed in after

Photographs courtesy of Mechanical Enterprises, Inc.

Figure 6. Selecting an adaptor (left) and placing it on the typewriter (right).

a drawing has been made, or drawn in as those shown in Figure 3. How did the letters in Figure 3 come out so neat and uniform? They were drawn with a template, as shown in Figure 4. There are also special typewriters which can produce numbers and letters similar to those in Figure 4. These typewriters are very versatile and elaborate; they are equipped with almost every letter and symbol that an engineer or scientist will ever require. But these special typewriters are not commonly found in engineering offices. If your company maintains a publications department which is involved in the preparation of government proposals or reports, it will usually have one such machine. What about tables? A good one is shown in Figure 5.

Some Additional Words About Typewriters.   It is possible to acquire a great variety of replaceable keys for most typewriters. These include almost all known mathematical symbols as well as Greek letters. The manufacturer of your machine usually will sell such replaceable keys if you request them. In fact, you may find it desirable to ask a typewriter serviceman to make certain replacements permanent by inserting a symbol or letter that you commonly use in place of one that you rarely use. It can save you a great deal of work if you just have keys such as α, β, and γ installed.

There is also a way of dealing with this problem of unusual symbols without modifying your typewriter. You may make use of little devices consisting of letters mounted in plastic holders, which fit on the typewriter carriage at exactly the place where the keys normally strike. You hold one of these adaptors in place with one hand while you strike a typewriter key with the other hand. The struck key hits the letter in the holder and causes it to print the desired symbol. Figure 6 illustrates how this is done. These adaptors are available for the entire Greek alphabet as well as for hundreds of other letters and symbols. An added feature is the availability of outsize symbols (as tall as the width of a typewriter ribbon) such as parentheses, brackets, and integral signs.

Some Examples.   The examples of well-typed pages from the fields of chemistry, mathematics, physics, and electronics given below come from actual internal memos and reports written in a typical science-oriented company. (See Figures 7 through 14.) They may be a little more complex than those the average technical secretary usually encounters —but not much! As you study these examples you will acquire some understanding of the techniques that were used. The simplest and best way to learn how to reproduce similar material is to copy and practice. Copy the pages that contain material similar to that being worked on in your office. Then you will have not only an understanding of what has been done in these examples, you will also have a *feel* for it. As time goes on you will find that the best techniques for technical typing come out of a combination of understanding the general sense of what you are typing and using common-sense principles of neatness —and practice.

When the reacting compounds go into water solution it is possible to hypothesize that a series of events occur involving peroxydisulfate and phosphorous acid as follows

$$S_2O_8^{-2} \rightarrow 2SO_4^{-} \tag{1}$$

$$S_2O_8^{-2} + H_2PO_3^{-} \rightarrow SO_4^{-} +$$
$$HSO_4^{-} + HPO_3^{-} \tag{2}$$

$$SO_4^{-} + H_2O \rightarrow HSO_4^{-} + OH \tag{3}$$

$$OH + H_2PO_3^{-} \rightarrow H_2O + HPO_3^{-} \tag{4}$$

$$HPO_3^{-} + S_2O_8^{-2} \rightarrow HPO_3 + SO_4^{-2} + SO_4^{-} \tag{5}$$

$$HPO_3^{-} + HPO_3^{-} \rightarrow HPO_3 + HPO_3^{-2} \tag{6}$$

followed by a rapid acid-base type reaction of HPO_3 with water.

$$HPO_3 + H_2O \rightarrow H_2PO_4^{-} + H^{+} \tag{7}$$

Application of the steady-state treatment leads to the rate law

$$-d\,(S_2O_8^{-2})/dt = \left[e^2 a/f + e^2 b/f(H_2PO_3^{-}) \right]^{1/2} X$$
$$(S_2O_8^{-2})^{3/2} \tag{8}$$

where a, b, etc are the rate constants for the corresponding reactions in the mechanism. Equation 7 agrees with the experimentally derived Eq. 4, when

$$k_1 = e^2 a/f \text{ and } k_2 = e^2 b/f \tag{9}$$

Figure 7. Inorganic chemistry.

D. Oxidation of unsaturated compounds

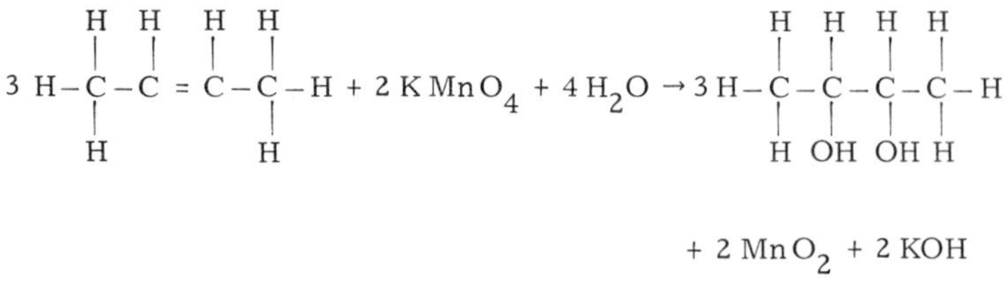

$$3 \; H-\overset{\overset{\textstyle H}{|}}{\underset{\underset{\textstyle H}{|}}{C}}-\overset{\overset{\textstyle H}{|}}{C} = \overset{\overset{\textstyle H}{|}}{C}-\overset{\overset{\textstyle H}{|}}{\underset{\underset{\textstyle H}{|}}{C}}-H + 2 \; K\,MnO_4 + 4 \; H_2O \rightarrow 3 \; H-\overset{\overset{\textstyle H}{|}}{\underset{\underset{\textstyle H}{|}}{C}}-\overset{\overset{\textstyle H}{|}}{\underset{\underset{\textstyle OH}{|}}{C}}-\overset{\overset{\textstyle H}{|}}{\underset{\underset{\textstyle OH}{|}}{C}}-\overset{\overset{\textstyle H}{|}}{\underset{\underset{\textstyle H}{|}}{C}}-H$$

$$+ \; 2 \; MnO_2 + 2 \; KOH$$

continuing as:

$$3 \; H-\overset{\overset{\textstyle H}{|}}{\underset{\underset{\textstyle H}{|}}{C}}-\overset{\overset{\textstyle H}{|}}{\underset{\underset{\textstyle OH}{|}}{C}}-\overset{\overset{\textstyle H}{|}}{\underset{\underset{\textstyle OH}{|}}{C}}-\overset{\overset{\textstyle H}{|}}{\underset{\underset{\textstyle H}{|}}{C}}-H + 6 \; K\,MnO_4 \rightarrow 6 \; H-\overset{\overset{\textstyle |}{}}{\underset{\underset{\textstyle H}{|}}{C}}-\overset{\overset{\textstyle \|}{}}{C}-OK + 6 \; MnO_2$$

$$+ \; 6 \; H_2O$$

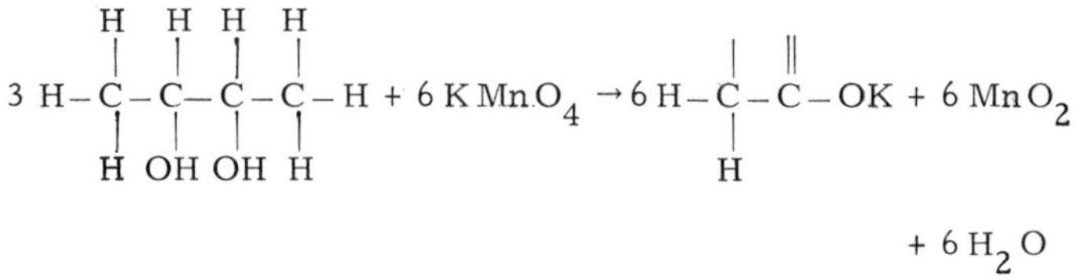

In summary, reaction is:

$$3 \; C\,H_3 - C\,H = C\,H - C\,H_3 + 8 \; K\,MnO_4 \rightarrow 6 \; C\,H_3 - C\,OOK + 8 \; MnO_2$$

$$+ \; 2 \; H_2O + 2 \; KOH$$

If there is no H on C = C, oxidation goes only as far as the ketone:

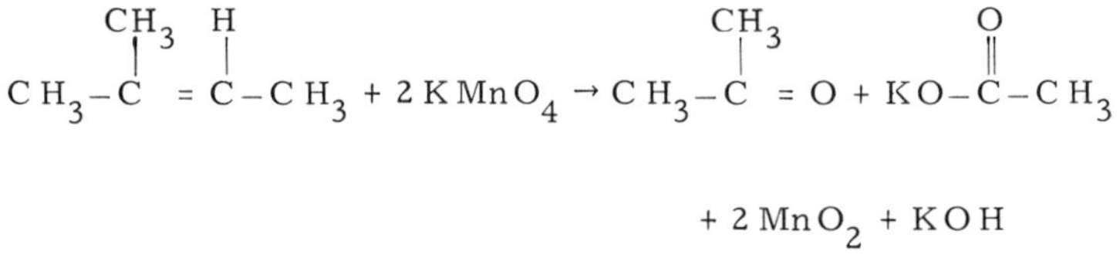

$$C\,H_3 - \overset{\overset{\textstyle CH_3}{|}}{C} = \overset{\overset{\textstyle H}{|}}{C} - C\,H_3 + 2 \; K\,MnO_4 \rightarrow C\,H_3 - \overset{\overset{\textstyle CH_3}{|}}{C} = O + K\,O - \overset{\overset{\textstyle O}{\|}}{C} - C\,H_3$$

$$+ \; 2 \; MnO_2 + KOH$$

Figure 8. Organic chemistry.

6. VOLUME DENSITY OF THE ELECTRONS

The volume density of the electrons $n(\underline{r})$ can be obtained by integrating the phase space density function $n(\underline{r}, \underline{w})$ with respect to $\underline{w}$.

$$n(\underline{r}) = \int n(\underline{r}, \underline{w})\, d\underline{w} \tag{6-1}$$

Fig. 4 provides the appropriate limits of integration. Substituting in eq. (6-1), we obtain for $0 \leq X < X_2$,

$$n(\underline{r}) = 2\pi^{-3/2} n_T e^{\eta} \int_{-\infty}^{\infty} dw_z \int dw_y \int \exp\{-(w_x^2 + w_y^2 + w_z^2)\}\, dw_x$$

$$= n_T e^{\eta} \frac{2}{\pi} \left\{ \int_{-\infty}^{w_{y4}} dw_y \int_{w_{xB}}^{\infty} \exp\{-(w_x^2 + w_y^2)\}\, dw_x + \int_{w_{y4}}^{w_{y5}} dw_y \int_{w_{xC}}^{\infty} \exp\{w_x^2 + w_y^2\}\, dw_2 \right.$$

$$\left. + \int_{w_{y5}}^{\infty} dwy \int_{w_{xA}}^{\infty} \exp\{-(w_x^2 + w_y^2)\}\, dw_x \right\}$$

$$= n_T e^{\eta} \left\{ 1 - \frac{1}{\sqrt{\pi}} \int_{-\infty}^{w_{yx}} \exp(-w_y^2)\, \mathrm{erf}\, w_{xB}\, dw_y - \frac{1}{\sqrt{\pi}} \int_{w_{yx}}^{w_{y6}} \exp(-w_y^2\, \mathrm{erf}\, w_{xC} dw_y) \right.$$

$$\left. + \frac{1}{\sqrt{\pi}} \int_{w_{y6}}^{w_{y5}} \exp(-w_y^2)\, \mathrm{erf}\, w_{xC}\, dw_y + \frac{1}{\sqrt{\pi}} \int_{w_{y5}}^{\infty} \exp(-w_y^2\, \mathrm{erf}\, w_{xA}) dw_y \right\}$$

$$\tag{6-2}$$

Figure 9. Mathematical physics.

corresponds to η'. First of all we note that g'_c curve coincides with the η' curve at the cathode, as it should by definition (see Fig. 1). From this, putting $g'_{tc} = \eta'_c$ we find that the corresponding value of the tangential initial velocity is given by $w_{yc} = \frac{1}{2}\eta'_c$. The next interesting g curve is that for which g' is tangential to η' in Fig. 3. We find that at that point $\eta'' = g'' = 2$. Once η is known, this gives us the appropriate point $X = X_2$. Since there $\eta' = g'$, we find that the initial tangential velocity which defines the right parabola is given by $w_{yc} = \frac{1}{2}\eta'_c - X_2$, where $\eta'_2 = (d\eta/dX)_{X = X_2}$. Finally, it is interesting to get the value of $w_{yc} = w^a_{yc}$, for which the electrons just graze the anode for the first time. This value is more difficult to obtain, since it corresponds to the following conditions: the $\eta(X) + w^2_{xc}$ curve, see Fig. 1, must be tangential at a point, say $X = X_1$, to a given g curve and at the same time $\eta_a + w^2_{xc}$ must be equal to $g(Xa)$ for the same curve. Thus, first of all we must eliminate w_{xc} between $\eta_1 + w^2_{xc} = g(X_1)$ and $\eta_a + w^2_{xc} = g(Xa)$. This gives

$$\eta_a - \eta_1 = (X_a^2 - X_1^2) + 2w_{yc}(X_a - X_1) \qquad (4\text{-}4)$$

Then w_{yc} has to be eliminated between eq. (4-4) and eq. (4-5) which defines the point X_1 at whicn $\eta' = g'$

$$\eta'_1 = g'(X_1) = 2(X_1 + w_{yc}) \qquad (4\text{-}5)$$

To complete our discussion, we have to derive suitable expressions for the limiting curves A, B, and C shown in Fig. 2. Curve A is obtained by assuming that $w_x = 0$ just when the electrons reach the anode. Substituting this condition in Eq. (4-1) we obtain

$$w_x^2 = (X_a + w_{yc})^2 - (X - w_{yc})^2 - (\eta_a - \eta) \qquad (4\text{-}6)$$

Figure 10. Physics.

Here we have assumed that the magnetic field is in the +z-direction and that

$$\eta = \frac{e}{kT} (\phi - \phi_c) \qquad (2-4)$$

$$\underline{w} = \sqrt{\frac{m}{2kT}} \ \underline{v} \qquad (2-5)$$

$$\underline{R} = \sqrt{\frac{m}{2kT}} \ \omega_c (\underline{r} - \underline{r}_c) \qquad (2-6)$$

where

$\omega_c = \frac{eB}{m}$ = cyclotron frequency

ϕ = electrostatic potential

$\underline{v}$ = electron velocity

-e, m = electron charge and mass

$\underline{r}$ = electron position vector

k = Boltzmann's constant

T = temperature of the cathode

Equation (2-1) expresses the principle of conservation of energy, and eq. (2-2) describes the linear dependence of the y-component of velocity w_y on X.

3. VELOCITY DISTRIBUTION OF THE ELECTRONS

As in I, our calculations will be based on the concept of the phase space density function $n(\underline{r}, \underline{w})$. From eq. (3-4) of I, we find that

$$n(\underline{r}, \underline{w}) = 2\pi^{-3/2} n_T \exp \eta \exp \{-(w_x^2 + w_y^2 + w_z^2)\}, \qquad (3-1)$$

where

$$n_T = (\frac{m}{h})^3 (\frac{2\pi kT}{m})^{3/2} \exp (\frac{-E_\phi}{kT}) \qquad (3-2)$$

is the volume density of the electrons at the surface of the cathode which is emitting full saturation current J_s. Here, h is Planck's constant and E_ϕ is the work function of the cathode.

Figure 11. Physics.

TABLE II

Pauling Valencies and Radii for the Elements
of the Alpha Tin Isoelectronic Series and for Copper[6]

	Ag	Cu	In	Alpha Sn	Sb	Te	I	Cu
Valence	5.44	4.44	3.44	4	3	2	1	5.44
r (CN12)	1.442	1.543	1.66	1.542	1.59	1.60		1.276
r (1)	1.339	1.413	1.497	1.399	1.41	1.37	1.334	1.173
r (cov)	1.53	1.48	1.44	1.40	1.41	1.37	1.33	1.35

r (CN12) = radius for the structures of the coordination number 12 (metallic bond).

   r (1)= radius of a single bond.

  r (cov)= radius for covalent (diamond) crystal structures.

Ternary compounds of the family $A^{II} B^{IV} C_2^{V}$ all crystallize in the chalcopyrite structure with the ratio of lattice parameters c/a between 1.89 and 1.97 and easy cleavage in the (111) plane. X-ray diffraction data for some of them are:

$$CdGeAs_2 : a = 5.942 \pm 0.002 \text{ Å}, \frac{c}{a} = 1.889 \pm 0.002 [7]$$

$$ZnSiP_2 : a = 5.398 \text{ Å} , \frac{c}{a} = 1.934 [8]$$

$$CdSnAs_2 : a = 6.093 \pm 0.001 \text{ Å}, \frac{c}{a} = 1.959 \pm 0.001 [9]$$

$$AnGeAs_2 : a = 5.670 \pm 0.002 \text{ Å}, \frac{c}{a} = 1.967 \pm 0.002 [8]$$

$$ZnGeP_2 : a = 5.46 \pm 0.01 \text{ Å} , \frac{c}{a} = 1.97 \pm 0.01 [8]$$

6   L. Pauling, The Nature of the Chemical Bond, Third Edition, Cornell University Press, Ithaca, New York (1960). Also: L. Pauling, J. Amer. Chem. Soc. 69, 542 (1947).

7   H. Pfister, Acta. Cryst. 11, 221-224 (1958).

8   O.G. Folberth and H. Pfister, Halbleiter and Phosphore, Vieweg, Braunschweig (1958, p. 474-476).

9   D.B. Gasson, P.J. Holmes, I.C. Jennings, B.R. Marathe and J.E. Parrott, J. Phys. Chem. Solids 33, 1291-1302 (1962).

Figure 12. Crystal physics.

In the referenced network, if the signal S_1 is scaled until it arrives at a level of unit energy and if the oscillation O_2 is damped to a minimum as a result of adding capacitive impedance to network N, then the amplified output signal maximizes. One module of the network takes the form

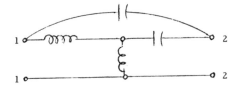

where at a frequency of $f = f_p$, $V_{11} > V_{22}$. In this case two different voltage distributions in the network obey Kirchhoff's law and are therefore scaled replicas of one another.

Another example of significance concerns itself with the condition where a current impulse of strength $1/n \sqrt{k^j}$ is applied to the resultant terminal pair in a condition where the sinusoidal voltage is a function of inductance. Then it can be shown that the operation is essentially lossless and the impedance of the two paths are compact at $s = \pm jf_p$.

Notice now that when the network is excited by a unit impulse of current at the resultant terminal pair in Fig. 7, the subsequent activity of N is identical to that which occurs when the same network is excited under the condition of Fig. 8. This illustrates that the problem of network synthesis proceeds under these conditions in a conventional manner regardless of the impulse magnitude. This leads to the conclusion that the functional relationship previously given (Eq. 5) may now be represented in the function of Equation 12

12) $$z_{11} = \frac{3k_p}{s^2 + n^2} + R_{11(n)}$$

Figure 13. Electronics.

The word format defined for the move instruction is as follows:

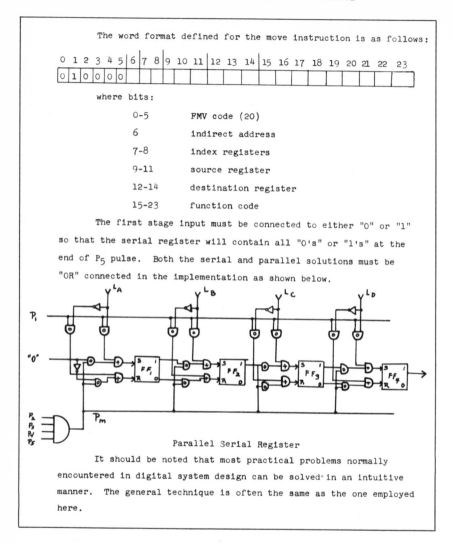

where bits:

0-5	FMV code (20)
6	indirect address
7-8	index registers
9-11	source register
12-14	destination register
15-23	function code

The first stage input must be connected to either "0" or "1" so that the serial register will contain all "0's" or "1's" at the end of P_5 pulse. Both the serial and parallel solutions must be "OR" connected in the implementation as shown below.

Parallel Serial Register

It should be noted that most practical problems normally encountered in digital system design can be solved in an intuitive manner. The general technique is often the same as the one employed here.

Figure 14. Computers.

Glossaries of Technical Terms

The following glossaries are presented in this section:

1. Prefixes
2. Suffixes
3. Technical and Scientific Abbreviations
4. The Chemical Elements and Their Abbreviations
5. Frequently Encountered Names of Scientists and Engineers
6. The Greek and Some Other Foreign Alphabets
7. The Secretary's Glossary of Scientific and Engineering Terms

These seven glossaries list the important words and parts of words a technical or scientific secretary is likely to meet. Remember, no such list can ever truly be complete, because scientists never stand still. They are always finding new facts, studying new phenomena, and labeling them with new words. In the course of your job, you will inevitably come across words and parts of words that are not listed here but which should be listed. When this happens, you are urged to record these new terms in your own "secretarial notes." Orderly note-keeping of this sort will make a valuable supplement to this book because it will pertain to the *specific* job that you are working on.

Glossaries 1 and 2
Prefixes and Suffixes

The lists of prefixes and suffixes contain many of the terms you have already met in Part I. As has been pointed out before, these "pieces" of words, added before or after a base word, enrich and enlarge the meaning of the base word. A familiarity with prefixes and suffixes will often be all the help you need to figure out the meanings and spellings of unfamiliar words. Most of the terms listed here also occur in Glossary 7, which lists scientific and engineering terms.

Glossary 1. Prefixes

aceto-, pertaining to the acetic radical

aero-, relating to flight or the science of aeronautics

amino-, a class of chemical compounds containing the radical NH_2

bi-, two

calc-, calci-, calco-, pertaining to calcium

centi-, a hundredth

chemi-, relating to chemical

chloro-, pertaining to chlorine

co-, con-, together

cryp-, pertaining to low temperatures

deci-, one-tenth

demi-, partly

di-, two

duo-, two

e-, out, not

electro-, pertaining to electricity

epi-, after

equi-, equal

ex-, out

extra-, outside

ferri-, pertaining to iron

ferro-, pertaining to iron

giga-, a million

gon-, angle

heli-, helio-, pertaining to the sun

hepto-, seven

hetero-, different

hex-, six

homo-, homeo-, the same

hydro-, pertaining to water

hygro-, pertaining to humidity

hyper-, greater than or above

hypo-, less than or below

in-, in

infra-, below, less than

inter-, between

intra-, withing during

intro-, within

is-, iso-, the same

kilo-, a thousand

kilomega-, a billion

lum-, relating to light

macro-, large

magneto-, relating to magnets

mal-, bad or ill

mega-, million

meso-, middle

meta-, after, later

mid-, middle

milli-, a thousandth

mini-, tiny

mon-, mono-, one

morph-, relating to form or shape

mult-, many

nano-, one-billionth

ne-, neo-, new

non-, no

ob-, against

octo-, eight

orth-, straight

oxy-, containing oxygen

para-, beside, similar

pent-, penta-, five

per-, through, *also* containing the largest amount

peri-, enclosing near

petr-, pertaining to stone

phil-, having a liking or affinity for

phon-, sound

phot-, photo-, light

pico-, one-trillionth

plumb-, pertaining to lead

pneumo-, pertaining to air

poly-, many

post-, after

pre-, before

pro-, in favor of

proto-, first

pyr-, pyro-, fire

quad-, four

quasi-, similar to

radi-, referring to something being emitted radially

re-, again
retro-, back
rheo-, flow
self-, directed toward itself
semi-, half
spectro-, spectrum
state-, resting
stereo-, solid
strati-, in layers
sub-, under
sulfa-, relating to sulfur
super-, in addition, greater than
supra-, above
sur-, over
syn-, with

synchro-, referring to simulta-
neous action
taut-, same
tax-, arrangement
techno-, technical
tel-, at a distance
tetra-, four
thermo-, heat
thio-, sulfur
trans-, across
tri-, three
ultra-, beyond
un-, contrary to, not
uni-, single, one
vari-, varied

Glossary 2. Suffixes

-age, amount of
-ance, amount of
-ane, a type of hydrocarbon
-ate, designates a radical of a salt
which contains oxygen in greater
proportion than "-ite"
-ene, a type of hydrocarbon
-gon, angle
-ic, designates an acid which contains oxygen in greater proportion than "-ous"; *also* having
the nature of
-ide, a compound of two elements
-ile, relating to
-ite, designates a radical of a salt
which contains oxygen in lesser
proportion than "-ate"
-ium, Latin ending for certain
nouns usually applied to the
chemical elements
-ive, tending toward
-ivity, concerning a unit amount

-ode, an electronic path
-oid, resembling
-ous, designates an acid which
contains oxygen in lesser proportion than "-ic"
-phil, -philic, having an affinity or
liking for
-phobic, having an aversion for
-phore, carrying
-phoresis, transmission
-scope, instrument for viewing
-tron, a device or instrument
-tuple, multiply times; as quin-
tuple, multiply times five
-ular, relating to
-ulent, abounding in
-ure, process
-urgy, art of dealing with material
-um, *see* -ium
-yl, a chemical radical
-yne, a type of hydrocarbon

Glossary 3
Technical and Scientific Abbreviations

You are already quite aware that engineers and scientists have their own shorthands. This list of approximately three hundred abbreviations is drawn from the ones used most commonly. It is important to preserve *every detail* in writing abbreviations. The careless substitution of a capital letter for a small letter, or the introduction of a space where it does not belong can change the meaning drastically. On the other hand, you must be just as aware of the fact that some abbreviations can be represented acceptably in many ways; for example, there are six acceptable ways to write the abbreviation for alternating current. But when alternative acceptable abbreviations are given, you must pick one and stick with it. *Never* switch abbreviations in the middle of a report or a group of closely related reports. Notice also that a large proportion of these abbreviations refers to scientific units.

Scientific abbreviations are usually written without periods, unless an abbreviation itself spells some other word. For example, the standard abbreviation for "inch" is "in." because "in" is itself a meaningful word. However, there are no completely hard and fast rules for writing scientific abbreviations, so if you have a question check with your employer. And always remember to be consistent.

abscissa	absc	atmosphere	atm
absolute	abs	atomic number	at no
acceleration	accel	atomic weight	at wt
accumulative	acc, accum	audio frequency	af, AF, a-f
activity	act	azimuth	az
algebraic	alg	backward wave	
alternating current	ac, a-c, a.c.,	oscillator	BWO
	AC, A-C, A.C.	barometric	bar
altitude	alt	battery	batt
ambient	amb	boiling point	bp, B.P.
ampere	A, a, amp	British thermal unit	BTU, Btu
amplitude modulation	AM, am,	calculated	calc
	a-m	caliber	cal
Ångstron unit	Å, A.U.	calorie	cal
anode	an	candlepower	cp
antenna	ant	capacitance	C, c
antilogarithm	antilog	capacity	cap
approximate	approx	carat	Kt
assembly	assby	cathode	cath

cathode-ray tube	CRT	degree Kelvin (abso-	
center of gravity	cg, c.g.	lute)	°K
centimeter	cm	degree Rankine	°R
centimeter-gram-	cgs, CGS	degree Réaumur	°Ré
second		denominator	denom
centimeters per sec-	cm/sec	dependent	dep
ond		diagonal	diag
centimeters per sec-	cm/sec²	diagram	diag
ond per second		diameter	diam
chemical	chem	differential	diff
chemically pure	cp, C.P.	dimension	dim
circuit	cct	diopter	diopt
circular mil	circ mil	direct current	dc, d-c, d.c.,
circular mil foot	circ mil ft		DC, D-C, D.C.
clockwise	cw	distribution	distrib, dist
coefficient	coeff	divergence	div
colinear	colin	double pole, double	DPDT
concentration of		throw	
hydrogen	pH	double pole, single	DPST
congruent	congr	throw	
constant	const	electric	elec
continuous wave	cw, CW, c-w	electromagnetic	e.m., e-m
cosecant	csc	electromagnetic	
cosine	cos	force	emf, EMF
cotangent	ctn or cot	electromagnetic unit	emu
coulomb	C	electron volt	eV
counterclockwise	ccw, CCW		
counter electromo-		electrostatic unit	esu
tive force	cemf	equation	eq., Eq.
cubic	cu	equilibrium	equilib
cubic centimeter	cc, cm³	equivalent	equiv
cubic foot	cu ft, ft³	error function	erf
cubic inch	cu in., in.³	experimental	exptl
cubic millimeter	cu mm, mm³	exponent	exp
cubic yard	cu yd, yd³	expression	expn
curie	cu, Cu, Ci	extrapolate	extrap
cutoff	co	farad	F, f
cycle	c	foot, feet	ft
cycles per second	cps	foot-candle	ft-c
deceleration	decel	foot-pound	ft-lb
decibel	db, dB	freezing point	fp
definition	def	frequency	freq
degree	deg, °	frequency modula-	
degree Baumé	°B	tion	FM, f-m
degree centigrade	°C	fugacity	fug
(Celsius)		function	fn
degree Fahrenheit	°F	gallon	gal

gallons per minute	gal/min	kilowatt-hour	kwh, KWH
gas	g	kinetic energy	KE
gauss	G	Lambert	L
geometric	geom	left	lt
giga-	G	limit	lim
gigawatt	GW	liquid	liq, l
gilbert	Gi	liquid oxygen	LOX
gradient	grad	liter	l
grain	gr	logarithm	log
gram	g	loudspeaker	spkr
gram-calorie	g-cal	lumen	lu
gravity	g	Mach number	M
ground	gnd	magnetic	mag
gyroscope	gyro	magnetomotive force	mmf
harmonic	harm	material	matl
henry	H	mathematical	math
high frequency	h-f, HF	maximum	max
high voltage	h-v, HV	mega-	M
horizontal	horiz	megacycle	Mc
hundred	C, c	megavolt	MV
hyperbolic cosecant	csch	megawatt	MW
hyperbolic cosine	cosh	melting point	mp
hyperbolic cotangent	ctnh	meter	m, mtr
hyperbolic secant	sech	micro-	μ
hyperbolic sine	sinh	microampere	μA
hyperbolic tangent	tanh	microfarad	μF
inch	in.	microgram	μg
inch-pound	in.-lb	microhenry	μH
increment	inc	micromho	μmho
independent	ind, indep	micromicrofarad	$\mu\mu$f
infrared	IR	micromicrohenry	$\mu\mu$H
inside diameter	ID	micromicron	$\mu\mu$
instrument	inst	micron	μ
integral	int, integ	microsecond	μsec
intermediate frequency	if, i-f, IF	microvolt	μV
inverse	inv	microwatt	μW
joule	J	mile	mi
junction	jct	miles per hour	mph
kilo-	k	milli-	m
kilocalorie	kcal	milliampere	ma
kilocycle	kc	milligram	mg
kilogram	kg	milliliter	ml
kilogram-calorie	kg-cal	millimeter	mm
kilometer	km	million	M
kilovolt	kV	millisecond	msec
kilovolt-ampere	kVA	millivolt	mV
kilowatt	kW, kw	milliwatt	mW

minimum	min	research and devel-	R & D
minute	min	opment	R & D
modulation	mod	residue	res
modulus	mod	revolutions per minute	rpm
molecular weight	mol wt	revolutions per second	rps
multiplication	mult	right	rt
nano-	n	roentgen	R
nanosecond	nsec	root mean square	rms
natural logarithm	ln	second	sec
negative-positive- negative	NPN	section	sect
number	No., #	series	ser
numerator	num	signal	sig
ohm-centimeter	ohm-cm	silicon controlled	
optimum	opt	rectifier	SCR
ordinate	ord	sine	sin
oscillate	osc	single pole, double	
ounce	oz	throw	SPDT
outside diameter	OD	single pole, single	
parallel	par	throw	SPST
parts per billion	ppb	solid	sol, s
parts per million	ppm	solute	solu
perimeter	perim	solution	soln
periodic	per	solvent	solv
phase	ϕ, ph	speaker	spkr
pico-	p	specific gravity	sp gr
picofarad	pF	square centimeter	sq cm, cm^2
point	pt	square inch	sq in., in.^{2}
positive	pos	summation	sum
positive-negative-		superheterodyne	superhet
positive	PNP	switch	sw
post alloy diffused		synchronous	sync, synch
transistor	PADT	tangent	tan
potential	poten	temperature	temp, T
pound	lb	tentative	tent, tenta
pound-feet	lb-ft	terminal	term
power factor	pf	thousand	k
precipitate	ppt	tolerance	tol
Program Evaluation		transformer	Xfmr
Review Technique	PERT	traveling wave	
quadrant	quad	tube	TWT
quantity, quantitative	quant	ultimate	ult
quart	qt	ultrahigh fre-	
quotient	quot	quency	uhf, UHF
radian	rad	ultrahigh voltage	uhv, UHV
radio frequency	rf, r-f, RF	ultraviolet	UV, U.V., uv
reciprocal	recip	vacuum	vac

value	val	viscosity	visc
vapor pressure	vp	volt	V, v
vector	vect	volt-ampere	VA, va
velocity	vel	watt	W, w
versus	vs	weber	Wb
vertical	vert	weight	wt
verh high frequency	vhf, VHF	yard	yd
video frequency	Vf, v-f, VF	year	yr
		yield	y

Glossary 4
The Chemical Elements and Their Abbreviations

This glossary gives a list of abbreviations for the chemical elements. Refer to the chapter on chemistry for explanations of what the chemical elements are, and for the rules to be followed in using these abbreviations.

actinium	Ac	europium	Eu
aluminum	Al	fermium	Fm
americium	Am	fluorine	F
antimony	Sb	francium	Fr
argon	A	gadolinium	Gd
arsenic	As	gallium	Ga
astatine	At	germanium	Ge
barium	Ba	gold	Au
berkelium	Bk	hafnium	Hf
beryllium	Be	helium	He
bismuth	Bi	holmium	Ho
boron	B	hydrogen	H
bromine	Br	indium	In
cadmium	Cd	iodine	I
calcium	Ca	iridium	Ir
californium	Cf	iron	Fe
carbon	C	krypton	Kr
cerium	Ce	lanthanum	La
cesium	Cs	lawrencium	Lw
chlorine	Cl	lead	Pb
chromium	Cr	lithium	Li
cobalt	Co	lutetium	Lu
columbium*	Cb	magnesium	Mg
copper	Cu	manganese	Mn
curium	Cm	mendelevium	Md
dysprosium	Dy	mercury	Hg
einsteinium	Es	molybdenum	Mo
erbium	Er	neodymium	Nd

neon	Ne	scandium	Sc
neptunium	Np	selenium	Se
nickel	Ni	silicon	Si
niobium*	Nb	silver	Ag
nitrogen	N	sodium	Na
nobelium	No	strontium	Sr
osmium	Os	sulfur	S
oxygen	O	tantalum	Ta
palladium	Pd	technetium	Tc
phosphorus	P	tellurium	Te
platinum	Pt	terbium	Tb
plutonium	Pu	thallium	Tl
polonium	Po	thorium	Th
potassium	K	thulium	Tm
praseodymium	Pr	tin	Sn
promethium	Pm	titanium	Ti
protactinium	Pa	tungsten*	W
radium	Ra	uranium	U
radon	Rn	vanadium	V
rhenium	Re	wolfram*	W
rhodium	Rh	xenon	Xe
rubidium	Rb	ytterbium	Yb
ruthenium	Ru	yttrium	Y
samarium	Sm	zinc	Zn
zirconium		Zr	

*Columbium is another name for niobium; wolfram is another name for tungsten

Glossary 5
Frequently Encountered Names of Scientists and Engineers

The names listed in this glossary are used so often that they have ceased to be just names and have become scientific words. Like other scientific words they are now fair game to be modified with prefixes and suffixes. In such cases they may even be written without capitalizing their first letters.

When a name is used an an adjective, to describe something, as, for example,

Laplace transform	Poynting vector	Poisson ratio
Wheatstone bridge	Venturi nozzle	Taylor series
d'Arsonval galvanometer	Avogadro's number	Heaviside layer
van de Graaf generator	Young's modulus	Fermi level
Bunsen burner	Barkhausen effect	Dewar flask
Van Allen belt	Stokes' law	Planck's constant
	Bohr atom	

the capital remains at the front of the word as it would for any name. On the other hand, when a name has been made into a unit, the first letter is small, and the word is prey to the addition of prefixes and suffixes. For example,

watt,   wattage,   kilowatt
volt,   voltage,   microvolt
ohms,   microohm
farad,   micromicrofarad

An exception is the Ångstrom Unit, called the Ångstrom or Ångstrom Unit, with the little Scandinavian circle over the capital A.

There are also many cases where usage is not so standard where a name has prefixes and suffixes added to it but does not stand for a physical unit. So, sometimes, "Hamiltonian" is written with a capital, and sometimes it is written "hamiltonian." The same is true for "Lagrangian," "Laplacian," and many other words. As always, the important thing for you to do when you meet such a term is to check with your employer, and then be *consistent* in using the style he prefers.

Ampere	Carnot	Fermi	Jeans
Ångstrom	Celsius	Fresnel	Joule
Archimedes	Clausius	Fahrenheit	Kelvin
Armstrong	Clapeyron	Fourier	Kepler
Avogadro	Clerk-Maxwell	Fraunhofer	Kirchhoff
Barkhausen	Colpitts	Galileo	Lambert
Baumé	Coulomb	Galvani	Laplace
Bell	Curie	Gauss	Laue
Bernoulli	Dalton	Gay-Lussac	Lenz
Berzelius	d'Alembert	Gibbs	Leibniz
Bessemer	d'Arsonval	Gilbert	Lissajous
Bohr	Debye	Haber	Lorentz
Boltzmann	De Forest	Haldane	Maxwell
Boole	Descartes	Hall	Mendeleev
Bose	Dewar	Hamilton	Michelson
Boyle	Dirac	Heaviside	Morley
Bragg	Doppler	Heisenberg	Morse
Brahe	Edison	Helmholtz	Nernst
Bridgman	Einstein	Henry	Newton
Bunsen	Euclid	Hertz	Oersted
Cavendish	Euler	Hooke	Ohm
Cantor	Faraday	Huygens	Pascal
Compton	Fermat	Jacobi	Pauli

Pauling	Rankine	Solvay	van de Graaff
Peirce	Raoult	Sommerfeld	van der Waals
Peltier	Réaumur	Steinmetz	van't Hoff
Pitot	Reimann	Stokes	Venn
Planck	Reynolds	Szilard	Venturi
Poisson	Rumford	Taylor	Volta
Poynting	Russell	Tesla	Von Braun
Priestley	Rydberg	Thomson	Watt
Purcell	Seebeck	Torricelli	Wheatstone
Pythagoras	Shockley	Urey	Wiener
Rabi	Snell	Van Allen	Young

Zeeman

Glossary 6
The Greek and Some Other Foreign Alphabets

The Greek alphabet is the most important foreign alphabet used in scientific work. It has come into universal acceptance in all fields of science and engineering. Greek letters are used as distinctive symbols to represent concepts, physical quantities, and physical qualities. In some cases a Greek letter has become so identified with what it stands for that the object has no other name; the symbol, the Greek letter, has become the name. The name of the Greek letter, spelled out, is often used instead of the letter itself

Perhaps a few examples will clear this up. Nuclear engineers talk of the emanation known as

gamma rays

Electronics men refer to the transconductance of a radio tube as its

mu

and if they want to talk of the amplification factor of a transistor they talk of its

beta

Sometimes these "letter words" are spelled out as in the preceding examples, and sometimes the Greek letters are themselves used:

γ ray, μ, β

But in general a Greek letter is just another kind of symbol that your boss will use, and you must learn to recognize it and write it—both as a capital letter and as a small letter, and as handwritten script. As has been mentioned, it is possible to acquire replaceable keys or plastic adaptors for the Greek letters, which can be inserted into most typewriters. There is also another way to make Greek letters. You may modify some conventional English letters. Some Greek letters are of course the same as English letters. But even when this is not so there is often enough similarity so that you can successfully "touch up" the English letters and make them fairly presentable as Greek letters. Here are a few examples, and you can probably think of a few others:

beta	add a vertical line to an 8	β
delta	add a little curl to an o	δ
theta	add a hyphen to an 0	θ
mu	add a vertical tail to a u	μ
rho	add a vertical tail to an o	ρ
sigma	add a horizontal line to an o	σ
phi	add a diagonal to an 0	ϕ
chi	use a diagonal and draw what is left	χ
psi	use a diagonal and draw what is left	ψ

Now that you know how to make Greek letters out of English letters you are confronted with some questions of judgment. What really is the best way to make Greek letters so that the reader is most satisfied and least distracted? I think that the best thing to do is to fit your typewriter with the Greek letters you use most frequently. Where this is not practical, I prefer having the complete letter drawn in by hand. This puts the technique of "tricking out" normal typewriter letters and symbols so that they look like Greek letters in third place, as an acceptable, but least preferable, practice.

The Hebrew letters are included in this glossary because they are sometimes used by mathematicians, especially to represent numbers beyond infinity. The Russian letters are also given because there seems to be a tendency to use them once in a while, particularly by those who read Russian technical literature.

The Greek Letters and Their Scientific Uses*
A number of scientific terms that are commonly symbolized by
Greek letters are listed after the symbolizing letters

Name	Capital	Lower Case	
alpha	A	α	absorption factor, angles, angular acceleration, attenuation constant, common-base current amplification factor, deviation of state parameter, temperature coefficient of linear expansion, temperature coefficient of resistance, thermal expansion coefficient, thermal diffusivity
beta	B	β	angles, common-emitter current amplification factor, flux density, phase constant, wavelength constant
gamma	Γ	γ	electrical conductivity, Grueneisen parameter, nuclear radiation
delta	Δ decrement increment	δ	angles, damping coefficient (decay constant), decrement, increment, secondary-emission ratio
epsilon	E electric field intensity	ϵ	capacitivity, dielectric coefficient, electron energy, emissivity, permittivity, base of natural logarithms (2.718 ...)
zeta	Z	ζ	
eta	H	η	chemical potential, dielectric susceptibility (intrinsic capacitance), efficiency, hysteresis, intrinsic impedance of a medium, intrinsic standoff ratio

Name	Capital		Lower Case	
theta	Θ	angles, thermal resistance	θ	angle of rotation, angles, angular phase displacement, reluctance, transit angle
iota	I		ι	
kappa	K	coupling coefficient	κ	susceptibility
lambda	Λ		λ	line density of charge, permeance, photosensitivity, wavelength
mu	M		μ	amplification factor, magnetic permeability, micron, mobility, permeability, prefix "micro"
nu	N		ν	reluctivity
xi	Ξ		ξ	
omicron	O		o	
pi	Π		π	Peltier coefficient, ratio of circumference to diameter (3.1416 ...)
rho	P		ρ	reflection coefficient, reflection factor, resistivity, volume density of electric charge
sigma	Σ	summation	σ	conductivity, Stefan-Boltzmann constant, surface density of charge
tau	T	period	period	propagation constant, Thomson coefficient, time-phase displacement, transmission factor
upsilon	Y	admittance	ν	
phi	Φ	magnetic flux, radiant flux	ϕ	angles, coefficient of performance, contact potential, magnetic

Name	Capital		Lower Case	
				flux, phase angle, phase displacement
chi	X		χ	angles
psi	Ψ	angles	ψ	dielectric flux, displacement flux, phase difference
omega	Ω	resistance	ω	angular frequency, angular velocity, solid angle

---

*Adapted, with permission, from *Electrical Design News*, June, 1963.

The Hebrew Alphabet

א	(not vocalized)	ל		l
		מ ם		m
ב	b, bh			
		נ ן		n
ג	g, gh			
		ס		s
ד	d, dh			
		ע		(not vocalized)
ה	h			
		פ ף		p, ph
ו	w			
		צ ץ		ts
ז	z			
		ק		q
ח	ch			
		ר		r
ט	t			
		שׂ		s
י	y			
		שׁ		s, sh
כ ך	k, kh	ת		t, th

The Russian Alphabet

А а	a		С с	s	
Б б	b		Т т	t	
В в	v		У у	u	
Г г	g		Ф ф	f	
Д д	d		Х х	kh	
Е е	e		Ц ц	ts	
Ж ж	zh		Ч ч	ch	
З з	z		Ш ш	sh	
И и Й й	i		Щ щ	shch	
К к	k		Ъ ъ	(not vocalized)	
Л л	l		Ы ы	y	
М м	m		Ь ь	(not vocalized)	
Н н	n		Э э	é	
О о	o		Ю ю	yu	
П п	p		Я я	ya	
Р р	r				

Glossary 7
The Secretary's Glossary of Scientific and Engineering Terms

This section is a dictionary of some 3,000 words compiled expressly for you, the technical secretary. While most of the words may be found in a standard dictionary, and certainly in one of the many technical dictionaries, this dictionary is different because it is written in a way to give you, the technical secretary, just the information that you may need. Thus, the definitions are quite short (a large number have only one or two words), and based on the simplest answers to your questions; The hyphens indicate end-of-the-line division points. If you do not need to know more than a one- or two-word definition in order to get the drift of what you are typing, why burden yourself with more detail? In other words, this dictionary was created to help make you a better technical secretary and not to make you into a scientist. Of course, if you decide some day that you want to become a scientist or an engineer (and one of my secretaries once did just that), this is as good a place as any to begin to become familiar with important scientific words and concepts.

A

ab-er-ra-tion (*n.*), an imperfection in a lens

ab-la-tion (*n.*), the removal of material by erosion, or melting and evaporation

abort (*v.*), to end (an experiment) earlier than planned, usually because of failure

abrade (*v.*), to wear away by rubbing (friction)

ab-scis-sa (*n.*), the horizontal base line of a graph; *also* one of the coordinates of a point on a graph

ab-so-lute (*adj.*), fundamental, basic, not relative to anything else, complete in itself

ab-sorb (*v.*), to suck in, dissolve, or assimilate another material; *note difference from* adsorb

ab-sorp-tion (*n.*), *see* absorb

ac (*adj., n.*), alternating electrical current; *also* AC, A.C., a.c., or a-c

ac-celer-ate (*v.*), to increase (or add to) speed

ac-cel-er-omet-er (*n.*), a meter to measure acceleration

ac-cep-tor (*n.*), one of a small group of atomic additives to semiconductors, the opposite of donor

ac-cu-mu-la-tive (*adj.*), that which accumulates; added up

ac-cu-mu-la-tor (*n.*), that which takes in; *also* a type of electronic circuit

ace-tic acid (*n.*), an organic acid

ace-to- (*prefix*), *see* acetic acid

ac-e-tone (*n.*), an organic chemical compound, a solvent

ace-tyl (*n.*), a radical of acetic acid

a-cet-y-lene (*n.*), an organic chemical compound

ach-ro-mat-ic (*adj.*), that light which, in passing through a compound lens, is not broken into its constituent colors

acid (*n.*), from sour, a class of chemical compounds containing the hydrogen ion (H^+); can combine with a suitable base or alkali to form a salt

acid-ic (*adj.*), that which is acid

acid-i-fy (*v.*), to make acid; to turn into an acid

acid-i-ty (*n.*), the degree to which something is acid

acid-u-late (*v.*), to make slightly acid

acous-tics (*n.*), the science of sound

acryl-ic (*n.*), an organic chemical compound; *also* a synthetic plastic

ac-tin-ic (*adj.*), pertaining to light rays that hit a surface and bring about a chemical change

ac-tin-i-um (*n.*), a radioactive chemical element, Ac

ac-tiv-i-ty (*n.*), a measure of the tendency of a chemical to react

ac-tu-ate (*v.*), to set into action

acute an-gle (*n.*), an angle smaller than $90°$

adapt-er (*n.*), a gadget or structure used to connect two parts or to change the possible uses of a piece of equipment

ad-dend (*n.*), a number which is to be added to another number; *see* augend add-er (*n*.), an electrical circuit, usually in a computer

add-ing (*adj*.), pertaining to a kind of electronic circuit

addi-tive (*adj*.), able to be added, produced by addition; (*n*.), a substance added to another to effect some change

ad hoc (*adv*.), for this particular situation only

adi-a-batic (*adj*.), pertaining to an occurrence which proceeds without loss or gain of heat

ad in-fi-ni-tum (*adv*.), without end or limit

ad-mix (*v*.), to mix together

ad-sorb (*v*.), to adhere to the surface of another material; *note difference from* absorb

ad-sorp-tion (*n*.), *see* adsorb

aer-ate (*v*.), to cause air to flow through something

ae-ri-al (*n*.), a device to "catch" radio signals for a radio or television receiver; an antenna

aer-o- (*prefix*), relative to flight or the science of aeronautics

aer-o-dy-namics (*n*.), the science of movement through the air

aero-sol (*n*.), a cloud of fine particles floating in the air

af-fect (*v*.), to produce an effect on, to influence

af-fini-ty (*n*.), a measure of the tendency of two specified materials to react chemically

age (*v*.), a treatment involving exposure to some condition for a certain period of time

ag-glomer-ate (*v*.), to cluster together; (*n*.), a cluster

ag-gre-gate (*v*.), to cluster together loosely; (*n*.), a loose cluster; material used in mixing concrete, plaster, etc.

aile-ron (*n*.), a movable part of the wing of an airplane or other flying structure

air-borne (*adj*.), supported or transported by air

air-foil (*n*.), a structure which will have a desired reaction when it moves through the air

air-frame (*n*.), the basic structure of a air or space vehicle

al-che-my (*n*.), the medieval science and philosophy of chemistry

al-co-hol (*n*.), an organic chemical compound

al-de-hyde (*n*.), an organic chemical compound

aleph (*n*.), the first letter of the Hebrew alphabet

al-ge-bra (*n*.), the branch of mathematics which treats numerical problems using a technique where items are represented by symbols (generally letters of the alphabet)

al-i-phat-ic (*adj*.), pertaining to a class of chemical compounds

al-ka-li (*n*., *adj*.), a class of chemical compounds containing the hydroxide radical (OH); *also called* a base

al-ka-line (*adj*.), *see* alkali

al-ka-lin-i-ty (*n*.), *see* alkali

al-ka-loid (*adj*.), *see* alkali

al-kyd (*n*.), a class of synthetic chemical compounds

al-kyl (*n*.), a class of organic chemical radicals

al-lo-trope (*n.*), a variation of structure for a given chemical or element, implying two or more forms; for example, two different crystal formations

al-lot-ro-py (*n.*), *see* allotrope

al-loy (*n.*), a mixture of metals; (*v.*), to melt metals together

al-lu-vi-al (*adj.*), silt deposited by running water

al-lu-vi-um (*n.*), *see* alluvial

al-lyl (*n.*, *adj.*), a class of organic chemical radicals

Al-ni-co (*n.*), a magnetic alloy of iron, aluminum, nickel, and, in different combinations, cobalt, copper, or titanium

al-pha (*n.*), the first letter of the Greek alphabet α; used as a symbol in many scientific terms, such as alpha metal, alpha ray, alpha particle

al-pha-nu-mer (-ic) (*n.*, *adj.*), a code of characters made up of both letters and numbers

al-ter-nate (*n.*), every other one; (*adj.*), to occur in turns or succession

al-ter-nat-ing cur-rent (*n.*), an electric current which changes its direction (or polarity) in a regular manner; ac, AC, a.c., A.C., or a-c

al-ter-na-tor (*n.*), an electric generator which produces alternating current

al-ti-tude (*n.*), height

al-um (*n.*), a chemical compound; a salt

alu-mi-na (*n.*), the chemical compound aluminum oxide, Al_2O_3

alu-mi-nate (*n.*), a chemical radical of aluminum and oxygen

al-u-min-i-um (*n.*), aluminum (British)

alu-mi-num (*n.*), a metallic chemical element, Al

al-u-nite (*n.*), a chemical compound; a mineral

amal-gam (*n.*), an alloy of mercury and another metal; a mixture of different metals

amal-ga-mate (*n.*), to mix to form a single compound

am-bi-ent (*n.*, *adj.*), the surrounding environment; completely surrounding

am-big-u-ous (*adj.*), uncertain; having more than one meaning

am-er-i-ci-um (*n.*), a chemical element, Am

amine (*n.*), a class of chemical compounds derived from ammonia

ami-no (*adj.*, *prefix*), a class of chemical compounds containing a particular radical (NH_2) or related radicals

am-me-ter (*n.*), a meter for measuring electrical current in amperes

am-mo-nia (*n.*), the chemical compound NH_3

am-mo-ni-a-cal (*adj.*), pertaining to the compound ammonia

amor-phous (*adj.*), noncrystalline; having no definite shape

am-per-age (*n.*), the unit of electric current flow, one coulomb per second; current strength

am-pere (*n.*), the unit of electric current flow

ampere-hour (*n.*), a unit describing the number of electrons that flow in an hour when there is a steady current of one ampere

ampere-second (*n.*), the same as ampere-hour except the time interval is one second

ampere-turn (*n.*), an electrical unit related to transformers

am-pho-ter-ic (*adj.*), pertaining to a compound capable of reacting either as an acid or as an alkali

am-pli-dyne (*n.*), a type of electrical-current generator

am-pli-fi-ca-tion (*n.*), the act of making something bigger (usually an electrical quantity)

am-pli-fi-er (*n.*), something which amplifies; a type of circuit

am-pli-fy (*v.*), to make bigger

am-pli-tron (*n.*), a class of high-power microwave tube

am-pli-tude (*n.*), the size of a wave (height, loudness, or intensity)

amplitude modulation (*n.*), regulation of wave size to achieve certain effects; *abbreviated* A.M., AM, a.m., a-m

am-pul *or* am-poule *or* am-pule (*n.*), a small vial or container

amyl (*n.*), a class of chemical radicals

an-a-log or an-a-logue (*n.*), similar to or like another

anal-o-gous (*adj.*), resembling, corresponding, like

anal-o-gy (*n.*), resemblance, similarity; inference that if substances, things, or ideas are similar in some respects that they may be similar in other respects

anal-y-sis (*n.*), intellectual investigation; the identification of components or constituents of a substance

an-a-lyst (*n.*), one who analyzes

an-a-lyt-ic (*adj.*), *see* analysis

an-a-lyz-able (*adj.*), *see* analysis

an-a-lyze (*v.*), *see* analysis

an-as-tig-mat-ic (*adj.*), relating to a property of a lens

AND (*n.*), a designation used in computer programming to indicate the operation of adding (*always* capitalized)

an-echo-ic (*adj.*), without echoes; referring to a soundless room or chamber

an-gle (*n.*), the geometric shape formed by two straight lines meeting at a point

ång-strom unit (*n.*), one ten billionth of a meter; also Ångstrom or A.U.

an-gu-lar (*adj.*), having or forming an angle or angles

an-hy-dride (*n.*), the compound that remains when water is removed from one that normally has water associated with it

an-ion (*n.*), a negatively charged ion

an-iso-trop-ic (*adj.*), having different properties or reactions in different directions or circumstances

an-isot-ropy (*n.*), *see* anisotropic

an-neal (*v.*), to heat a metal in order to soften it and make it less brittle an-nu-lar (*adj*.), having a ring or doughnut shape

an-nu-lus (*n*.), a structure with a ring shape

an-ode (*n*.), the positive terminal of a battery

an-od-ize (*v*.), to subject a metal to electrolytic action (in an electrolytic cell)

anom-a-lous (*adj*.), having no explanation, not conforming to the expected or to the rule

anom-a-ly (*n*.), that which does not conform to the general rule

an-ten-na (*n*.), the wire or rod which receives electromagnetic (radio) waves and brings these signals into a radio or television set

an-ti-log-a-rithm (*n*.), the number corresponding to a given logarithm; *abbreviated* anti log

an-ti-mo-ny (*n*.), a chemical metallic element, Sb

apex (*n*.), the topmost part

ap-er-ture (*n*.), a small opening, usually in an optical system

arc (*n*.), something arched or curved; a spark

ar-gon (*n*.), an inert gaseous element, A

ar-ma-ture (*n*.), part of a motor or dynamo

ar-senic (*n*.), a metallic chemical element, As

aspher-i-cal (*adj*.), not quite spherical

as-ta-tine (*n*.), a radioactive chemical element, At

astig-ma-tism (*n*.), a lens defect

as-tral (*adj*.), relating to the stars

as-tro-nau-tics (*n*.), the science of the construction and operation of space vehicles

as-tro-phys-ics (*n*.), the physics and chemistry of the stars and planets

asym-met-ric (*adj*.), not symmetric, askew, unbalanced

asymp-tote (*n*.), a line on a graph that gets nearer and near to another line but never touches it

at-mos-phere (*n*.), the layer of air around the earth; *also* any surrounding gaseous environment

at-om (*n*.), the smallest particle of an element that can exist and still show all the properties of that element

atom-ic (*adj*.), referring to atoms or atomic energy

at-om-ize (*v*.), to break up into tiny particles

at-ten-u-ate (*v*.), to reduce or make something less

at-ten-u-a-tion (*n*.), *see* attenuate

at-trac-tion (*n*.), a force pulling objects together

at-tri-bute (*n*.), a basic quality or characteristic of something

at-tri-tion (*n*.), wearing down by grinding or rubbing

atyp-i-cal (*adj*.), not as expected, not typical

au-di-ble (*adj*.), able to be heard

au-dio (*adj*.), pertaining to sound

au-gend (*n*.), a number to which

another is added; *see* addend

aus - ten - ite (*n.*), a constituent of some types of steel made up of a solid solution of carbon in iron

au-to-mate (*v.*), to change over to automatic production

au-to-ma-tion (*n.*), the operation of machinery with a minimum of human operation, decision-making, or tending

av-a-lanche (*n.*), a great rush of something, usually sudden

avi-on-ics (*n.*), the science or study of electrical and electronic instruments used in flying vehicles

ax-i-al (*adj.*), in the neighborhood of the axis of something, where the axis is a straight center line

ax-i-om (*n.*), a proposition or statement considered to be true without proof

ax-is (*n., pl.* axes), *see* axial

ax-le (*n.*), the shaft on which a wheel rotates

azide (*n.*), a group of chemical compounds containing an NH_3 group

az-i-muth (*n.*), a navigational or astronomical measurement

azine (*n.*), a group of organic chemical compounds

B

Bab-bitt met-al (*n.*), an alloy used in parts that bear or wear on each other (as bearings)

baf-fle (*n.*), a surface or other

device used to deflect or regulate the flow of something

bal - ance (*v.*), to equalize in weight; *in chemistry*, to make two sides of an equation come out equal in terms of amounts used and valences

bal - last (*n.*), heavy material used in a vehicle of any sort in order to stabilize it

bal-lis-tics (*n.*), the study of any object in flight or its flight characteristics

band (*n.*), a range or spread of frequency or energy

bar-i-um (*n.*), a metallic chemical element, Ba

ba-rom-e-ter (*n.*), an instrument used to measure air pressure (an aid in weather forecasting) or height of ascent

bas - al (*adj.*), referring to a basic quality or to the base of something

ba-salt (*n.*), a kind of mineral or rock

base (*n.*), a class of chemical, also called an alkali; *also* the number to which an exponent or a logarithm is applied

ba-sic-ty (*n.*), the degree of alkalinity in a chemical solution

batch (*n.*), the quantity of something treated or processed at any one time

bath (*n.*), a liquid in a vessel for some specific purpose (as heating, cooling); the vessel containing the liquid

bat - tery (*n.*), a device which generates electricity as a result of a continuous chemical reaction; the device has two terminals, one positively charged, the other negatively charged

baux-ite (*n.*), a mineral

bea-con (*n.*), a radio transmitter that sends a signal used by aircraft or ships for guidance

bead (*n.*), the track or path of a weld joint in metals or plastics

bea-ker (*n.*), a cup-like container used in chemistry

beam (*n.*), a vertically supported horizontal number used in construction

bear-ing (*n.*), a structure used in machinery in which a pin or axle turns

beat (*n.*), the difference frequency between two frequencies

bell jar (*n.*), a dome-shaped chamber in which a vacuum or other gaseous environment may be produced; *also* a cover for something

bel-lows (*n.*), an extendible or expandable part, usually used for blowing or stretching (to increase a distance)

ben-zene (*n.*), an organic chemical used as a solvent or a fuel

ben-zene ring (*n.*), an arrangement of chemical bonds, in organic chemistry

ben-zol (*n.*), benzene; *also* a mixture of benzene with similar liquids

berke-li-um (*n.*), a radioactive element, Bk

ber-yl (*n.*), a mineral

beryl-li-um (*n.*), a metallic element, Be

be-ta (*n.*), the second letter of the Greek alphabet β, used as a symbol in physics and chemistry (beta-rays, etc.)

be-ta-tron (*n.*), an electron accelerator

beth (*n.*), the second letter of the Hebrew alphabet

bev-el (*n.*), an angle, made by two intersecting parts, which is other than a right angle

bi- (*prefix*), two, twice

bi-as (*n.*), a voltage impressed on a given point, particularly on the electrodes of a tube or transistor

bi-ax-i-al (*adj.*), having two axes

bib-li-og-ra-phy (*n.*), a list of books and/or articles on a given subject

bi-fi-lar (*adj.*), having two linear marks or threads, usually scribed or scratched on a lens

bi-fur-cate (*v.*), to divide into two branches

bi-met-al (*n.*), a strip made up of two different kinds of metal joined or layered onto each other

bi-me-tal-lic (*adj.*), *see* bimetal

bi-na-ry (*adj.*), made up of two parts; *also* a numbering system

bin-au-ral (*adj.*), relating to sound received from two directions

bi-nis-tor (*n.*), a solid-state component with two leads

bin-oc-u-lar (*adj.*), relating to

receiving a light image from two lens systems, as with a telescope having a separate eyepiece for each eye

bi-no-mi-al (*adj.*), a mathematical expression having two terms connected by a plus or minus sign

bi-o-chem-is-try (*n.*), the science that involves the chemical reactions of living materials

bio-lu-mi-nes-cence (*n.*), giving off light as a result of biological action; the light itself

bi-phe-nyl (*n.*), a chemical radical; *see* diphenyl

bi-re-frin-gence (*n.*), refraction of light through a system or substance in two separate directions to produce two rays

bi-sect (*v.*), to cut into two separate parts, usually of equal size

bis-muth (*n.*), a metallic element, Bi

bisque (*n.*), a piece of hard-fired unglazed ceramic

bit (*n.*), the smallest possible piece of information in computer language, a choice between "yes" or "no"

bi-va-lent (*adj.*), having a valence of two, *i.e.*, a chemical element capable of taking on or giving off two ionic charges

black-body (*n.*), a surface so black that it reflects no light

bleed-er (*n.*), an electronic circuit

boil (*v.*), to go through a change of state from liquid to gas; to raise to the boiling point

bo-lom-e-ter (*n.*), a sensitive thermometer

bomb (*n.*), a chamber for containing compressed gases

bom-bard (*v.*), to subject to particles or rays

bond (*n.*), the force of attraction that holds atoms or ions together in chemical compounds

bond-er-ize (*v.*), to coat metal with a chemical primer base

boom (*n.*), a long strut or spar used in construction cranes

bor-ane (*n.*), a chemical compound of boron and hydrogen

bo-rate (*n.*), a salt containing boron

bo-rat-ed (*adj.*), mixed or combined with borate

bo-rax (*n.*), a chemical compound, essentially sodium borate

bore (*v.*), to drill a hole

bo-ron (*n.*), a metalloid element, B

bort (*n.*), an imperfect diamond or diamond fragment used abrasively

boss (*n.*), a projection

boule (*n.*), a rough lump of artificial sapphire or ruby

brack-et (*n.*), one of the pair of marks used to enclose a chemical or mathematical expression that must be marked off as an entity

brake (*v.*), to stop or slow down

brass (*n.*), an alloy of the metals copper and zinc

Bri-nell hard-ness (*n.*), a numerical measure of the hardness of metal

Brit-ish ther-mal unit (*n.*), a

unit amount of heat; B.T.U.

brit-tle (*adj.*), easily broken or cracked

bro - mine (*n.*), a nonmetallic element, Br

bronze (*n.*), an alloy of the metals copper and tin

brush (*n.*), part of a motor or generator

buff-er (*v.*), to add a substance capable of stabilizing the acid level of a solution

bul-lion (*n.*), gold or silver

Bun - sen burn - er (*n.*), a gas burner used in chemistry to produce a very hot, torchlike flame

buoy-an-cy (*n.*), the tendency of an object to float in a liquid

bu - rette (*n.*), a glass tube marked off in cubic centimeters, used to measure out accurate quantities of liquid

burr (*n.*), a sharp projection or roughness formed accidently as a result of machining

bu-ta-di-ene (*n.*), a flammable organic compound

bu-tane (*n.*), a flammable organic compound

bu-ta-nol (*n.*), an alcohol

butt (*n.*), the heavier, thicker end of something; (*v.*), to place two things together, end to end

butt weld (*n.*), the joint between two objects welded end to end

bu-tyl (*n.*), a chemical radical

bu-tyl-ene (*n.*), an organic compound

C

cad-mi-um (*n.*), a metallic element, Cd

calc-, calci-, calco- (*prefix*), pertaining to calcium

cal-car-e-ous (*adj.*), resembling the mineral calcite; containing calcium

cal-ci-fer-ous (*adj.*), containing or producing calcium compounds

cal-cine (*v.*), to heat in order to cause certain physical and chemical changes

cal-cite (*n.*), a mineral containing calcium

cal-ci-um (*n.*), a metallic element, Ca

cal-cu-la-ble (*adj.*), able to be determined by calculation

cal-cu-late (*v.*), to determine mathematically

cal - cu - lus (*n.*), a branch of mathematics

cal-i-ber (*n.*), the diameter of a round object or the inside diameter of a cylinder

cal - i - brate (*v.*), to determine exactly with reference to a standard the value of readings on a meter or some other device

cal-i-for-ni-um (*n.*), a radioactive chemical, Cf

cal-i-per *or* cal-i-pers (*n.*), an instrument for measuring small distances

ca-lo-ric (*adj*.), related to heat

cal - o - rie (*n.*), a unit of heat energy; the amount of energy; the amount of energy required to raise the temperature of one gram of water one degree centigrade; *abbreviated* cal

cal-o-rif-ic (*adj.*), producing heat

cal-o-rim-e-ter (*n.*), a device for measuring quantities of heat

cam (*n.*), in machinery, a sliding part which controls the movements of other parts

cam-ber (*n.*), a slight curvature

cam-phor (*n.*), a crystalline organic compound

can-dle-power (*n.*), a unit of light intensity

can-ti-le-ver (*n.*), a structural beam that extends horizontally, held only at one end

ca-pac-i-tance (*n.*), a quality of an electrical device that permits the storage of energy

ca-pac-i-tor (*n.*), a component of an electrical system which can store electrical energy; *also called* a condenser

ca-pac-i-ty (*n.*), the ability of a capacitor to store electrical energy

cap-il-lar-i-ty (*n.*), the rising of a liquid in a small tube

cap-il-lary (*n.*), a long narrow tube

cap-sule (*n.*), a small closed container

car-at (*n.*), a unit of weight used to measure precious stones, equal to one-fifth of a gram

car-bide (*n.*), a chemical compound of carbon

car-bo-hy-drate (*n.*), a class of chemical compounds containing carbon, hydrogen, and oxygen

car-bol-ic (*adj.*), referring to a class of chemicals; *also called* carbolic acid *or* phenol

car-bon (*n.*), a nonmetallic element, C

car-bo-na-ceous (*adj.*), containing carbon

car-bon-ic (*adj.*), referring to carbon - containing compounds

car-bon-if-er-ous (*adj.*), containing carbon

car-bon-ize (*v.*), to dissociate a chemical compound of carbon, leaving uncombined carbon as a residue; *see also* carburize

car-bon-yl (*n.*), a class of chemical compounds containing the radical CO

car-box-yl (*n.*), a class of organic radicals

car-boy (*n.*), a large cylindrical container for dangerous liquids

car-bu-ret (*v.*), combining chemically with carbon

car-bu-ret-or (*n.*), a device which measures and mixes a fuel with air

car-bu-rize (*v.*), to impregnate a material with carbon; *see also* carbonize

car-ri-er (*n.*), an electrical wave upon which signals are impressed (as modulation)

Car-te-sian (*adj.*), referring to a system for making graphs

cas-cade (*adj.*), a series; (*n.*), an electronic circuit

case (*n.*), a skin or surface

ca-sein (*n.*), a chemical compound produced from milk

cast (*v.*), to shape liquid or a semisolid in a mold so that the solid material which results takes on the shape of the mold

cast-ing (*n.*), an item which has

been cast

ca-tal-y-sis (*n.*), the process in which a chemical reaction is speeded up by the presence of a material that does not itself enter into the reaction

cat - a - lyst (*n.*), substances which can produce catalysis

cat-a-lyze (*v.*), *see* catalysis

cat-e-go-rize (*v.*), to put into a group or classification

cat - e - go - ry (*n.*), a group or classification

cat-e-na-ry (*n.*), the shape of a flexible line or cord when it is held loosely between two points

cath-ode (*n.*), the negative electrode of a battery; the electrode that emits electrons in a vacuum tube

ca-thod-ic (*adj.*), pertaining to the cathode

ca - thod - o - lu - mi -nes-cence (*n.*), light resulting from electron impact

cat - ion (*n.*), a positively charged ion, attracted toward the negative electrode (cathode)

caulk (*v.*), to fill up a hole to prevent leakage

caus-tic (*adj.*), having alkaline qualities, a chemical; corrosive

ce-les-tial (*adj.*), referring to the sky

cell (*n.*), the smallest functional unit of an organized mechanism or structure, a small enclosure

cel-lu-lar (*adj.*), consisting of or related to cells

cel-lu-lose (*n.*), a carbohydrate

in plant cell walls

ce - ment (*n.*), a material that binds particles together

ce-ment-ite (*n.*), a constituent of steel

centi- (*prefix*), referring to a hundred or a hundredth

cen-ti-grade (*adj.*), referring to a temperature scale where the range between the freezing and boiling points of water is divided into a hundred equal parts

cen - ti - me - ter (*n.*), a unit of distance in the metric system, a little less than a half inch

cen-trif-u-gal (*adj.*), referring to a direction away from the center

cen-tri-fuge (*n.*), a machine that makes use of centrifugal force, rotating solutions in a circle to separate substances of differing weights

cen-trip-e-tal (*adj.*), referring to a direction toward the center

ce-ram-ics (*n.*), the technology of making structures out of clay and like materials

ce - ram - ist *or* ce-ram-i-cist (*n.*), one who works in ceramics

ce-ri-um (*n.*), a metallic element, Ce

cer-met (*n.*), an alloy of a heat-resistant substance and a metal

cer - ti - fy (*v.*), to claim that something is true, in the sense of guarantee

ce-si-um (*n.*), an alkali metallic element, Cs

ce-tane (*n*.), a hydrocarbon found in petroleum

cgs (*adj*.), abbreviation for centimeter-gram-second system of measurement (also known as the metric system)

chan-nel (*n*.), a U- or V-shaped groove in a metal bar; a frequency band for radio or television

chan-nel-ize (*v*.), to direct a certain way

cha-os (*n*.), a confusion, with no order or regularity

char (*v*.), to burn partly

char-ac-ter-is-tic (*n*.), a particular distinguishing quality or trait

charge (*n*.), the amount of voltage on a point; (*v*.), to place voltage on a point

chas-sis (*n*.), the metal frame or shelf on which electrical circuit components are mounted

che-late (*v*.), a variety of chemical reaction

chem-i-lu-mi-nes-cence (*n*.), light resulting from a chemical reaction

chi (*n*.), a letter of the Greek alphabet; used as a symbol in mathematics

chip (*n*.), a small fragment; (*v*.), to break off small fragments

chis-el (*n*.), a tool with a wedge-shaped cutting or hacking edge

chlo-rine (*n*.), a nonmetallic element, Cl

chlo-ro-form (*n*.), a toxic organic solvent containing chlorine

chlo-ro-phyll (*n*.), the green photosynthetic chemical, naturally occurring in plants

choke (*n*.), a coil used to provide inductance in an electronic circuit

chop-ping (*n*.), an electronic circuit

chro-mat-ic (*adj*.), relating to color

chro-mi-um (*n*.), a metallic element, Cr

chro-no-log-i-cal (*adj*.), in regular time sequence

chro-nom-e-ter (*n*.), a very accurate instrument for measuring time

cin-der (*n*.), residue, ash, or slag after burning

ci-pher (*n*.), zero, denoting absence of magnitude or quality

cir-cuit (*n*.), a path ending where it started, an electrical setup consisting of the conventional electrical components and performing a given electrical function

cir-cu-i-tous (*adj*.), indirect, roundabout

cir-cuit-ry (*n*.), the study or plans of electric circuits

cir-cum-scribe (*v*.), to enclose by a circle or boundary

cir-cum-vent (*v*.), to avoid or check

cite (*v*.), to quote, generally as an authority

cit-ric (*adj*.), referring to an organic acid

clad (*adj*.), covered with a metallic sheet, metal bonded on metal

clad-ding (*n*.), the clad metal sheath

clamp - ing (n.), an electronic circuit

clear - ance (n.), the space by which objects are separated from each other

cleav-age (n.), the ability of a mineral or a crystal to be split along a (crystal) plane

cleave (v.), see cleavage

co-ag-u-lant (n.), a substance or process producing coagulation

co-ag-u-la-tion (n.), the clustering together in a jelly-like mass of particles in a suspension

co-ax-i-al (adj.), two or more structures having the same axis

co-balt (n.), a metallic element, Co

co - ef - fi - cient (n.), a number describing the quantity of something and written as part of that thing

co-er-civ-i-ty (n.), an attribute of a magnetizable material

co-ex-ten-sive (adj.), sharing the same space and extending to the same limits

cog (n.), a tooth on a gear or wheel

co-here (v.), to stick together firmly

co-her-ence (n.), see cohere

co - her - ent (adj.), consistent; also light beams whose waves act together (in phase)

co - he - sion (n.), the state of cohering

coil (n.), a spiral-wound wire

coin (v.), to make a pattern in metal by pressing or stamping

co-in-ci-dent (adj.), occupying the same space or occurring at the same time

co-lin-e-ar (adj.), lying in the same straight line

col-late (v.), to compare carefully; also to set in order

col-lat-er-al (adj.), parallel

col-lec-tor (n.), the electrode that collects electrons to ions; also the anode of a transistor

col-li-mate (v.), to make rays of light parallel

col-li-ma-tor (n.), a device to produce the effect of parallel rays of light

col - loid (n.), a suspension of extremely fine particles

col-loi-dal (adj.), see colloid

col-or-im-e-ter (n.), an instrument used to discriminate between colors

Col - pitts (n.), an electronic circuit

co-lum-bi-um (n.), a metallic element, Cb; also called niobium

col-umn (n.), a vertical structural member

col-um-nar (adj.), in columns or rows

com - bus - tion (n.), the act of reacting rapidly with oxygen: oxidation, burning

com-mon (adj.), shared

com-mu-ta-tor (n.), part of an electrical motor; also a switch

com-pact (v.), to press into a limited space, to increase in density; (n.), a pressed mass

com-pa-ra-tor (n.), an instrument used to compare sizes

and shapes of objects

com-part-men-tal-ize (*v.*), to separate into groups or categories

com-pat-i-ble (*adj.*), able to exist together without damage

com-pen-sate (*v.*), to counterbalance or neutralize

com-ple-ment (*n.*), the angle added to a given angle that makes the sum of the two equal to 90°; *also* whatever must be added to something to make it complete

com-ple-men-ta-ry (*adj.*), mutually beneficial; *also* one color which neutralizes another in combination; *see also* complement

com-plex (*adj.*), in mathematics, the sum of a real and an imaginary number; *also* a more-than-simple grouping

com-pli-ant (*adj.*), yielding easily into a required shape or condition

com-po-nent (*n.*), a part of something; *also* a device used in electronics; *also* a vector

com-pound (*n.*), a chemical formed by the combination of two or more other chemicals (elements, radicals)

com-press (*v.*), to squeeze or flatten

com-pres-sion (*n.*), *see* compress

com-prise (*v.*), to make up, constitute

com-pute (*n.*), to calculate

com-put-er (*n.*), a machine for calculating

con-cave (*adj.*), rounded inward

con-cav-i-ty (*n.*), a concave surface

con-cen-trate (*v.*), to make less dilute, to make more intense

con-cen-tra-tion (*n.*), the strength of a solution referring to the amount of a specified component

con-cen-tric (*adj.*), having the same center point

con-crete (*adj.*), real; *also* formed by a solid particulate mass

con-cur-rent (*adj.*), happening at the same time

con-den-sate (*n.*), material that condenses

con-den-sa-tion (*n.*), the physical change where material in vapor form changes to liquid or solid

con-dens-er (*n.*), an apparatus for condensing; *also* a capacitor

con-duct (*v.*), to serve as a medium in which movement of material or electrons can occur

con-duc-tance (*n.*), the capacity for conduction

con-duc-tiv-i-ty (*n.*), the measure of an object's conductance

con-duc-tor (*n.*), a medium in which conduction occurs

cone (*n.*), a geometrical figure, circular at the bottom and coming to an evenly tapered point

con-fig-u-ra-tion (*n.*), arrangement of parts

con-form (*v.*), to agree with or be similar to

con-gru-en-cy (*n.*), the state of being identical in size and shape; coincidence

con-ic (*n.*), a piece cut from a cone; (*adj.*), relating to a cone

con-jec-ture (*n.*), a guess

con-ju-gate (*adj.*), joined together

con - junc - tion (*n.*), something which has been joined together from parts

con - se - quence (*n.*), resulting from a cause or a certain condition

con-ser-va-tion (*n.*), the act of saving or preserving

con-serve (*v.*), *see* conservation

con - sis - tent (*adj.*), in agreement with other factors; *also* of a firm or coherent nature

con-sol-i-date (*v.*), to bring together into a single unit

con-stant (*n.*), a number or condition that does not change while one or more others do

con-stit-u-ent (*n.*), a component, part, or element

con - straint (*n.*), an imposed limit

con-strict (*v.*), to squeeze or draw together

con-sume (*v.*), to use up or use fully

con-tent (*n.*), that which is contained

con-ti-gu-ity (*n.*), the state of being next to and touching

con-tig-u-ous (*adj.*), *see* contiguity

con - tin - gent (*adj.*), depending on something else

con-tin-gen-cy (*n.*), something that may happen

con-ti-nu-i-ty (*n.*), something

that keeps happening without interruption

con - tin - u - um (*n.*), the same continuous thing or happening

con-tour (*n.*), outline

con - tract (*v.*), to become smaller

con-vec-tion (*n.*), the movement of a gas or liquid in a roughly circular path

con-verge (*v.*), to come together

con - ver - gence (*n.*), *see* converge

con-vex (*adj.*), rounded outward

cool-ant (*n.*), a cooling agent

co-or-di-nate (*n.*), a set of numbers or variables used to show the position, state, or motion of something in space

co-pol-y-mer (*n.*), a molecule which is the result of polymerizing other molecules together

cop-per (*n.*), a metallic element, Cu

core (*n.*), the inside of something; *also* the metal rod in a coil or transformer

cor - ol - lar - y (*n.*), something that follows naturally from a preceding argument

co-ro-na (*n.*), a glowing region that surrounds an object, as a glow on a conductor at high voltage

cor-pus-cu-lar (*adj.*), in separate particles

cor - re - late (*v.*), to show the relationship between

cor-re-spon-ding (*adj.*), equivalent or parallel

cor-rob-o-rate (*v.*), to make a position stronger by presenting supporting data cor - rode (v.), to eat away a material, usually with a chemical

cor-ru-gat-ed (adj.), shaped in regular ridges and grooves

co - sec - ant (n.), the trigonometric ratio of the hypotenuse over the side opposite an angle in a right triangle

co-sine (n.), the trigonometric ratio of the side adjacent over the hypotenuse of an angle in a right triangle

cos-mic ray (n.), a stream of atomic nuclei from outer space

cost-plus (adj.), a contractual payment based on the cost with a fee added on

co-tan-gent (n.), the trigonometric ratio of the side adjacent over the side opposite an angle of a right triangle

cot-ter pin (n.), a pin used to fasten parts of machinery

cou-lomb (n.), the number of electrons moved in one ampere of electrical current in one second

count - er (adv.), against, opposed to

coun-ter-act (v.), to make ineffective

coun-ter-bal-ance (v.), to offset

coun-ter-clock-wise (adv.), in a direction opposite to that in which the hands of a clock move

coun - ter - sink (v.), to drill a hole to leave space to accommodate the head of a screw

count - ing (n.), an electronic circuit

co-va-lent (adj.), referring to atoms that join together by reason of shared electrons

craze (v.), to produce a network of fine cracks on a surface

creep (n.), the slow changing of shape of a material

cre-o-sote (n.), a liquid chemical used in preserving

cres-cent (n.), arc shaped

cross hair (n.), a thread or wire in an optical system used as a reference line

cross sec-tion (n.), the surface of something exposed when it is cut through at a right angle to its axis

cross - talk (n.), electrical interference in a communication line

cru-ci-ble (n.), a container with high heat-resistance used for melting materials

crude (adj.), not refined or processed chemically

cry-o-gen-ics (n.), the science of very low temperatures

cryo-stat (n.), equipment used to maintain very low temperatures

crys-tal (n.), a type of formation where the atoms occur in a regular (periodic) arrangement

crys-tal-line (adj.), made of or resembling a crystal

crys-tal-lize (v.), to produce a crystal or crystals

crys-tal-log-ra-pher (n.), one who studies crystals

crys-tal-log-ra-phy (n.), the science of crystals

cube (n.), a solid made up of six

sides of equal size at right angles to each other; (*v.*), to raise to the third power

cu-bic (*adj.*), *see* cube

cu-bic cent - i - me - ter (*n.*), a metric system measure of volume equal to 0.06 cubic inch

cull (*n.*), a reject piece; (*v.*), to select and separate out the good from the bad

cum (*prep.*), with

cu-mu-la-tive (*adj.*), to add up with successive additions

cu-pric (*adj.*), relating to copper

cu-rie (*n.*), a unit to measure radioactivity, cu, Cu, Ci

cu - ri - um (*n.*), a radioactive element, Cm

curl (*n.*), a mathematical operation with vectors

cur-rent (*n.*), a flow; in electricity, of electrons

cur-tail (*v.*), to shorten

cur-vi-lin-ear (*adj.*), referring to a curved line or boundary

cush-ion (*v.*), to protect against shock; (*n.*), a structure to protect against shock

cusp (*n.*), a sharp point made by two intersecting curves

cut-off (*n.*), the point at which an electric circuit ceases to work

cy - an - a - mide (*n.*), an acidic compound of cyanide

cy-a-nide (*n.*), a salt of hydrocyanic acid

cy-cle (*n.*), a complete sequence that repeats itself; (*v.*), to repeat regularly

cy-clic (*adj.*), *see* cycle

cyc-loid (*n.*), a particular shape of curve

cy-clo-tron (*n.*), a machine that accelerates atomic particles

cyl-in-der (*n.*), geometrically, an object shaped like a round, straight-walled tube

cy-lin-dri-cal (*adj.*), *see* cylinder

D

damp (*v.*), to restrain or check vibration

da - tum (*n. sing., pl:* data) a piece of factual information, usually quantitative

de - cal - ci - fy (*v.*), to remove calcium from

de-cant (*v.*), to pour liquid from one container to another leaving lower liquid levels or solid matter behind

de-car-bon-ize (*v.*), to remove carbon from

de-car-bur-ize (*v.*), to remove carbon from a metal, usually steel

de - cel - er - ate (*v.*), to lessen speed

deci-bel (*n.*), a unit for measuring the loudness of sound or the voltage of an electrical signal; DB, db

dec - i - mal (*n.*), fraction expressed in powers of ten

dec - li - na - tion (*n.*), an angle pointing downward

de-code (*v.*), to convert a coded message to ordinary language

de-com-pose (*v.*), to break up a compound into its constituent parts

de - com - press (*v.*), releasing pressure

de-con-tam-i-nate (*v.*), to be rid of contamination

de-duce (*v.*), to draw conclusions from data or a general principle

de-fer (*v.*), to put aside, to delay

de-flate (*v.*), to release gas from

de-flect (*v.*), to turn aside

de-form (*v.*), to alter the shape of something

de-for-ma-tion (*n.*), the act or state of being deformed

de-gauss (*v.*), to demagnetize

de-gen-er-ate (*adj.*), having lower standards or at a lower standard

de-gen-er-a-ting (*n.*), an electronic circuit

de-gen-er-a-tion (*n.*), deterioration

de-grade (*v.*), in chemistry, to make simpler; *also* to wear down

de-gree (*n.*), unit of temperature; *also* a relative level

de-hy-drate (*v.*), to remove water

de-lay line (*n.*), an electronic circuit that builds in lag in phase of a wave

del-e-te-ri-ous (*adj.*), harmful

de-lete (*v.*), to remove

de-lim-it (*v.*), to impose boundaries or limits

del-i-ques-cence (*n.*), said of a material which takes up available water or water vapor, becoming moist or dissolving

del-ta (*n.*), the fourth letter of the Greek alphabet used as a symbol for an increment involving a changing factor; also: an electronic circuit

del-ta star (*n.*), an electronic circuit

del-ta wye (*n.*), an electronic circuit

demi- (*prefix*), partly or half

de-mod-u-late (*v.*), to remove a modulating electrical signal from a carrier wave

de-mon-strate (*v.*), to show, prove, or illustrate

den-drite (*n.*), a crystalline constituent in alloys

de-nom-i-na-tor (*n.*), the below-the-line number in a fraction

den-si-tom-e-ter (*n.*), an instrument used to measure the darkness of regions in a photographic film, used in X-ray diffraction or spectrographic analysis

den-si-ty (*n.*), the weight of a unit volume of a material

de-ox-y-ge-nate (*v.*), to remove oxygen from

de-pen-dence (*n.*), the relationship in which the condition of one factor is determined by another factor

de-plete (*v.*), to use up, to make less

de-po-lar-ize (*v.*), to remove or prevent polarity

de-press (*v.*), to cause to flatten vertically; *also* to lessen

de-riv-a-tive (*n.*), the mathematical function that is the result of differentiating; *also* the result of a chemical process

de-salt (*v.*), to remove salt

de-sign (*n.*), a plan derived from

a concept

de-sorb (*v.*), to release an adsorbed or absorbed gas from a material

de-tail (*v.*), to add the fine points to a design

de-tec-tion (*n.*), demodulation of an electrical signal

de-tec-tor (*n.*), a kind of electronic circuit

de-ter-mi-nant (*n.*), an array of numbers used in carrying out a mathematical manipulation

det-o-nate (*v.*), to cause to explode

deu-te-ri-um (*n.*), an isotope of the element hydrogen

de-vi-ate (*v.*), not conforming to a norm; to cause deviation

de-vice (*n.*), a gadget

de-vise (*v.*), to conceive; to invent

Dew-ar flask (*n.*), a flask that keeps its contents hot or cold

dew point (*n.*), the temperature at which vapor in a gas condenses to moisture on a surface

dex-trose (*n.*), an organic compound, a sugar

di- (*prefix*), two

di-ag-no-sis (*n.*), analysis of the cause of a condition

di-ag-on-al (*n.*), a straight line connecting two corners of a geometrical figure

di-a-gram (*n.*), a line drawing

di-al-y-sis (*n.*), the process of separating particles in solution from each other

di-a-mag-net-ic (*adj.*), describing the magnetizability of a material

di-a-met-ric (*adj.*), completely opposite to

di-a-mond (*n.*), a carbon crystal

di-a-phragm (*n.*), a thin, flexible disc; a partition

dia-ther-my (*n.*), generating heat in organic materials by electrical means

di-atom-ic (*adj.*), consisting of two atoms

di-chot-o-my (*n.*), a division into two parts

di-chro-ism (*n.*), color changes in a material by transmitted light as through a crystal or layers of varying thickness, or with changes in solution concentration

die (*pl.* dice) (*n.*), a small, cubicle object; *also* a tool used to give a desired shape to a material

di-elec-tric (*n.*), a nonconductor of electricity, a fundamental part of the condenser or capacitor

die-sel en-gine (*n.*), a kind of internal combustion engine

dif-fer-en-tial (*n.*), an increment or difference in amount between two quantities, a term used in calculus

dif-fer-en-ti-ate (*v.*), to perform a mathematical operation which shows how one function varies with another

dif-fer-en-ti-at-ing (*adj.*), a kind of electronic circuit

dif-frac-tion (*n.*), an effect produced on light rays passing through narrow slits

dif-fuse (*adj.*), all spread out; (*v.*), to undergo diffusion; *see* diffusion

dif-fu-sion (*n.*), the intermingling of particles; an equalizing of physical states thereby

di-ges-tion (*n.*), the breaking down of materials by solution and chemical reaction

dig-it (*n.*), any number from 0 to 9

dig-i-tal (*adj.*), involving the use of numbers

di - he - dral (*adj.*), made up of two intersecting planes

di-late (*v.*), to spread wide

di - la - tom - e -ter (*n.*), instrument to measure expansion

di-lute (*v.*), to make thinner or less concentrated

di-men-sion (*n.*), measurement of size in one direction

dim - mer (*n.*), a device for making light less intense

di-mor-phic (*adj.*), having the qualities of two kinds of things at once

dim-ple (*n.*), a small indentation; (*v.*), to make a small indentation

di-ode (*n.*), a type of tube having two terminals; a semiconductor rectifier

di-op-ter (*n.*), a unit of measure of the power of a lens to bend light rays

di-ox-ide (*n.*), an oxide containing two atoms of oxygen

di - phe - nyl (*n.*), a chemical radical; *see* biphenyl

di-plex (*adj.*), relating to two electromagnetic signals being sent together

di-pole (*n.*), a usually small, or atomic size object having its two ends oppositely charged with static electricity or oppositely magnetized

di-rect cou-pled (*adj.*), referring to a type of electronic circuit

di-rect cur-rent (*n.*), an electric current that flows in one direction only; DC, D.C., d.c., dc, or d-c

dis-as-so-ci-ate *or* dis-so-ci-ate (*v.*), to separate into its constituents

disc (*n.*), *see* disk

dis-charge (*v.*), to release potential voltage or energy; to remove a charge; (*n.*), the action that results from the release of voltage or energy

dis-crete (*adj.*), separate, not continuous (not to be confused with "discreet," meaning having good judgement)

dis-crim-i-nate (*v.*), to notice the difference between things

dis-crim-i-na-tor (*n.*), a device, usually an electric circuit, that discriminates

dis-in-te-grate (*v.*), to break into fragments

disk (*n.*), a flat, round object

dis-lo-ca-tion (*n.*), a defect in crystal regularity

dis - or - dered (*adj.*), without regularity

dis-ori-ent (*v.*), to cause to lose position or relationship

dis - pense (*v.*), to give out in measured quantities

dis-perse (*v.*), to cause to separate and spread out

dis-per-sion (*n.*), a dispersed material

dis-pro-por-tion-ate (*adj.*), out

of proportion

dis-sect (*v.*), to cut up for examination; to analyze

dis-si-pate (*v.*), to cause to break up and disappear

dis-so-ci-ate (*v.*), see disassociate

dis-solve (*v.*), to cause something to break up or go into solution or both

dis-till (*v.*), the process of boiling a liquid to its vapor and then recondensing the vapor to a liquid in order to purify it

dis-til-late (*n.*), the resulting product of the process of distillation

dis-tor-tion (*n.*), an abnormal change in shape

dis-trib-ute (*v.*), to spread out

dis-tri-bu-tion (*n.*), the way something is spread out, indicating exactly how much of it is in each place

di-ver-gence (*n.*), a spreading apart

di-vert (*v.*), to turn aside

di-vide (*v.*), to separate into parts

di-vid-end (*n.*), a number that is to be divided

di-vid-ers (*n.*), an instrument, resembling a compass, that consists of two sharp points hinged together

di-vi-sor (*n.*), the number by which the dividend is divided

do-deca- (*prefix*), twelve

do-main (*n.*), a sphere of influence; *also* a basic magnetic region

do-nor (*n.*), a source of a material; a source of electrons

in semiconductors

dop-ant (*n.*), the material added in doping; the doping agent

dope (*v.*), to add a small amount of something

dop-pler (*adj.*), a type of electronic circuit

Dopp-ler effect (*n.*), changes in wave frequency (sound or light) as the wave source moves

dor-mant (*adj.*), quiescent

do-sim-e-ter (*n.*), an instrument for measuring the amount of exposure to X-rays

doub-ler (*n.*), a kind of electronic circuit

dou-blet (*n.*), a pair of identical objects

dow-el (*n.*), a pin of wood or metal that fits into a particular hole

DPDT (*adj.*), double pole, double throw; a type of electric switch

DPST (*adj.*), double pole, single throw; a type of electric switch

dregs (*n.*), sediment or sludge remaining in a container after liquid has been drained or decanted off

drone (*n.*), a pilotless vehicle

du-al (*adj.*), referring to an object that consists of two parts

duo- (*prefix*), two

du-plex (*adj.*), double

du-ra-tion (*n.*), the amount of time that something lasts

dy-nam-ic (*adj.*), active

dy-nam-ics (*n.*), a branch of mechanics dealing with movement dy-na-mo (*n.*), a generator of electricity

dy-na-mom-e-ter (*n.*), an instrument for measuring mechanical force

dy-na-tron (*n.*), a type of vacuum tube

dyne (*n.*), a unit of force

dyne cen-ti-me-ter (*n.*), a unit of energy

dy-node (*n.*), a part of a type of vacuum tube

dys-pro-si-um (*n.*), a chemical element, Dy

E

e- (*prefix*), out, not

ec-cen-tric (*adj.*), not following a circular path; having a center different from that of a related sphere

Ec-cles–Jor-dan (*adj.*), a type of electronic circuit

ech-e-lon (*n.*), a grade or level

echo (*n.*), a reflected sound

eclipse (*n.*), the obscuring of an object by another object or its shadow

ed-dy (*n.*), a circular current

ef-fect (*n.*), the result of an action; (*v.*), to cause to happen

ef-fer-vesce (*v.*), to bubble out

ef-fi-cien-cy (*n.*), a measure of the amount of production of an effort

ef-flo-resce (*v.*), to lose water to the extent that a substance crumbles into powder

ef-flu-ence (*n.*), that which flows out

ein-stein-i-um (*n.*), a chemical element, Es

e-ject (*v.*), to cast out from within with force

elab-o-rate (*adj.*), with great detail

elas-tic (*adj.*), able to resume its original shape after stretching

elas-tic-i-ty (*n.*), *see* elastic

elas-to-mer (*n.*), one of a class of elastic, rubbery materials

el-bow (*n.*), a piece of pipe having a right angle

elec-tric-i-ty (*n.*), the phenomenon relating to charged particles and their movement

elec-tro- (*prefix*), referring to electricity

elec-tro-chem-is-try (*n.*), the science dealing with the interaction of electricity and chemicals

elec-trode (*n.*), a metallic contact point of an electric circuit; a basic element of an electrical component

elec-tro-form (*v.*), to form structures by building up metal by electroplating

elec-to-lu-mi-nes-cence (*n.*), voltage-produced light

elec-trol-y-sis (*n.*), producing an electric current through an electrolyte to effect chemical change

elec-tro-lyte (*n.*), a chemical solution which conducts electric current by means of ions

elec-tro-lyze (*v.*), to subject to electrolysis

elec-tro-mag-net (*n.*), a magnet operating as a result of an electrical current passing through it

elec-trom-e-ter (*n.*), an instrument used to measure small

voltages

elec-tro-mo-tive (*adj.*), relating to the voltage force that moves electrons

elec-tron (*n.*), a basic subatomic particle having a negative charge and essentially no weight

elec-tron-ics (*n.*), the science dealing with the behavior of electrons

elec-tro-pho-re-sis (*n.*), the movement of particles in a liquid suspension by means of electrical forces

elec-tro-plate (*v.*), the deposition of metal on an electrode by electrochemical processes

elec-tro-stat-ics (*n.*), the science dealing with the behavior of electrical charges without continuous current flow

elec-tro-ther-mal (*adj.*), relating to the production of heat by electrical means

el-e-ment (*n.*), one of 103 basic constituents of matter that ordinarily cannot be subdivided; *also* a basic part

el-e-men-ta-ry (*adj.*), simple, basic

el-e-va-tion (*n.*), a kind of drawing made by a draftsman; *also* altitude

el-lipse (*n.*), oval

el-lip-soi-dal (*adj.*), *see* ellipse

elu-tri-ate (*v.*), to remove by washing

em-a-na-tion (*n.*), that which is sent out of something

em-bed (*v.*), to enclose an object in another substance

em-boss (*v.*), to raise a surface in desired places for ornamental or other purposes

em-bryo (*n.*), the early and undeveloped state of something

em-ery (*n.*), an abrasive powder used in grinding and polishing

emf (*n.*), abbreviation for electromotive force; *also* EMF, e.m.f.

emis-sion (*n.*), the act of sending material out from within

emis-siv-i-ty (*n.*), the ease with which something is emitted

em-pha-sis (*n.*), the giving of particular importance to something

em-pir-i-cal (*adj.*), based upon actual experimental data and observation

emul-si-fy (*v.*), *see* emulsion

emul-sion (*n.*), a liquid in which tiny droplets of another liquid are suspended

enam-el (*v.*), to form a glassy layer on metal; (*n.*), a glassy layer which may be formed on metal

en-cap-su-late (*v.*), to enclose in a capsule or packaging structure

en-code (*v.*), to convert information into a code, usually for computer programming

en-do-ther-mic (*adj.*), a chemical reaction in which heat is absorbed

en-er-gy (*n.*), the capability of doing work

en-gine (*n.*), a machine that converts one form of energy usually into mechanical energy

en-gi-neer-ing (*n.*), the science

of making use of the properties of materials and of energy

en-grave (v.), to cut a pattern
into a surface

en-hance (v.), to heighten, to
intensify

enig-ma (n.), something difficult to understand

enig-mat-ic (adj.), see enigma

en-thal-py (n.), a measure of the
amount of heat involved in any
chemical or physical change,
ΔH

en-ti-ty (n.), something that is
complete in itself

en-tro-py (n.), a thermodynamic quantity relating to the
amount of disorder in a system, ΔS

en-ve-lope (n.), that which surrounds and encloses

en - vi - ron - ment (n.), all the
factors and materials that
surround something

epi- (prefix), after, outer

ep-i-sode (n.), an occurrence
complete in itself

epit-o-me (n.), a summary or
an ideal

ep-oxy (n.), a type of arrangement of oxygen atoms in a
chemical compound, usually
a plastic

ep-si-lon (n.), a Greek letter, ε

equal-ize (v.), to make equal

equate (v.), to treat mathematically as equals

equa-tion (n.), a mathematical
or chemical statement that
shows the relationship between two things

equi- (prefix), equal

equi - an - gu - lar (adj.), having

equal angles

equi - lat - er - al (adj.), having
equal sides

equi-lib-ri-um (n.), a condition
of balance which tends to remain stable

equi-po-ten-tial (adj.), having
the same voltage

equiv - a - lent (adj.), virtually
identical, having the same
significance; also a kind of
electronic circuit

equiv-o-cal (adj.), uncertain

equiv-o-cate (v.), to take an uncertain position

erad - i - cate (v.), to remove
completely

er-bi-um (n.), a chemical element, Er

erg (n.), a unit of work

er-go (adv.), therefore

erode (v.), to wear away

ero-sive (adj.), having the ability to erode

er-ra-ta (n. pl., sing: erratum),
list of errors accompanying
a publication or appearing in
a subsequent issue

er - rat - ic (adj.), following no
predictable course, eccentric

erupt (v.), to burst forth

es-pouse (v.), to support

ester (n.), an organic chemical grouping

es-tim-ate (n.), a detailed analysis and appraisal

eta (n.), a Greek letter, η

etch (v.), to dissolve away
some of the surface of
a material

eth-ane (n.), a chemical compound

eth-a-nol (n.), an alcohol

eth-ene (*n.*), a chemical compound

ether (*n.*), a chemical compound

ethyl (*n.*), a chemical radical

eth-yl-ene (*n.*), a chemical radical; *also* a chemical compound

Eu-clid-e-an (*adj.*), referring to the geometry of Euclid, conventional geometry

eu-ro-pi-um (*n.*), a chemical element, Eu

eu-tec-tic (*n.*), the lowest melting point of an alloy system

evac-u-ate (*v.*), to empty, to create a vacuum

evap-o-rate (*v.*), to dissipate as a vapor, to cause to vaporize

evolve (*v.*), to emit; *also* to develop

ex- (*prefix*), out, former

ex-ci-ta-tion (*n.*), the state in which certain atomic or quantum phenomena occur

ex-e-cute (*v.*), to carry out, perform

ex-fo-li-ate (*v.*), to grow by spreading leaves, sheets, or laminates; to unfold

ex-haust (*v.*), to empty, to evacuate; (*n.*), a gas that is given off

ex-hib-it (*n.*), a display for illustrating a point

ex-o-ther-mic (*adj.*), referring to chemical reactions that give off heat

ex-pan-sion (*n.*), increase in size

ex-pan-siv-i-ty (*n.*), expansion of a unit-sized piece of material

ex-pe-di-ent (*adj.*), makeshift, done to achieve an end

ex-pel (*v.*), to eject

ex-pend (*v.*), to use up

ex-per-i-ment (*n.*), test or trial carried out under controlled conditions

ex-per-tise (*n.*), expertness

ex-plor-ato-ry (*adj.*), relating to a search or examination

ex-po-nent (*n.*), a number written half a line above a mathematical symbol to show a power or root

ex-pression (*n.*), a mathematical statement (usually in the form of an equation)

ex-tra- (*prefix*), outside

ex-tract (*v.*), to get something out of something, as to extract a metal from ore

ex-trap-o-late (*v.*), to project or extend (a line on a graph or an idea)

ex-trem-i-ty (*n.*), a farthermost part

ex-trin-sic (*adj.*), outside, not forming part of

ex-trude (*v.*), to push through to shape, as toothpaste is squeezed from a tube

eye-piece (*n.*), the lenses nearest the eye in an optical instrument such as a microscope or telescope

F

fac-et (*n.*), a small plane face on a crystal

fac-tor (*n.*), a number or algebraic expression that is multiplied by one or more others; (*v.*), to separate a number or expression into the fundamental quantities that equal it when multiplied together

fac-to-ri-al (*n.*), the product of

all the positive whole numbers from one to a given number

Fahr-en-heit (*adj.*), the temperature scale in common use on which the freezing point of water is 32° and the boiling point of water is 212°; referred to as °F

fa-rad (*n.*), a unit of capacitance

far-a-day (*n.*), a unit used in electrolysis

fat-ty ac-id (*n.*), a type of organic compound

fault (*n.*), a defect or discontinuity in a mineral deposit or in a crystal

fea-si-bil-i-ty (*n.*), the likelihood that something—a theory, a machine, or an experiment—will work

feed-back (*n.*), influence of an electrical signal on a preceding circuit; *also* a type of electronic circuit

fer-men-ta-tion (*n.*), a type of chemical reaction

fer-mi-um (*n.*), an iron radical

ferri- (*prefix*), relating to iron

fer-ric (*adj.*), relating to iron

fer-rite (*n.*), a type of magnet; *also* a group of iron compounds

ferro- (*prefix*), relating to iron

fer-ro-mag-net-ic (*adj.*), strongly magnetic

fer-rous (*adj.*), relating to iron

fer-rule (*n.*), a ring of metal placed around a shaft

fi-ber (*n.*), a structure that is threadlike in shape

fi-brous (*adj.*), *see* fiber

field (*n.*), a region in which a force acts

fil-a-ment (*n.*), a threadlike structure (often one used to conduct electricity)

fi-lar (*adj.*), of or relating to a filament

film (*n.*), a thin layer

fil-ter (*n.*), an apparatus to separate solids from liquids; a type of electronic circuit

fil-trate (*n.*), the liquid passed through a filter

fin (*n.*), a flat projection

fi-nite (*adj.*), having definable limits

fis-sile (*adj.*), referring to something that can be split or divided

fis-sion (*n.*), *see* fissionable

fis-sion-able (*adj.*), splitting of an atomic nucleus to release energy; *see* fissile

flint (*n.*), a very hard form of the mineral quartz

flip-flop (*n.*), a kind of electronic circuit

floc (*n.*), a cluster of particles

floc-cu-la-tion (*n.*), the separation of particles according to their relative abilities to cluster and sink

flow chart (*n.*), a diagram showing the movement of material through a process (generally a manufacturing process)

fluc-tu-a-tion (*n.*), a back-and-forth variation

flu-id (*n.*), a gas or liquid

flu-id-i-ty (*n.*), a measure of the "runniness" of a material

flu-o-res-cence (*n.*), the emission of light from a material as a result of its being hit by some kind of radiation

flu-o-rine (*n.*), a chemical element, F

flux (*n.*), the rate of transfer of energy across a surface (often used in discussing electric and magnetic fields)

FM (*n.*), frequency modulation

foam (*n.*), froth

fo-cal (*adj.*), of or relating to a focus

fo - cus (*n.*), a point at which rays converge and meet

fog (*n.*), a fine mist

foil (*n.*), a very thin piece of metal

foot-pound (*n.*), a unit of work equal to that done in moving one pound of substance a distance of one foot

force (*n.*), a push

forge (*v.*), to form or shape a piece of metal by hammering it when it is hot

for-mal (*adj.*), done exactly according to accepted procedure

for-mu-la (*n.*), a mathematical or chemical expression written using the symbols of mathematics and chemistry

for-tu-i-tous (*adj.*), accidental

fran-ci-um (*n.*), a chemical element, Fr

fray (*v.*), to wear

freez-ing point (*n.*), the temperature at which a liquid changes to a solid; *also* the temperature at which the solid and liquid may exist together

French curve (*n.*), a device used in drafting

fre-quen-cy (*n.*), the number of cycles that a repeating phenomenon makes in a given time interval

fri-a-ble (*adj.*), easily crumbled

fric-tion (*n.*), the resistance to movement offered by two surfaces being rubbed together

fringe (*n.*), an edge; *also* a dark band observed in optics

frit (*n.*), powdered glass

fron-tal (*adj.*), at the front

fu-gac-i-ty (*n.*), a thermodynamic property of a gas

ful-crum (*n.*), the point around which a lever rotates

fume (*n.*), a smoke or vapor

func-tion (*n.*), a mathematical expression that shows how one variable changes as a result of changes in another

func - tion - al (*adj.*), working, performing

fun-da-men-tal (*adj.*), basic

fuse (*v.*), to melt *or* to melt together

fu-se-lage (*n.*), the main body of a flying vehicle

fus-ible (*adj* .), able to be melted

fu-tile (*adj.*), serving no purpose, wasted

G

gad-o-lin-i-um (*n.*), a chemical element, Gd

gain (*n.*), a measure of electrical amplification

ga-le-na (*n.*), a mineral crystal

gall (*v.*), to wear away mechanically

gal-li-um (*n.*), a chemical element, Ga

gal-van-ic (*adj.*), related to direct-current electricity

gal-va-nom-e-ter (*n.*), an instrument used to measure voltage

gam-ma (*n.*), a Greek letter, Γ and γ

gan-try (*n.*), a moveable tower used in servicing rockets

gar-net (*n.*), a mineral

gas-eous (*adj.*), relating to gas

gauge *or* gage (*n.*), a measure of thickness of metal sheet or wire; *also* an instrument for measuring; (*v.*), to measure

gear (*n.*), equipment; *also* a toothed wheel in a machine

Gei-ger count-er (*n.*), an instrument for measuring radioactivity

gel (*n.*), a jellylike substance; (*v.*), to cause to become a gel

ge-lat-i-nous (*adj.*), jellylike

gem (*n.*), a stone used as a jewel

gen-er-al-ize (*v.*), to make an over-all conclusion from available information

gen-er-ate (*v.*), to bring into being

gen-er-a-tor (*n.*), a machine that converts mechanical energy to electrical energy

ge-ner-ic (*adj.*), referring to a whole group

geo-de-sic (*adj.*), a kind of dome structure

ge-ol-o-gy (*n.*), the study of the history and structure of the earth

ge-om-e-try (*n.*), a branch of mathematics that deals with points, lines, surfaces, angles, and solids

geo-phys-ics (*n.*), the physics of the earth

germ (*n.*), the originating part or beginning of something

ger-ma-ni-um (*n.*), a chemical element, Ge

get-ter (*n.*), a material used to absorb gases in a vacuum tube

giga- (*prefix*), a billion

gilt (*n.*), a surface layer of gold or a material resembling gold

gim-bal (*n.*), a mechanical support that allows a rod to incline in any direction

gim-mick (*n.*), a clever device or feature of a device

gird-er (*n.*), a horizontal structural member

girth (*n.*), the distance around something

gla-cial (*adj.*), resembling ice

glanc-ing (*adj.*), not direct

glaze (*n.*), a smooth, glassy coating; (*v.*), to coat with a smooth glassy layer

glide (*v.*), to move smoothly

glob-u-lar (*adj.*), spherical

glob-ule (*n.*), a small, spherical object

gloss (*n.*), a surface sheen

glu-cose (*n.*), a sugar

glut (*n.*), an overabundance

glyc-er-ine *or* glyc-er-ol (*n.*), a chemical compound

gneiss (*n.*), a rock formation

gold (*n.*), a chemical element, Au

gon (*prefix* and *suffix*), angle

go-ni-om-e-ter (*n.*), an instrument for measuring angles

grad (*n.*), a mathematical function

gra-da-tion (*n.*), a step in a series

grade (*v.*), to smooth off

gra - di - ent (*n*.), the rate of change

grad-u-at-ed (*adj*.), marked in units of measurement

grain (*n*.), texture; *also* a metal crystal

gram (*n*.), a unit of mass or weight (454 grams equals one pound)

gran-ule (*n*.), a small particle

graph (*n*.), a diagram showing the variations or a variable in comparison with other variables; (*v*.), to draw a graphical diagram

graph-ic (*adj*.), clear

graph - ite (*n*.), a black, shiny mineral, a form of carbon

grat-ing (*n*.), a metal screen or mesh used in optical instruments

gravi-met-ric (*adj*.), referring to weight measurement

grav-i-tate (*v*.), to move toward

grav-i-ta-tion (*n*.), the force that pulls one object toward another

grav - i - ty (*n*.), the force that pulls objects toward the earth

grid (*n*.), a mesh, network, or perforated piece of metal; *also* the element that controls the flow of electrons in a vacuum tube

gross (*adj*.), referring to the overall amount; (*n*.), the main body, mass

ground (*n*.), the return lead touching the earth in an electrical circuit (often the chassis or plate on which the circuit is mounted); (*adj*.), basic

guid-ance (*n*.), control of a moving vehicle by automatic elec-tronic means

gy-rate (*v*.), to revolve around

gy-ro (*n*.), *abbreviation* for gy-roscope

gy-ro-scope (*n*.), a device having complicated, spinning parts, used in stabilization and guidance of vehicles

H

hab-it (*n*.), the pattern or form of a crystal

haf-ni-um (*n*.), a chemical ele-ment, Hf

ha-la-tion (*n*.), a ring of light surrounding an image

half-life (*n*.), the time it takes for half the amount of a ra-dioactive substance to disin-tegrate

ha-lide (*n*.), a chemical com-pound that contains either chlorine, fluorine, iodine, or bromine

ha-lo (*n*.), a ring of light sur-rounding an object

halo-gen (*n*.), a group of chem-ical elements including chlo-rine, iodine, bromine, and fluorine

har - mon - ic (*adj*.), able to be described in terms of the functions sine and cosine; (*n*.), an overtone, or a tone whose frequency is a whole number of times faster than a basic frequency

Hart-ley (*n*.), a kind of elec-tronic circuit

heat-er (*n*.), the part of a vac-uum tube that heats the cath-ode

heli- *or* helio- (*prefix*), relating to the sun

he-li-cal (*adj*.), *see* helix

he-li-um (*n.*), a chemical element, He

he-lix (*n.*), a spiral coil

hemi-sphere (*n.*), half a sphere

hep-tane (*n.*), an organic chemical compound

hep-to- (*prefix*), seven

her-met-ic (*adj.*), airtight

hertz (*n.*), electrical frequency unit, one cycle per second; *abbreviated* Hz

het-ero- (*prefix*), different

het-ero-dox (*adj.*), unorthodox, contrary to standards

het-ero-dyne (*v.*), to get a difference frequency from two frequencies of electrical waves

hex- (*prefix*), six

hex-a-gon (*n.*), a geometrical shape with six sides

hex-ag-o-nal (*adj.*), *see* hexagon

hex-al (*n.*), an organic chemical compound

hex-ane (*n.*), an organic chemical compound

hi-a-tus (*n.*), a break or pause

hi-er-ar-chy (*n.*), a listing or ranking in order of importance

hi-fi (*n.*), "high fidelity," accuracy of sound reproduction

his-to-gram (*n.*), a graph shown by an array of vertical bars of differing heights

hole (n.), in electronics the absence of an electron

ho-log-ra-phy (*n.*), a technique of handling light waves to create three-dimensional representations of objects

hol-mi-um (*n.*), a chemical element, Ho

home- *or* hom-eo- (*prefix*), the same

ho-mog-e-neous (*adj.*), uniform; sometimes homogeneous

ho-mog-e-nize (*v.*), to blend into a smooth mixture

ho-mol-o-gous (*adj.*), having the same, or a corresponding, position or function

hook-up (*n.*), an arrangement of components in an electrical circuit

hop-per (*n.*), a box for holding particles of material

ho-rol-o-gy (*n.*), the science of measuring time

horse-pow-er (*n.*), a unit of power; *abbreviated* hp

hub (*n.*), the central part of a wheel

hue (*n.*), color

hu-mid-i-fy (*v.*), to moisten a gas

hu-mid-i-ty (*n.*), the amount of moisture in a gas

hunt (*n.*), the back-and-forth movement of a mechanical or electrical mechanism as it attempts to settle at a particular value

hy-brid (*n.*), an object composed of two or more different types

hy-brid-ize (*v.*), to cause to produce hybrids

hy-drate (*n.*), a chemical compound having "attached" water molecules

hy-drau-lic (*adj.*), relating to water

hy-drau-lics (*n. sing. or pl.*), the science that deals with liquids in motion

hy-dra-zine (*n.*), a chemical

compound

hy-dride (*n.*), a chemical compound containing hydrogen

hy-dro- (*prefix*), pertaining to water

hy-dro-car-bon (*n.*), a chemical compound of hydrogen and carbon

hy-dro-foil (*n.*), a winglike structure designed to move through water

hy-dro-gen (*n.*), a chemical element, H

hy-drol-y-sis (*n.*), a chemical reaction associated with dissolving in water

hy-dro-lyze (*v.*), *see* hydrolysis

hy-dro-phil-ic (*adj.*), having a strong attraction for water

hy-dro-pho-bic (*adj.*), having a strong aversion for water

hy-dro-stat-ic (*adj.*), relating to the pressure exerted by a quantity of water

hy-drox-ide (*n.*), a chemical compound having a hydroxyl ion

hy-drox-yl (*n.*), the chemical radical, (OH)⁻

hy-gro- (*prefix*), relating to humidity

hy-grom-e-ter (*n.*), an instrument for measuring humidity

hyper- (*prefix*), more, excessive

hy-per-bo-la (*n.*), a kind of curve

hy-per-bol-ic (*adj.*), *see* hyperbola

hypo- (*prefix*), meaning less, under

hy-pot-e-nuse (*n.*), the side of a triangle opposite a right angle

hy-poth-e-sis (*n.*), an assumption

hy-poth-e-size (*v.*), to make a hypothesis

hy-po-thet-i-cal (*adj.*), conditional, conjectural

I

I beam (*n.*), a structural beam shaped like an ''I''

-ic (*suffix*), character of; *see* -ous

-ide (*suffix*), indicating a chemical compound of two elements

idler (*n.*), a kind of wheel or gear

if (*n.*), abbreviation for intermediate frequency; also: I.F., IF, i.f., i-f

ig-ne-ous (*adj.*), referring to rock that has solidified from magma (hot liquid rock)

ig-nite (*v.*), to set on fire

ig-ni-tron (*n.*), a type of vacuum tube

-ile (*suffix*), relating to

il-lu-mi-nate (*v.*), to give light

il-lu-so-ry (*adj.*), deceptive

im-age (*n.*), representation of an object

imag-i-nary (*adj.*), referring to an unreal number (such as $\sqrt{-1}$)

im-mi-nent (*adj.*), about to happen

im-mis-ci-ble (*adj.*), unable to be mixed together

im-mo-bile (*adj.*), unable to be moved

im-mo-bi-lize (*v.*), to prevent

movement

im-mune (*adj.*), not affected by

im-mu-ta-ble (*adj.*), unable to change

im-pact (*n.*), a forceful colli-sion; (*v.*), to collide suddenly

im-part (*v.*), to give

im-par-tial (*adj.*), unbiased

im-passe (*n.*), a deadlock, pre-dicament for which there is no easy solution

im-ped-ance (*n.*), electrical re-sistance

im-pede (*v.*), to be in the way, to hinder

im-ped-i-ment (*n.*), an obstacle

im-pel (*v.*), to push

im-pel-ler (*n.*), an engine part, usually a blade or a fan, that pushes a fluid forward

im-pend-ing (*adj.*), about to happen very soon

im-per-me-able (*adj.*), not able to be penetrated or diffused through

im-per-vi-ous (*adj.*), not able to be penetrated or affected by external environment

im-pe-tus (*n.*), a stimulus

im-pinge (*v.*), to strike or hit

im-plant (*v.*), to insert perma-nently

im-plau-si-ble (*adj.*), not likely to be so, unbelievable

im-ple-ment (*n.*), a tool; (*v.*), to make happen, to carry out

im-plic-it (*adj.*), understood from previous information

im-plode (*v.*), to burst inward

im-plo-sion (*n.*), *see* implode

im-pon-der-a-ble (*adj.*), not able to be weighed or meas-ured

im-pose (*v.*), to place upon

im-po-tent (*adj.*), powerless

im-pound (*v.*), to confine

im-preg-na-ble (*adj.*), unable to be overcome

im-preg-nant (*n.*), a substance that permeates another ma-terial

im-preg-nate (*v.*), to cause a material to be soaked with another substance

im-press (*v.*), to dent, to make a mark by pressure

im-pres-sion (*n.*), the mark made by indenting or impres-sing

im-promp-tu (*adj.*), on the spur of the moment

im-pro-vise (*v.*), to do some-thing on the spur of the mo-ment

im-pulse (*n.*), a sudden force

in-ac-ti-vate (*v.*), to render in-active

in-an-i-mate (*adj.*), not alive

in-au-di-ble (*adj.*), unable to be heard

in-board (*adv.*), toward the cen-ter of a vehicle

in-cal-cu-la-ble (*adj.*), unable to be calculated, extremely great; unpredictable

in-can-des-cence (*n.*), light given off by a heated surface

in-can-des-cent (*adj.*), *see* in-candescence

in-ca-pac-i-tate (*v.*), to render incapable of acting

in-cen-di-ary (*adj.*), relating to materials that easily burst into flame

in-cep-tion (*n.*), the beginning

in-ci-dence (*n.*), the rate of oc-curring; *also* the act of hit-ting upon a surface in-cin-er-ate (*v.*), to cause to burn

in-cip-i-ent (*adj.*), beginning to appear or to happen

in-cise (*v.*), to cut into

in-cli-na-tion (*n.*), a dipping, bending, or deviation from the vertical or horizontal

in-clined (*adj.*), having inclination, leaning

in-co-her-ent (*adj.*), without pattern, scattered

in-com-men-su-ra-ble (*adj.*), lacking a common basis of measurement

in-com-men-su-rate (*adj.*), *see* incommensurable

in-com-pat-i-ble (*adj.*), two or more things that cannot work together

in-con-tro-vert-ible (*adj.*), without doubt

in-cor-po-rate (*v.*), to include and blend in thoroughly

in-cre-ment (*n.*), a small increase or decrease

in-crus-ta-tion (*n.*), a hard, crusty top layer

in-cu-bate (*v.*), to maintain conditions favorable to development

in-cur (*v.*), to become subject to some condition

in-de-fin-able (*adj.*), incapable of being exactly described

in-def-i-nite (*adj.*), not precise

in-dent (*v.*), to form a depression by pressing

in-den-ta-tion (*n.*), a depression on a surface, a dent

in-de-pen-dent (*adj.*), occurring on its own, not affected by other factors

in-de-ter-mi-nate (*adj.*), vague

in-dex (*n.*), a mark or pointer on a measuring device; *also* a number having a special significance; (*v.*), to move position to effect a given sequence or operation

in-di-cate (*v.*), to point out; *also* to suggest the likelihood of an occurrence

in-di-ca-tor (*n.*), something that shows an effect; *also* a pointer in a measuring device

in-di-um (*n.*), a chemical element, In

in-di-vis-i-ble (*adj.*), not able to be separated into smaller pieces

in-duce (*v.*), to cause induction

in-duc-tance (*n.*), a quality of an electric circuit that causes electrical waves to lag

in-duc-tion (*n.*), the passage of electricity from a charged object to another object

in-duc-tive (*adj.*), *see* induction

in-duc-tor (*n.*), the electrical component (such as a coil) that passes on electricity

in-ef-fi-cient (*adj.*), not productive, wasteful

in-elas-tic (*adj.*), having no elasticity

in-ert (*adj.*), incapable of chemical reaction

in-er-tia (*n.*), the tendency of a moving object to keep moving in the same direction, and of a stationary object to remain unmoving

in-fal-li-ble (*adj.*), incapable of making a mistake

in-fil-trate (*v.*), to penetrate into something little by little

in-fi-nite (*adj.*), without limit,

having no end

in-fin-i-tes-i-mal (*adj.*), extremely tiny

in-flex-i-ble (*adj.*), rigid

in-flux (*n.*), a flowing in

infra- (*prefix*), below

in-fra-red (*n.*), light waves invisible to the human eye; *also* heat waves

in-fra-son-ic (*adj.*), sound waves too low in frequency to be heard by the human ear

in-fuse (*v.*), to pour something into something else

in-ge-nu-ity (*n.*), inventiveness

in-got (*n.*), a mass of refined metal before its final processing

in-her-ent (*adv.*), referring to a basic character

in-hib-it (*v.*), to hold back

in-hib-i-tor (*n.*), *see* inhibit

ini-tial (*adj.*), referring to the first

in-ject (*v.*), to push into or force in

in-lay (*v.*), to insert one metal into the surface of another; (*n.*), the inlaid metal

in-no-vate (*v.*), to introduce something new

in-op-er-a-tive (*adj.*), out of order, not functioning

in-or-gan-ic (*adj.*), relating to chemicals other than carbon; *also* materials that have never lived, inanimate

in si-tu (*adj.* or *adv.*), in place (Latin)

in-sol-u-ble (*adj.*), unable to be dissolved

in-su-la-tor (*n.*), a material incapable of conducting electricity or heat

in-te-ger (*n.*), a whole number without decimals or fractions

in-te-grate (*v.*), to perform an operation in calculus; *also* to incorporate

in-te-gra-tor (*adj.*), a kind of electronic circuit

in-ten-si-ty (*n.*), the strength or amount

inter- (*prefix*), between

in-ter-act (*v.*), to act on each other

in-ter-ac-tion (*n.*), *see* interact

in-ter-cept (*v.*), to interrupt the progress of

in-ter-com (*n.*), an intercommunication system

in-ter-de-pen-dent (*adj.*), depending on each other

in-ter-elec-trode (*adj.*), between electrodes

in-ter-face (*n.*), the plane separating two regions

in-ter-fer-ence (*n.*), the effect of light waves or electrical waves on each other

in-ter-fer-ence fringe (*n.*), a dark line caused by interference

in-ter-fer-om-e-ter (*n.*), an instrument that measures light interference

in-ter-im (*n.*), the time between

in-ter-ject (*v.*), to throw into the midst of

in-ter-lin-ear (*adj.*), placed between lines

in-ter-mit-tent (*adj.*), separated at intervals

in-ter-po-late (*v.*), to insert

in-ter-re-late (*v.*), to show the relationship between different things

in-ter-sect (*v.*), to meet and

cross (said of lines)

in-ter-sec-tion (*n.*), *see* inter-sect

in-ter-sperse (*v.*), to place things into a system at inter-vals

in-ter-stice (*n.*), the space be-tween things

in-ter-sti-tial (*adj.*), relating to the space between

in-tra- (*prefix*), within; during

in-tri-cate (*adj.*), complex

in-trin-sic (*adj.*), basic, funda-mental, essential

intro- (*prefix*), within

in-tro-duce (*v.*), to bring in

in vac-uo (*adv.*), in a vacuum (Latin)

in-val-id (*adj.*), without basis or foundation

in-val-i-date (*v.*), to destroy or nullify

in-vari-able (*adj.*), constant

in-ven-to-ry (*n.*), a list of the items in a system

in-verse (*adj.*), opposite or backwards

in-ver-sion (*n.*), a reversal of order

in-vert (*v.*), to turn upside-down

in-vert-er (*n.*), a kind of elec-tronic circuit

in-vest-ment (*n.*), a kind of casting done in foundries

in-vo-lute (*adj.*), relating to spiral-like curves

io-dine (*n.*), a chemical ele-ment, I

ion (*n.*), an atom or chemical radical having an electrical charge

ion-ic (*adj.*), *see* ion

ion-ize (*v.*), *see* ion

ion-o-lu-mi-nes-cence (*n.*), a light glow as a result of ion activity

iono-sphere (*n.*), a layer of the atmosphere starting about 25 miles up which contains charged particles

io-ta (*n.*), a Greek letter; *also* a very small amount

ip-so fac-to (*adv.*), the nature of the situation

ir-i-des-cent (*adj.*), having varying colors

irid-i-um (*n.*), a chemical ele-ment, Ir

iris (*n.*), a diaphragm having a circular hole

iron (*n.*), a chemical element, Fe; the primary constituent of steel

ir-ra-di-ate (*v.*), to cast rays on

ir-ri-gate (*v.*), to wash with flowing water

is- (*prefix*), meaning the same, equal

iso- (prefix), meaning the same, equal

iso-bar (*n.*), a line on a weather map connecting areas of equal air pressure

iso-met-ric (*adj.*), in mechani-cal drawing, using three per-pendicular axes

iso-mor-phic (*adj.*), having the same shape

isos-ce-les (*adj.*), referring to a triangle having two equal sides

iso-ther-mal (*adj.*), having the same temperature

iso-tope (*n.*), an atom in which the number of neutrons varies from those of other atoms of the same element

is-sue (*n.*), result, outcome

-ite (*suffix*), designating a chemical radical having less oxygen than an -ate radical

it-er-ate (*v.*), to repeat ("re-iterate" means to repeat again)

J

jam (*v.*), to press into a cramped space; *also* to interfere with radio signals

jar (*v.*), to subject to a sudden jolt

jer - ry - built (*adj.*), poorly or cheaply made

jet (*n.*), a forceful stream of gas or liquid

jig (*n.*), a structure for holding in position pieces that are being worked on

joint (*n.*), the place at which two parts are joined

joist (*n.*), a structural member

joule (*n.*), a unit of energy

junc - tion (*n.*), the region between two types of conductors in a semiconductor device

K

ka-o-lin (*n.*), a kind of clay

kap-pa (*n.*), a Greek letter, κ

keel (*n.*), the center beam at the bottom of a boat

kerf (*n.*), the width of a cut made by a saw

ker - nel (*n.*), the central or basic part of something

ke-tene (*n.*), an organic chemical compound

ke-tone (*n.*), an organic chemical compound

ki-lo- (*prefix*), a thousand

kilo-cal-o-rie (*n.*), one thousand calories

kilo-cy-cle (*n.*), one thousand cycles

kilo - gram (*n.*), one thousand grams

kilo-mega- (*prefix*), one billion

kilo-me-ter (*n.*), one thousand meters

kilo-volt (*n.*), one thousand volts

kilo-watt-hour (*n.*), a thousand watt-hours; KWH, kwhr

ki-ne-mat-ics (*n.*), the science of the motions of objects

kin-e-scope (*n.*), a cathode-ray tube, the picture tube in a television set

ki-net-ic (*adj.*), relating to motion

ki-net-ics (*n.*), the science of the effect of forces on moving objects

kit (*n.*), a set of parts to be assembled to form a finished object

kly-stron (*n.*), a type of micro-wave vacuum tube

knurl (*n.*), a series of projections on the surface of a piece of metal that make the part easy to grasp; (*v.*), to make such projections

kryp-ton (*n.*), a chemical element, Kr

KVA (*n.*), kilovolt-ampere

KWH (*n.*), kilowatt-hour

L

lab - y - rinth (*n.*), a structure consisting of many complex passages or tunnels or both lab-y-rin-thine (*adj.*), *see* labyrinth

lag (*v.*), to fall behind; (*n.*), the amount by which something falls behind

lamb - da (*n.*), a Greek letter, Λ, λ

lam - bert (*n.*), a unit of the brightness of light

la-mel-la (pl. lamellae) (*n.*), a layer

la-mel-lar (*adj.*), *see* lamella

lam-i-na (pl. laminae) (*n.*), the same as lamella, a layer

lam-i-nar (*adj.*), *see* lamina

lam-i-nate (*v.*), to press layers together

lan-tha-num (*n.*), a chemical element, La

lap (*v.*), to grind gently, to smooth and polish; (*n.*), the instrument used in lapping

lap joint (*n.*), a joint made by overlapping the edges of two pieces

large sig-nal (*adj.*), a condition of electronic circuit operation

la-ser (*n.*), a device that generates a narrow, extremely intense beam of light

la-tent (*adj.*), quiescent, dormant, inactive

lat-er-al (*adj.*), to one side

la-tex (*n.*), an emulsion of rubber

lathe (*n.*), a machine used to cut and shape parts

lat-tice (*n.*), a regular arrangement of points or positions; crystal structure

law-renc-i-um (*n.*), a chemical element, Lw

leach (*v.*), to dissolve material by percolating liquid through it

lead (*n.*), a heavy metallic element, Pb; (*v.*), to move ahead, the opposite of lag

lead - ing edge (*n.*), the front edge of an electromagnetic wave

lens (*n.*), a piece of glass shaped to refract and focus light

lever (*n.*), a bar used to move or lift objects

lev-i-tate (*v.*), to cause to rise or float

lift (*n.*), the amount of upward force on an aircraft

lig-nite (*n.*), a type of coal

lim-it-er (*n.*), a kind of electronic circuit

lin - ear (*adj.*), arranged in a series or sequence; *also* pertaining to a mathematical function in which one element is directly dependent on another

li-qui-dus (*n.*), the temperature range at which a component in a liquid mixture starts to solidify

list (*v.*), to lean to one side

li-ter (*n.*), a measure of volume in the metric system, equals about a quart

li-tharge (*n.*), a chemical compound of lead, lead monoxide

lith-ic (*adj.*), relating to stone

lith-i-um (*n.*), a light metallic element, Li

li-thog-ra-phy (*n.*), a printing process

lit-mus (*n.*), a material that indicates if a solution is acid or alkaline

load (*n.*), a resistor or resistive component that carries electrical current

lo-cal (*adj.*), in one place

lock-ing (*n.*), a kind of electronic circuit

lo-co-mo-tion (*n.*), the act of moving

lo-cus (*n.*), a place set by mathematical considerations

lode-stone (*n.*), a magnetic mineral, magnetite

log (*n.*), abbreviation for logarithm

log-a-rithm (*n.*), the exponent that tells the power to which a number is to be raised in order to equal another number

lo-gis-tic (*adj.*), relating to a kind of mathematical reasoning

loop (*n.*), a circular path

lo-ran (*n.*), a kind of navigation using electronic systems

loss (*n.*), electrical power that is lost from a system

loud-speak-er (*n.*), the electronic transducer that converts electric current to sound

lu-bri-cate (*v.*), to make slippery by applying a liquid

Lu-cite (*n.*), a kind of plastic

lug (*n.*), a projection to which wires can be fastened

lu-men (*n.*), a unit of light intensity

lu-mi-nes-cence (*n.*), a glow of light due to factors other than heat

lu-mi-nous (*adj.*), glowing, shining

lu-nar (*adj.*), relating to the moon

lu-te-tium (*n.*), a chemical element, Lu

lye (*n.*), a strong alkaline chemical solution

M

Mach num-ber (*n.*), a number indicating how much faster than the speed of sound an object is moving

ma-chine (*v.*), to cut and shape using a rotary automatic tool; (*n.*), a device which advantageously uses force

mac-ro- (*prefix*), large

mac-ro-scop-ic (*adj.*), large enough to be seen by the naked eye

mag-ma (*n.*), hot, liquid rock

mag-nes-ia (*n.*), a chemical compound, magnesium oxide (MgO)

mag-ne-sium (*n.*), a light metallic element, Mg

mag-net (*n.*), a material that can attract certain materials toward itself

mag-ne-tite (*n.*), a magnetic mineral of iron

mag-ne-to (*n.*), a generator of electrical current

mag-ne-to-hy-dro-dy-nam-ic (*adj.*), relating to the effect of magnetism on fluids; MHD

mag-ne-tom-e-ter (*n.*), an instrument for measuring magnetic intensity

mag-ne-to-mo-tive (*adj.*), relates to the mechanical force exerted by a magnetic field

mag-ne-to-stric-tion (*n.*), a change in the dimensions of a body as a result of exposure to a magnetic field

mag-ne-tron (*n.*), a microwave vacuum tube that operates in a magnetic field

mag-ni-fy (*v.*), to increase in size, to enlarge

make-up (*n.*), the way in which something is put together

mal- (*prefix*), bad

mal-a-chite (*n.*), a mineral of copper

mal-func-tion (*v.*), to fail to work effectively; (*n.*), the failure to operate

mal-lea-ble (*adj.*), bendable

man-drel (*n.*), a metal shaft that serves as a core around which other metal is shaped

man-ga-nese (*n.*), a chemical element, Mn

man-i-fest (*adj.*), easily apparent

man-i-fes-ta-tion (*n.*), an action or circumstance that demonstrates a principle

man-i-fold (*n.*), a pipe to which many smaller pipes are attached

ma-nip-u-late (*v.*), to manage or control

ma-nom-e-ter (*n.*), an instrument that measures pressure

man-u-al (*n.*), a handbook; (*adj.*), able to be worked by hand

mar-ble-ize (*v.*), to put in vein-like markings

mar-gin (*n.*), a spare amount

mar-gin-al (*adj.*), just barely achieving what is required

mar-tens-ite (*n.*), a constituent of steel

mas-er (*n.*), a device that gives off a strong, narrow beam of

microwave electromagnetic radiation; *compare with* laser

mass (*n.*), weight; *also* the greater part

mass spec-tro-graph (*n.*), an instrument that separates and measures isotopes of a chemical element

ma-trix (*n.*), an array of numbers; *also* a set pattern; *also* the parent structure in which another component is embedded

matte (*n.*), a mixture of molten minerals

max-i-mal (*adj.*), referring to the most

max-i-mize (*n.*), to increase to the maximum

max-i-mum (*n.*), the greatest amount attainable

max-well (*n.*), an electromagnetic unit

maze (*n.*), a network of channels and passages

mea-ger (*adj.*), scanty

mean (*n.*), an intermediate in a range of values; *similar to* average

mean free path (*n.*), the average distance a particle can travel

mea-sure (*n.*), a standard of comparison

mech-a-nism (*n.*), a piece of machinery; *also* the means whereby something is done

mech-a-nize (*v.*), to make automatic

me-dia (*n.*), plural of medium

me-di-an (*n.*), the number or position midway in a range

me-di-um (*n.*), the environment in which something is situated mega- (*prefix*), million

mega-cy-cle (*n*.), a million cycles

mega-ton (*n*.), a million tons

mega-volt (*n*.), a million volts

mega-watt (*n*.), a million watts

meg-ohm (*n*.), a million ohms

mel-a-mine (*n*.), a kind of plastic

melt-ing point (*n*.), *see* freezing point

mem-ber (*n*.), a part of something

mem-brane (*n*.), a thin, flexible sheet

mem-o-ry (*n*.), the part of a computer that stores information; *also* the ability of a computer to store information

men-de-le-vi-um (*n*.), a chemical element, Md

me-nis-cus (*n*.), the curved surface of a liquid that is contained in a column

men-su-ra-ble (*adj*.), able to be measured

mer-cap-tan (*n*.), a group of organic chemical compounds

Mer-ca-tor (*n*.), a way of drawing a map

mer-cu-ry (*n*.), a chemical element, Hg

merge (*v*.), to blend into

me-rid-i-an (*n*.), a circle drawn around a sphere, especially through the poles of the earth

me-sa (*n*.), an upward slope that ends with a flat table

mesh (*n*.), a network; (*v*.), to cause to engage (with reference to gears)

meso- (*prefix*), middle

me-son (*n*.), an atomic particle

meta- (*prefix*), after, later, beyond

met-al-lo-graph (*n*.), an apparatus for photographing microscopic metal crystals

met-al-loid (*n*.), a material that has some, but not all, the properties of a metal

met-al-lur-gist (*n*.), one who practices metallurgy

met-al-lur-gy (*n*.), the science and technology of metals

meta-sta-ble (*adj*.), only slightly stable

me-te-or-ite (*n*.), a small object from space that reaches the earth

me-te-o-rol-o-gy (*n*.), the study of weather

me-ter (*n*.), a device that measures amounts; *also* a measure of length, a little more than a yard; (*v*.), to measure out

meth-ane (*n*.), a gaseous organic compound

meth-a-nol (*n*.), an organic compound, a kind of alcohol

me-thod-i-cal (*adj*.), systematic

meth-od-ol-o-gy (*n*.), a set of rules by which something is to be done

meth-yl (*n*.), an organic radical

me-tic-u-lous (*adj*.), careful

met-ric (*adj*.), referring to the system of measurement that is based upon the centimeter, gram, second (cgs)

mho (*n*.), the unit of electrical conductivity, the reciprocal of ohm

mi-ca (*n*.), a mineral that is made up of lamellae

mi-cel-lar (*adj.*), *see* micelle

mi-celle (*n.*), a unit of structure of certain organic compounds

micro- (*prefix*), very small; *also* one millionth

mi-cro-gram (*n.*), one millionth of a gram

mi-cr-og-ra-phy (*n.*), microscopic examination

mi-crom-e-ter (*n.*), a tool for measuring small distances

mi-cron (*n.*), a unit of length, a millionth of a meter

mi - cro - pho - to - graph (*n.*), a photograph taken through a microscope

mi-cro-ra-dio-graph (*n.*), a microphotograph made with X-rays

micro-scop-ic (*adj.*), very tiny

micros - co - py (*n.*), the technique of using the microscope

mi-cro-struc-ture (*n.*), the microscopic structure of something

mi - cro - wave (*n.*), (*adj.*), a short, high-frequency electromagnetive wave

mi - cro - wave plumb-ing (*n.*), the wave guide used in conducting microwave current

mi - gra - tion (*n.*), movement from one place to another

mil (*n.*), a thousandth of an inch

mi-lieu (*n.*), environment

mill (*v.*), to machine a piece of metal by cutting with a rotary tool

Mil-ler in-dex (*n.*), a series of numbers used in identifying crystal faces

milli- (*prefix*), a thousandth

mil-li-am-pere (*n.*), a thousandth of an ampere

mil - li - gram (*n.*), one thousandth of a gram

mil - li - li - ter (*n.*), one thousandth of a liter, a cubic centimeter

mil-li-me-ter (*n.*), one thousandth of a meter

mil-li-volt (*n.*), one thousandth of a volt

min-er-al (*n.*), a naturally occurring chemical compound, usually crystalline

min-er-al-o-gy (*n.*), the study of minerals

mini- (*prefix*), tiny

min-a-tur-iza-tion (*n.*), the act of making a very small, operable object

min-ia-tur-ize (*v.*), *see* miniaturization

min-i-mize (*v.*), to reduce to a minimum

min-i-mum (*n.*), the smallest amount possible

minor (*adj.*), lesser

min-term (*n.*), the smallest number (in computer programming)

mi-nus (*prep.*), diminished by; (*adj.*), negative, in algebra; (*n.*), a deficiency

mi - nus - cule *or* min - is - cule (*adj.*), tiny

mi-nute (*adj.*), tiny

min-ute (*n.*), one sixtieth of an hour; one sixtieth of a degree of arc

mi-nu-tiae (*n.*), tiny details

mi-rage (*n.*), a type of optical illusion

mis-cal-cu-late (*v.*), to make an error in calculation

mis - ci - ble (*adj.*), able to be

mixed together

mis-in-ter-pret (v.), to understand or explain incorrectly

mis-no-mer (n.), a descriptive
name, wrongly applied

mis-sile (n.), something
thrown; an unmanned flying
weapon

mis-sile-ry (n.), the study of
the design, construction, and
use of missiles

mi-ter or mi-tre (n.), a corner
formed by joining two pieces
that have been cut at an angle; (v.), to make a miter joint

mit-i-gate (v.), to make less
intense

mix-er (n.), a kind of electronic
circuit

mne-mon-ic (n., adj.), a reference code used in programming

mo-bile (adj.), moveable

mo-bil-i-ty (n.), the ease with
which electricity moves

mock-up (n.), a full-sized model

mode (n.), a particular arrangement or pattern

mod-el (n.), a constructed representation of an object; or a
theoretical description; (v.),
to shape

mod-er-a-tor (n.), a substance
that slows down a chemical or
physical reaction

mod-u-lar (adj.), see module

mod-u-late (v.), to vary a property of a carrier signal, particularly in radio and electricity

mod-u-la-tor (n.), a kind of
electronic circuit

mod-ule (n.), a section of parts
of a large system

mod-u-lus (n.), a number or
coefficient used to describe
a condition

mo-dus ope-ran-di (n.), the
manner in which something
works

mod-us vi-ven-di (n.), a feasible way of operating

Moh's scale (n.), a scale used
to measure hardness of minerals

mol (n.), see mole

mol-al (adj.), relating to a solution containing one mole of a
chemical

mol-ar (adj.), relating to one
mole of a chemical compound

mold (v.), to shape into a given
form; to cast; (n.), the form
into which a liquid is poured
in order that it take on the
shape of that form after it
solidifies

mold-ing (n.), a border or frame

mole or mol (n.), the weight of
a chemical expressed in
grams numerically equal to
the weight, in atomic units,
of its molecules

mo-lec-u-lar (adj.), relating to
molecules

mol-e-cule (n.), the smallest
particle of a chemical compound

mol-ten (adj.), melted, fused

mo-lyb-de-num (n.), a heavy,
metallic element, Mo

mo-ment (n.), a measure of the
tendency of something to rotate around an axis

mon-, mono- (prefix), one

mon-atom-ic (adj.), having only
one atom

mon-au-ral (adj.), receiving

sound through a single transmitter

Mo-nel (*n.*), an alloy of copper and nickel

mon-i-tor (*n.*), an instrument that watches and checks a process; (*v.*), to watch and check a process

mo-no-clin-ic (*n.*), a crystal system

mo-no-lith-ic (*adj.*), having a massive structure consisting of a single stone

mon-o-mer (*n.*), form of organic chemical compound

mon - ox - ide (*n.*), a chemical compound having one oxygen atom

moot (*adj.*), not settled, open to discussion

mor-dant (*n.*), a substance that renders a dye permanent

morph- (*prefix* or *suffix*), relating to form or shape

morphol-o-gy (*n.*), the study of form and structure

mo-sa-ic (*n.*), a structure made up of small pieces

mould (*n.*), *see* mold

mount (*v.*), to set up; raise

mu (*n.*), a Greek letter, *also* a quality of a vacuum tube

mul-lion (*n.*), part of a door or a window

multi- (*prefix*), many

mul-ti-far-i-ous (*adj.*), having great variety

mul-ti-form (*adj.*), having many forms

mul-ti-lat-er-al (*adj.*), having many sides

mul-ti-plex (*adj.*), relating to the sending of many messages at once on one electrical channel

mul-ti-pli-cand (*n.*), a number that is multiplied by another

mul-ti-plic-i-ty (*n.*), a great number or variety

mul-ti-pli-er (*n.*), a type of circuit

mul-ti-vi-bra-tor (*n.*), a type of circuit

mu-ri-at-ic acid (*n.*), hydrochloric acid

mu-ta-ble (*adj.*), changeable

mu-tant (*n.*), the product of a changing process

mu-tate (*v.*), to cause to change

mute (*v.*), to soften the loudness of a sound

myr - i - ad (*n.*), a very great number

N

na-dir (*n.*), the lowest possible point

NAND (*n.*), a designation used in computer programming to indicate "not added" or Not AND; *the opposite of* AND

nano- (prefix), one billionth, 10^{-9}

naph-tha (*n.*), an organic compound

naph-tha-lene (*n.*), an organic compound

na-scent (*adj.*), newly existing

ne- or neo- (*prefix*), new

neb-u-la (*n.*), a cloud

neb-u-lar (*adj.*), pertaining to nebula

neb-u-lous (*adj.*), pertaining to nebula

neb-u-lous (*adj.*), vague, hazy

ne-gate (*v.*), to render ineffective, to deny

neg - a - tive (*adj.*), less than zero; unfavorable

ne-o-dym-i-um (*n.*), a chemical element, Nd

ne-on (*n.*), a chemical element, Ne

ne - o - prene (*n.*), a synthetic rubber

nep-tu-ni-um (*n.*), a chemical element, Np

net-work (*n.*), a system of interconnected parts

neu-ron (*n.*), a nerve cell

neu-tral (*adj.*), neither acid nor alkaline

neu-tral-ize (*v.*), to counteract, to nullify

neu-tron (*n.*), a particle in the atomic nucleus that has no electrical charge

neu - tron - o - lu-mi-nes-cence (*n.*), a glow as a result of impact by neutrons

nib (*n.*), a small projection

nick - el (*n.*), a chemical element, Ni

Nic-ol (*adj.*), a kind of prism used in optics

nil (*n.*), nothing

nim-bus (*n.*), a type of cloud

ni - o - bi - um (*n.*), a chemical element, Nb (sometimes called columbium, Cb)

ni - tro - gen (*n.*), a gaseous chemical element, N; the major constituent of the air

no-bel-i-um (*n.*), a chemical element, No

node (*n.*), a position that is free from vibrations on a vibrating structure

nod-u-lar (*adj.*), *see* nodule

nod-ule (*n.*), a small lump

noise (*n.*), meaningless sound that has no pattern or regularity

no-men-cla-ture (*n.*), the system of naming elements

nom-i-nal (*adj.*), in name only

no - mo - gram (*n.*), *see* nomograph

no-mo-graph (*n.*), a chart that allows one to find the value of a third variable when the values of two other variables are known

non- (*prefix*), no

non-fer-rous (*adj.*), an alloy or compound that does not contain iron

NOR (*n.*), a designation used in computer programming to indicate "not OR"; *or* do not use alternate operation

nor-mal-ize (*v.*), to reduce to a common basis

nose cone (*n.*), the front end of a rocket or missile

no-ta-tion (*n.*), the designation of parts of a system, especially by use of symbols

no-va (*n.*), a bright new star

nox - ious (*adj.*), harmful, unpleasant

noz-zle (*n.*), a small spout from which gas or liquid may flow

NPN (*n.*), a type of transistor construction; *also* npn

nth (*adj.*), the ultimate

n-type (*n.*), a type of semiconductor material, doped with n-material; *also* N-type

nu (*n.*), a Greek letter, ν

nu-ance (*n.*), a subtle variation or gradation

nub (*n.*), the point, the gist

nu-cle-ar (*adj.*), relating to the nucleus

nu - cle - ate (v.), to provide a nucleus or seed for something to grow on

nu-cle-on-ics (n.), the study of the properties of the atomic nucleus

nu-cle-us (n.), the center of the atom containing the protons and the neutrons

nu-clide (n.), a kind of atom

nug-get (n.), a solid lump

null (n.), zero; the place on a meter that indicates zero

nul-li-fy (v.), to make useless and ineffective

nul-li-ty (n.), something that is null

nu-mer-a-tion (n.), the act of designating by number

nu-mer-a-tor (n.), the bottom number in a fraction

nur-ture (v.), to give nourishment

O

ob- (prefix), against

ob-jec-tive (n.), the lens system at the end of a microscope nearest what is being looked at

ob-late (adj.), flattened

oblique (adj.), tilted

oblit-er-ate (v.), to destroy all trace

ob-scure (adj.), not clear, dark

ob-ser-va-tion (n.), the making and recording of an exact measurement

ob-so-les-cence (n.), becoming out of date

ob-so-lete (adj.), out of date, no longer used

ob-tuse an-gle (n.), an angle between 90° and 180°

oc-clude (v.), to obstruct; also to dissolve a gas into a material

oc-ta- or octo- (prefix), eight

oc-ta-gon (n.), an eight-sided figure

oc-ta-he-dral (adj.), relating to an eight-sided solid figure

oc-tane (n.), a kind of chemical compound

oc-u-lar (adj.), relating to what is seen; (n.), the eyepiece of a microscope or telescope

-ode (suffix), a path, usually electronic

ohm (n.), the unit of electrical resistance

ohm-ic (adj.), see ohm

ohm-me-ter (n.), an instrument for measuring ohms

-oid (suffix), resembling

ole-ag-i-nous (adj.), oily

oleic ac - id (n.), a chemical compound

ome-ga (n.), a Greek letter, Ω, ω

om-i-cron (n.), a Greek letter, o

opac-i-ty (n.), the property of obstructing the passage of light

opaque (adj.), not transparent

op-er-a-tion (n.), a mathematical process

op-tic (adj.), relating to vision

op-tics (n.), the science of light

OR (n.), a designation used in computer programming to indicate use alternate operation

or-bit (n.), the circular path of a satellite

or-der (n.), a pattern; also a ranking

or-dered (*adj.*), in a particular pattern

or-di-nal (*adj.*), numbered in sequence

or-di-nate (*n.*), the vertical axis of a graph; *also* one of the coordinates of a point on a graph

or-gan-ic (*adj.*), relating to the chemistry of carbon; *also* relating to living things

or-ga-nism (*n.*), a complex structure consisting of many parts

ori-ent (*v.*), to set in a particular direction or position

ori-en-ta-tion (*n.*), the process of orienting

or-i-gin (*n.*), the beginning; *also* an intersection of some primary lines on a graph

orth-, ortho- (*prefix*), straight

or-thi-con (*n.*), a camera used in television

or-tho-graph-ic (*adj.*), a type of projection used in drafting

or-tho-phos-pho-ric acid (*n.*), a chemical compound

or-tho-rhom-bic (*n.*), a form of crystal

os-cil-late (*v.*), to swing back and forth repeatedly

os-cil-la-tor (*n.*), a kind of electronic circuit

os-cil-lo-scope (*n.*), an electrical instrument in which wave forms are made visible on a screen

os-mi-um (*n.*), a heavy metallic element, Os

os-mo-sis (*n.*), diffusion of liquid through a membrane

-ous (*suffix*), designating a chemical radical with a lower valence than one ending in -ic

out-crop (*n.*), the part of a rock formation that emerges at the ground

out-gas (*v.*), to remove gas from materials

out-growth (*n.*), the result of a process

out-put (*n.*), what is produced from a system

over-lay (*n.*), a layer of something on top of a structure

over-tone (*n.*), a frequency that is a multiple of a fundamental frequency

ovoid (*adj.*), shaped like an egg

ox-i-da-tion (*n.*), the process of reacting with oxygen

ox-ide (*n.*), a chemical compound containing oxygen

oxy- (*prefix*), containing oxygen

ox-y-gen (*n.*), a chemical element, O

ox-y-lu-mi-nes-cence (*n.*), a glow produced by oxidation

ozone (*n.*), a gas whose molecules consist of three atoms of oxygen, O_3

P

pack-age (*v.*), to enclose in a protective container

PADT (*n.*), abbreviation for post alloy diffused transistor

pal-la-di-um (*n.*), a precious metallic chemical element, Pd

pal-mit-ic ac-id (*n.*), an organic acid

pal-pa-ble (*adj.*), able to be touched, tangible, easily understood

pan (*v*.), to rotate a camera so as to keep a moving object in view

pan-to-graph (*n*.), a tool used in copying a pattern, usually at a different size

par (*n*.), an amount taken as standard

para- (*prefix*), beside; similar

pa-rab-o-la (*n*.), a bowl-shaped curve

par-a-bol-ic (*adj*.), *see* parabola

pa-rab-o-loid (*n*.), a parabolic surface

par-a-dox (*n*.), a statement that seems contradictory but may be true

par-a-dox-i-cal (*adj*.), *see* paradox

par-af-fin (*n*.), a waxy material

par-a-gon (*n*.), a model of excellence

par-al-lax (*n*.), the apparent difference in position of an object as it is seen from two different angles

par-al-lel (*adj*.), lines or surfaces which are always the same distance apart; *also* comparable, analogous; *also* an electronic circuit

par-al-lel-ism (*n*.), the state of being parallel

par-al-lel-o-gram (*n*.), a foursided figure in which opposite sides are parallel; *also* a solid with parallel sides

par-al-lel-o-piped (*n*.), a prism with bases that are parallelograms

pa-ra-mag-net-ic (*adj*.), slightly magnetic

pa-ram-e-ter (*n*.), a character-istic quality of something

para-met-ric am-pli-fi-er (*n*.), an electronic circuit using solid-state devices

paramp (*n*.), abbreviation for parametric amplifier

par-a-sit-ic (*adj*.), relating to something that is dependent on something else

pare (*v*.), to shave off or trim

par-ent (*n*.), the source of something

par-i-ty (*n*.), the condition of being equivalent

pa-ro-chi-al (*adj*.), narrow

par-ti-cle (*n*.), a small object; *also* a substance of atomic size or smaller

par-tic-u-late (*adj*.), *see* particle

patch (*n*.), a particular area within a larger area

pa-ti-na (*n*.), a surface film acquired over a period of time

pat-tern (*n*.), a design, (*v*.), to imitate

pau-ci-ty (*n*.), a scarceness, a dearth

peak (*n*.), a maximum, a high point; (*v*.), to reach a maximum

pearl-ite (*n*.), a constituent of steel

pe-des-tri-an (*adj*.), ordinary, commonplace

peen (*v*.), to flatten by hammering

peg (*v*.), to fix or hold at a particular level

pel-let (*n*.), a small ball

pel-lu-cid (*adj*.), clear, transparent

pen-du-lum (*n*.), an object placed at the bottom of a line

and swinging back and forth

pen-e-tra-ble (*adj.*), able to be pierced

pen-e-trate (*v.*), to pierce, to pass through

pent (*adj.*), confined

pent- (*prefix*), five

pen-ta-gon (*n.*), a five-sided figure

pen-ta-he-dron (*n.*), a five-sided solid

pen-tane (*n.*), an organic chemical compound, a hydrocarbon

pen-tode (*n.*), a five-element vacuum tube or semiconductor device

pent-ox-ide (*n.*), an oxide with five oxygen atoms

pen-tyl (*n.*), an organic chemical radical

pe-num-bra (*n.*), a partial shadow

per- (*prefix*), through; *also* containing the largest amount

per an-num (*adv.*), yearly

per-bo-rate (*n.*), a chemical compound of boron

per cap-i-ta (*adv.*), for each person in a population

per-ceive (*v.*), to understood

per cent (*n.*), on the basis of one hundred

per-cen-tile (*n.*), within a one per cent range

per-cep-ti-ble (*n.*), detectable

per-cep-tu-al (*adj.*), able to be observed with the senses

per-chlo-rate (*n.*), a chemical compound of chlorine

per-co-late (*v.*), the trickling of a liquid through a porous mass of solid material

per-cus-sion (*n.*), the act of striking sharply

per-fect (*v.*), to bring to a final, desirable form

per-fo-rate (*v.*), to make a hole

per-func-to-ry (*adj.*), routine

peri- (*prefix*), enclosing; near

peri-gee (*n.*), the point in the orbit of a satellite when it is nearest the earth

per-i-he-li-on (*n.*), the point in the path of a satellite when it is nearest the sun

per-im-e-ter (*n.*), the distance around a figure

pe-ri-od (*n.*), the time required for one cycle in a repeating series

pe-ri-od-ic (*adj.*), recurring at regular intervals

pe-ri-od-ic-i-ty (*n.*), the degree or the state of recurring regularly

pe-riph-ery (*n.*), perimeter, outer boundary

peri-scope (*n.*), an instrument for looking around corners or over obstacles

per-ish-able (*adj.*), spoilable

per-man-ga-nate (*n.*), a chemical radical of manganese

per-me-abil-i-ty (*n.*), able to be diffused through; *also* the amount of magnetic effect made by a magnetic material

per-me-ance (*n.*), a unit describing magnetic qualities

per-mit-tiv-i-ty (*n.*), a unit describing the electrical quality of a dielectric material

per-mu-ta-tion (*n.*), a change

per-mute (*v.*), to change an arrangement

per-ox-ide (*n.*), a chemical compound of oxygen

per - pen - dic - u - lar (*adj*.), at right angles

per-spec-tive (*n*.), the rendering of a drawing so that the object shown appears on paper to be solid; *also* a view from a particular position

PERT (*n*.), program evaluation review technique, a method of planning a project; *also* pert

per-ti-nent (*adj*.), relevant

per-turb (*v*.), to cause a deviation

per-tur-ba-tion (*n*.), a disturbance of a regular situation

per-vade (*v*.), to penetrate and diffuse through something

per-vi-ous (*adj*.), permeable

pes-tle (*n*.), an implement used for crushing in a mortar

petr- (*prefix*), stone

pet-ri-fy (*v*.), to convert into a stony material

pet-ro-chem-i-cal (*adj*.), relating to chemicals in oil

pe-trog-ra-phy (*n*.), the study and classification of rocks

pe-trol-o-gy (*n*.), the study of the origin and composition of rocks

pew-ter (*n*.), an alloy of lead and tin

pf (*n*.), power factor

pH (*n*.), a numerical measure of acidity or alkalinity of a chemical solution (7 is neutral; less than 7 is acid; 7-14 is alkaline)

phan - tas - tron (*n*.), an electronic circuit

phase (*n*.), a condition or state of matter such as liquid, solid, gas; *also* a point in a periodically repeating cycle; (*v*.), to gradually merge from one stage to another

phase in-ver-ter (*n*.), an electronic circuit

phase shift - er (*n*.), an electronic circuit

phe-nol (*n*.), an organic chemical compound

phe-no-lic (*adj*.), *see* phenol

phe - nol - phtha - lein (*n*.), a chemical compound used as an indicator of acidity or alkalinity

phe-nom-e-no-log-i-cal (*adj*.), relating to true occurrences

phe-nom-e-non (pl. phenomena) (*n*.), an occurrence of a definable type

phe-nyl (*n*.), an organic chemical radical

phi (*n*.), a Greek letter, ϕ

phil- (*prefix*), having a liking or affinity for

-phil-ic (*suffix*), *see* phil-

pH me-ter (*n*.), an instrument for measuring pH

-pho - bic (*suffix*), having an aversion for; *opposite of* -philic

phon- (*prefix*), sound

pho-non (*n*.), a unit or quantum of mechanical energy in a crystal lattice

-phore (*suffix*), carrying

-pho-re-sis (*suffix*), transmission

phos - gene (*n*.), an organic chemical compound

phos - phate (*n*.), a chemical radical of phosphorus

phos - phor (*n*.), a substance which glows when subjected to radiation phos-pho-res-cence (*n.*), a glow that is the result of radiation and which persists after the radiation has ceased

phos-pho-rus (*n.*), a chemical element, P

phot- *or* photo- (*prefix*), light

pho-to-cell (*n.*), a device that responds electrically to the incidence of light

pho - to - chem - is -try (*n.*), the study of the effect of light on chemical reactions

pho - to - con - duc-tiv-i-ty (*n.*), electrical conductivity increased by light radiation

pho-to-de-po-si-tion (*n.*), the laying down of layers of materials by photographic means

pho-to-elec-tric (*adj.*), relating to the effect of light on electrical properties

pho-to-en-grave (*v.*), to make indentations in a metal surface by means of a photographic and chemical process

pho-to-lu-mi-nes-cence (*n.*), the giving off of light as a result of excitation by light

pho-tom-e-ter (*n.*), an instrument that measures light intensity

pho-tom-e-try (*n.*), the science of the measurement of light

pho - to - mi - cro - graph (*n.*), a photograph taken through a microscope

pho-ton (*n.*), a unit of light intensity; *also* a quantum of radiant energy

pho-to-syn-the-sis (*n.*), a type of chemical reaction in plants as a result of irra-

diation with light

pho-to-tube (*n.*), a vacuum tube that may be modulated by light

pho-to-vol-ta-ic (*adj.*), relating the generation of voltage as a result of the impact of light

phtha - lein (*n.*), a chemical compound used as a dye

phtha-lic (*n.*), a chemical radical

phys - i - cal (*adj.*), relating to material things

phys-ics (*n.*), the science of the structure and activities of matter, excluding its chemical properties

pi (*n.*), a Greek letter, π; *also* the ratio of the circumference of a circle to its diameter

pi-co (*prefix*), one trillionth

pic-ric (*adj.*), a kind of acid

piece - meal (*adv.*), piece by piece

pier (*n.*), a structural supporting member

pig-ment (*n.*), a material used to provide color

pig-men-ta-tion (*n.*), coloration

pi-las-ter (*n.*), a vertical supporting member

pile (*n.*), equipment used to generate atomic energy

pi - lot (*adj.*), referring to the first specimen of a given model

pin-a-coi-dal (*adj.*), a crystal system

pip (*n.*), a small vertical line on a cathode-ray tube screen indicating an incoming signal, an object signal in radar

pi-pette (*n.*), a glass tube used

in sucking up or measuring quantities of liquid

pis-ton (*n.*), a metal cylinder which moves in a cylindrical chamber, causing mechanical action of a machine

pit (*n.*), a tiny indentation on a surface; (*v.*), to make tiny indentations

Pi-tot tube (*n.*), an instrument used in hydraulics

piv-ot (*n.*), a pin on which something turns; (*v.*), to turn on a given spot

piv-ot-al (*adj.*), crucial

pla-nar (*adj.*), flat

pla-nar tran-sis-tor (*n.*), a type of transistor

plane (*adj.*) flat; (*n.*), a flat region; *also* a level for consideration; (*v.*), to make flat

plan-et (*n.*), a heavenly body (such as the earth) that resolves around the sun

plan-e-tar-y (*adj.*), having an orbit like a planet

pla-nim-e-ter (*n.*), an instrument that measures area

plant (*n.*), a factory building and its equipment

plas-ma (*n.*), an ionized gas with an admixture of charged particles

plas-tic (*adj.*), able to be formed or bent; (*n.*), a chemical material

plate (*n.*), the anode of a vacuum tube; a lamellar structure; a film of electrodeposited metal; (*v.*), to make a film of metal by electrochemical deposition

pla-teau (*n.*), a region of relatively small change

plat-en (*n.*), a metal form against which things may be pressed

plat-i-num (*n.*), a precious, metallic element, Pt

plat-i-num black (*n.*), a powdery form of platinum

plau-si-ble (*adj.*), believable

pleth-o-ra (*n.*), an excess

pli-able (*adj.*), flexible, easily yielding

pli-an-cy (*n.*), a state of being flexible

pli-ant (*adj.*), *see* pliable

plot (*n.*), a graphical diagram; (*v.*), to draw with careful planning

ploy (*n.*), a maneuver; a tactic

plumb (*adj.*), exactly vertical; (*v.*), to examine deeply

plumb- (*prefix*), pertaining to lead

plum-met (*v.*), to fall perpendicularly

plu-ral-i-ty (*n.*), a majority, or a comparatively greater number

plus (*v.*), to add; (*n.*), an advantage; (*adj.*), positive, in reference to electrical charge

plu-to-ni-um (*n.*), a chemical element, Pu

ply (*n.*), one of several layers

pneu-mat-ic (*adj.*), referring to a machine that uses air or another gas

pneumo- (*prefix*), air or gas

PNP (*n.*), a type of transistor; *also* pnp

po-lar (*adj.*), relating to objects having ends with opposite conditions of the same quality, such as positive and negative electricity; *also* opposite; *also* relating to coordinates what represent the position of an object

po-lari-scope (*n.*), an instrument for measuring the amount of polarization of light

po-lar-i-ty (*n.*), the quality of having two different poles or positions of opposite condition

po-lar-iz-able (*adj.*), the ability to be polarized

po-lar-ize (*v.*), to impart polarity; to make light waves vibrate in a particular pattern

pole (*n.*), one end of a polarized structure

pol-lute (*v.*), to render contaminated

po-lo-ni-um (*n.*), a chemical element, Po

poly- (*prefix*), many

poly-chro-mat-ic (*adj.*), having many colors

poly-es-ter (*n.*), a kind of chemical compound

poly-eth-yl-ene (*n.*), a chemical compound; a plastic

poly-gon (*n.*), a geometrical figure of many sides

po-lyg-o-nal (*adj.*), *see* polygon

poly-he-dral (*adj.*), relating to a polyhedron

poly-he-dron (*n.*), a solid made of many sides

poly-mer (*n.*), a type of chemical compound with many units

poly-mer-ic (*adj.*), relating to polymers

poly-mer-iza-tion (*n.*), the process of combining chemical molecules to form larger

molecules

poly-sty-rene (*n.*), a chemical compound; a plastic

poly-sul-fide (*n.*), a chemical compound of sulfur

poly-ure-thane (*n.*), a chemical compound; a plastic

poly-vi-nyl (*n.*), a chemical compound; a plastic

pon-der-a-ble (*adj.*), able to be weighed

pon-toon (*n.*), a float

pore (*n.*), a small opening

po-ros-i-ty (*n.*), the quality of having pores

po-rous (*adj.*), having pores

port (*n.*), an opening

por-ta-ble (*adj.*), able to be carried

pos-i-tive (*adj.*), having a plus electrical charge

pos-i-tron (*n.*), a sub-atomic particle

post (*v.*), to list data

post- (prefix), after

pot (*v.*), to embed in an encapsulating material

pot-ash (*n.*), a chemical compound, potassium carbonate

po-tas-si-um (*n.*), a chemical element, K

po-ten-cy (*n.*), *see* potent

po-tent (*adj.*), powerful

po-ten-tial (*adj.*), capable of action; latent

po-ten-ti-om-e-ter (*n.*), an instrument for measuring voltage; *also* a device to vary voltage

pow-der met-al-lur-gy (*n.*), the making of metal parts by pressing metal powders

pow-er (*n.*), energy in a unit time; *also* the exponent to which a number may be raised; *also* ability to act; (*v.*), to supply with force to act

prac-ti-ca-ble (*adj.*), able to be done, feasible

prac-ti-cal (*adj.*), able to be done

prac-tice (*n.*), the usual way of doing something

prac-ti-tion-er (*n.*), one who performs a professional function

prag-mat-ic (*adj.*), practical, factual

pra-seo-dym-i-um (*n.*), a chemical element, Pr

pre- (prefix), before

pre-car-i-ous (*adj.*), uncertain, unstable

pre-ce-dence (*n.*), coming first

pre-ce-dent (*n.*), something that occurred earlier used as an example for future action

pre-cess (*v.*), *see* precession

pre-ces-sion (*n.*), a tilting of a rotating object

pre-cip-i-tate (*n.*), a solid material which separates from a liquid; (*v.*), to cause a solid to deposit out of a liquid

pre-cis (*n.*), a summary of essential facts

pre-ci-sion (*n.*), exactness

pre-clude (*v.*), to make impossible

pre-con-di-tion (*n.*), something that must happen before something else can occur

pre-de-ter-mine (*v.*), to assure in advance that something will occur

pre-dict-able (*adj.*), able to be foreseen

pre-di-lec-tion (*n.*), a tendency toward, preference

pre-mier (*adj.*), first, chief

prem-ise (*n.*), an introductory statement that is the basis of an argument or discussion

pre-mi-um (*adj.*), best

pre-pon-der-ant (*adj.*), having greater quantity, dominant

pre-sage (*v.*), to foreshadow

pres-sur-ize (*v.*), to fill a chamber with gas at an elevated pressure

pri-ma fa-cie (*adj.*), on the first appearance

prin-ci-pal (*adj.*), most important; (*n.*), a leader, chief or head

prin-ci-ple (*n.*), a fundamental rule or law

pri-or-i-ty (*n.*), something that comes before something else

prism (*n.*), a solid of glass or crystal having regular, flat sides

pris-mat-ic (*adj.*), see prism; *also* a crystal system

pro- (*prefix*), in favor of, in front of

prob-a-bil-i-ty (*n.*), the likelihood of something happening

probe (*v.*), to examine thoroughly; to examine by feeling deeply into something with a long tool; (*n.*), a long tool used to contact something

prob-lem-at-i-cal (*adj.*), expressing some doubt

pro-cess (*n.*), an established way of doing something; (*v.*), to subject to a given procedure

pro-cliv-i-ty (*n.*), a tendency toward

pro-di-gious (*adj.*), very great in amount

pro-file (*n.*), an outline

pro-found (*adj.*), deep

pro-fuse (*adj.*), in great numbers

pro-fu-sion (*n.*), a great quantity

prog-no-sis (*n.*), a prediction

prog-nos-ti-cate (*v.*), to predict

pro-gram (*n.*), a sequence of instructions for a computer; *also* a sequence of plans for achieving a goal

pro-ject (*v.*), to plan, devise; *also* to represent in a drawing

proj-ect (*n.*), a set task

pro-jec-tile (*n.*), something thrown

pro-lif-er-ate (*v.*), to grow rapidly by adding many parts

pro-lif-ic (*adj.*), able to produce a great deal

pro-me-thi-um (*n.*), a chemical element, Pm

prom-i-nent (*adj.*), standing out

pro-mul-gate (*v.*), to make known; to declare

proof (*n.*), a printed sheet which is to be examined for errors; *also* a measure of the strength of alcohol

prop (*n.*), a support; (*v.*), to support

prop-a-gate (*v.*), to cause to extend

pro-pane (*n.*), a gaseous organic chemical compound

pro-pel (*v.*), to push forward

pro-pel-lant (*n.*), the material which causes something to be pushed forward

pro-pen-si-ty (*n.*), a tendency toward

pro-pin-qui-ty (*n.*), nearness

pro-pi-tious (*adj.*), favorable

pro-por-tion-al (*adj.*), having the same, unchanging ratio or relationship

pro-pri-etary (*adj.*), privately owned

pro-pul-sion (*n.*), the act of pushing something forward

pro-pyl (*n.*), an organic chemical radical

pro-rate (*v.*), to divide up in proportion

pro-sa-ic (*adj.*), ordinary

pro-scribe (*v.*), to prohibit

pro-spec-tus (*n.*), a detailed report giving plans for a new enterprise

prot-ac-tin-i-um (*n.*), a chemical element, Pa

pro-tag-o-nist (*n.*), one who supports a particular cause

pro-ti-um (*n.*), an isotope of hydrogen

proto- (*prefix*), first

pro-ton (*n.*), a positively charged particle in the nucleus of atoms

pro-to-plasm (*n.*), living material

pro-to-type (*n.*), an original model which is used as an example

pro-trac-tor (*n.*), a tool used in drawing and measuring angles

pro-tu-ber-ant (*adj.*), extending out

pro-vi-so (*n.*), a condition, stipulation

prox-im-i-ty (*n.*), nearness

pseud- or pseudo- (*prefix*),

false

psi (*n.*), a Greek letter, ψ

P-type (*adj.*), semiconductor material doped with P-dopants

pul-ley (*n.*), an arrangement of wheels and rope which aids in lifting and pulling

pulse (*n.*), a sudden jolt, usually of electrical force

pulse width (*n.*), the time a pulse of electrical energy lasts

pul-ver-ize (*v.*), to crush into powder

punc-ture (*v.*), to pierce

purge (*v.*), to cleanse thoroughly

push-pull (*adj.*), a type of electronic circuit

pyr-, pyro- (*prefix*), fire

pyr-a-mid (*n.*), a solid with a flat bottom and triangular sides that meet at a point

Py-rex (*n.*), a heat-resistant glass

pyr-i-dine (*n.*), an organic chemical compound

py-rite *or* py-ri-tes (*n.*), a mineral of iron

py-ro-chem-i-cal (*adj.*), referring to reactions at elevated temperatures

py-ro-lu-mi-nes-cence (*n.*), giving off of light as the result of heat

py-rol-y-sis (*n.*), a chemical reaction brought about by the action of heat

py-ro-lyt-ic (*adj.*), *see* pyrolysis

py-ro-lyze (*v.*), *see* pyrolysis

py-ro-met-al-lur-gy (*n.*), chemical reactions of metals at high temperatures

py-rom-e-ter (*n.*), an instrument for measuring temperature

py-ro-phor-ic (*adj.*), easily ignited

py-ro-phos-phate (*n.*), a radical of phosphorus and oxygen

Q

quad- (*prefix*), four

quad-rant (*n.*), one fourth of a geometrical figure; *also* an instrument for measuring altitudes

qua-drat-ic (*adj.*), an algebraic expression containing a term that is raised to the second power

quad-ri-lat-er-al (*adj.*), having four sides

quad-ri-va-lent (*adj.*), having a chemical valence of four

qual-i-fy (*v.*), to describe, to modify

qual-i-ta-tive (*adj.*), relating to the qualities of something; descriptive; *note difference from* quantitative

qual-i-ty (*n.*), a characteristic or parameter

quan-ti-fy (*v.*), to describe with exact numbers

quan-ti-ta-tive (*adj.*), referring to the measurement of amounts in exact numbers

quan-tize (*v.*), to express in terms of quantum mechanics

quan-tum (pl. quanta) (*n.*), an irreducible interval or quantity

quartz (*n.*), a mineral of silicon; *also* a glassy crystal having a very high melting point qua-si (*adv.*, *prefix*), similar to, as though

qua-ter-na-ry (*adj.*), consisting of four parts; *also* fourth in a series

quench (*v.*), to extinguish; to douse in water

que-ry (*n.*), question

quick-sil-ver (*n.*), mercury

qui-es-cent (*adj.*), quiet, inactive

R

rab-bet (*n.*), a groove or channel; (*v.*), to cut a groove or channel

race (*n.*), a groove in which ball bearings roll

rack (*n.*), a toothed bar used with a gear; a holder or support; (*v.*), to place objects into position on a rack

ra-dar (*n.*), an electronic system used to locate objects

ra-dar-scope (*n.*), the receiving screen of a radar set

ra-di-al (*adj.*), spreading out from the center, like the radius of a circle

ra-di-an (*n.*), a measure of angle

ra-di-ant (*adj.*), *see* radiate

ra-di-ate (*v.*), to emit rays

ra-di-a-tor (*n.*), *see* radiate

rad-i-cal (*n.*), in mathematics, a root; a mathematical expression under a radical sign, √; in chemistry, a fundamental part of a compound; (*adj.*), extreme

ra-dio- (*prefix*), referring to something being emitted radially

ra-dio-ac-tive (*adj.*), emitting subatomic particles and rays

ra-dio-chem-is-try (*n.*), the branch of chemistry that deals with the dissociation of elements into isotopes and rays

ra-dio fre-quen-cy (*n.*), the range of frequencies of electromagnetic waves used in radio and television, abbreviated rf or RF

ra-dio-graph (*n.*), an X-ray photograph

ra-di-og-ra-phy (*n.*), the process of taking pictures with X-rays

ra-dio-iso-tope (*n.*), a radioactive isotope

ra-dio-lu-mi-nes-cence (*n.*), a glow as a result of exposure to radiation

ra-di-om-e-ter (*n.*), an instrument used to measure radiant energy

ra-dio-sonde (*n.*), an electronic system for sending weather information from an unmanned balloon

ra-di-um (*n.*), a radioactive chemical element, Ra

ra-di-us (*n.*), a straight line from the center of a circle to the circumference

ra-dix (*n.*), a number taken as the base of a number system

ra-dome (*n.*), a dome-shaped structure for housing and protecting a radar antenna, usually on an airplane

ra-don (*n.*), a chemical element, Rn; a dissociation product of radium

ram-jet (*adj.*), a type of jet engine

ramp (*n.*), a sloping pathway

ran-dom (*adj.*), without pattern or plan

ran-dom-ize (*v.*), to mix up so as to eliminate any order or planned arrangement

range (*n.*), an extent

rank (*n.*), a position in a series; (*v.*), to arrange in positions according to some factor

Ran-kine (*n.*), a temperature scale

rar-efied (*adj.*), scant thin

rasp (*n.*), a coarse file

ratch-et (*n.*), a metal tooth which prevents a gear from turning in the wrong direction

rat-ed (*adj.*), a standard of performance

rat-ing (*n.*), classification according to performance ability

ra-tio (*n.*), a mathematical expression showing the relation of one factor to another

ra-tio-nal (*adj.*), reasonable

ra-tio-nale (*n.*), the basis

ra-tio-nal-ize (*v.*), to perform a certain mathematical manipulation

ray (*n.*), that which is radiated

re (*prep.*), with regard to

re- (*prefix*), again

re-act (*v.*), to act on each other, especially with regard to chemical action

re-ac-tance (*n.*), resistance to the flow of electrical current

re-ac-tion (*n.*), the interaction between different things, particularly chemicals

re-ac-ti-vate (*v.*), to render active again

read-out (*n.*), a type of electronic circuit

re-agent (*n.*), something that may take part in a chemical reaction

re-cep-ta-cle (*n.*), a container

re-cep-tor (*n.*), that which receives

re-cess (*n.*), an indentation or interruption

re-cip-ro-cal (*adj.*, *n.*), opposite; in reverse proportion

rec-la-ma-tion (*n.*), the process of returning something to use

re-coil (*v.*), to spring back

rec-on-cile (*v.*), to bring back into harmony

re-crys-tal-ize (*v.*), to crystallize again after having existed in an amorphous state

rec-ti-fy (*v.*), to convert alternating current to direct current

re-cur (*v.*), to happen again

re-duce (*v.*), to remove oxygen; or to cause a reaction in which one product goes to a lower valence

re-dun-dant (*adj.*), superfluous

re-en-trant (*adj.*), leading inward

re-fine (*v.*), to purify

re-flec-tion (*n.*), the return of energy or an image from a surface

re-flex (*adj.*), directed back

re-fract (*v.*), to cause light waves to bend

re-frac-tion (*n.*), the bending of light waves

re-frac-tor (*n.*), a kind of telescope

re-frac-to-ry (*adj.*), resistant

to heat

re-fute (*v.*), to disprove

re-gen-er-ate (*v.*), to restore

re-gen-er-a-tive (*adj.*), a kind of electronic circuit

re-gime (*n.*), a regular pattern

reg-i-men (*n.*), a set procedure

re-gress (*v.*), to turn back to an earlier stage

re-gres-sion (*n.*), the return to a less developed state

re-gres-sive (*adj.*), *see* regression

reg-u-late (*v.*), to make happen in accordance with rules

re-i-fy (*v.*), to consider as a real thing

re-in-force (*v.*), to strengthen

re-it-er-ate (*v.*), to say again

re-late (*v.*), to show a connection with

rel-a-tive (*adj.*), having a connection with

rel-a-tiv-i-ty (*n.*), a theory in physics showing that there is an equivalence between mass and energy

re-lax-ation os-cil-la-tor (*n.*), an electronic circuit

re-lay (*n.*), an electrical switch; *also* an electronic amplification station used in passing along television and other signals; (*v.*), to pass along

rel-e-vant (*adj.*), pertinent

re-lief (*n.*), something that stands out from a flat surface

re-luc-tance (*n.*), resistance to megnetic influence

re-luc-tiv-i-ty (*n.*), *see* reluctance

re-me-di-a-ble (*adj.*), able to be fixed

re-miss (*adj.*), negligent

re-mote cut-off (*n.*), an electronic circuit

re-nege (*v.*), to deny

re-pro-duce (*v.*), to duplicate

re-qui-site (*adj.*), essential

re-search (*v.*), to investigate

res-er-voir (*n.*), a place where something is stored

re-sid-u-al (*adj.*), left over

res-i-due (*n.*), that which is left over

re-sil-ient (*adj.*), springy, elastic

res-in (*n.*), a constituent of plastics

re-sis-tance (*n.*), impedance to electric flow, expressed in ohms

re-sis-tiv-i-ty (*n.*), the resistance offered by a unit volume of a substance

re-sis-tor (*n.*), an electrical component that impedes the flow of electrical current; (*adj.*), an electronic circuit

res-o-lu-tion (*n.*), the ability to make optical images distinct one from the other

re-solve (*v.*), *see* resolution

re-solv-ing pow-er (*n.*), the ability of a lens system to distinguish between two images lying close together

res-o-nant (*adj.*), echoing

re-spec-tive-ly (*adv.*), in a given order

re-sponse (*n.*), to react as a result of stimulation

re-spon-sive (*adj.*), reacting quickly

res-ti-tu-tion (*n.*), restoration

re-sume (*n.*), a short, sum-

ming-up, generally in reference to a career

re-ten-tiv-i-ty (*n.*), the power
of retaining magnetism

ret-i-cle (*n.*), an eyepiece used
in microscopic measure-
ments

re-triev-al (*n.*), getting desired
information from a computer
memory

retro- *(prefix)*, back, behind

retro-ac-tive *(adj.)*, make effective as of an earlier time

ret-ro-grade *(adj.)*, moving
backward

re-tro-gres-sion (*n.*), revert-
ing back to a lesser state

re-ver-ber-ate (*v.*), to echo, to
reflect

re-ver-ber-a-tion (*n.*), an echo

re-ver-ber-ato-ry *(adj.)*, echoing, reflecting

re-vers-i-ble *(adj.)*, able to be
reversed or to work in either
direction

rhe-ni-um (*n.*), a chemical element, Re

rheo- *(prefix)*, flow

rhe-ol-o-gy (*n.*), the science
that deals with the deforma-
tion of matter

rheo-stat (*n.*), a variable resistor for controlling electrical current

rho (*n.*), a Greek letter, ρ

rho-di-um (*n.*), a precious metallic chemical element, Rh

rhom-bo-he-dron (*n.*), a solid
geometrical figure having
four-sided faces

rhom-bus (*n.*), a parallelogram
having sides of equal length

rib (*n.*), a strut

rif-fling (*n.*), spiral grooves on
the inside wall of a cylinder

right an-gle (*n.*), an angle of
90°, formed by two perpendicular lines

riv-et (*n.*), a bolt used as a fas-
tener

ro-bot (*n.*), a machine that performs functions usually done
by humans

rock-et-ry (*n.*), the science of
the manufacture and operation of rockets

roent-gen (*n.*), a measure of
X-ray radiation

root (*n.*), a number which yields
an indicated number when
multiplied by itself a specified number of times

root mean square (*n.*), a spec-
cial mathematical average;
rms and RMS

ro-ta-me-ter (*n.*), an instrument for measuring the flow
of fluids

ro-ta-ry *(adj.)*, able to turn
around an axis

ro-tate (*v.*), to turn around an
axis

ro-ta-tion (*n.*), the act of rotating

ro-tor (*n.*), the moving part in a
motor

ru-bid-i-um (*n.*), a chemical
element, Rb

ru-by (*n.*), a crystal of aluminum oxide

rust (*n.*), iron oxide, the cor-
rosion product of iron

ru-the-ni-um (*n.*), a chemical
element, Ru

S

sac (*n.*), a non-rigid container
for fluid

sal (n.), salt

sal am-mo-ni-ac (n.), a chemical compound, ammonium chloride

sal-i-cyl-ic (n.), an organic chemical radical

sa-lient (adj.), noticeable; prominent

sa-line (adj.), salty; containing salts

sa-lin-i-ty (n.), the degrees of saltiness

salt (n.), a chemical compound, sodium chloride; also a compound that yields ions other than $(H)^+$ or $(OH)^-$ when it is dissolved

sal-vage (v.), to obtain something useful from something that may be partially destroyed

sa-mar-i-um (n.), a chemical element, Sm

sam-ple (v.), to remove a representative quantity from a group or from a mass for testing

sand-blast (v.), clean or roughen a surface by subjecting it to a rapid stream of sand

sand-cast (v.), to pour liquid metal for a casting into a sand mold

sap (v.), to drain

sa-po-na-ceous (adj.), soapy

sa-pon-i-fi-ca-tion (n.), the act of converting into a soap

sa-pon-i-fy (v.), to convert into soap

sap-phire (n.), a crystal of aluminum oxide; a precious stone

sat-el-lite (n.), a body that or-

bits around another body

sat-u-rate (v.), to completely penetrate and fill

saw-tooth (n.), a wave form; an electronic circuit

scan (v.), to sweep over something with a succession of rays of light or of electrons

scan-di-um (n.), a chemical element, Sc

scar-i-fy (v.), to make scratches in a surface

sche-mat-ic (n.), a diagram of an electrical, chemical, or mechanical system

schism (n.), a split, division, or separation

schist (n.), rock formation

scin-til-la (n.), a spark

scin-til-late (v.), to sparkle

scin-til-la-tion (n.), a spark or flash

scope (n.), range or extent; also abbreviation for oscilloscope

-scope (suffix), an instrument for viewing

score (v.), to scratch a surface

SCR (n.), abbreviation for silicon controlled rectifier, a semiconductor electronic device

scrap (n.), that portion of a product that does not pass requirements and is discarded; (v.), to throw away what is unsuitable

scru-ti-nize (v.), to examine closely

scru-ti-ny (n.), examination

seal (v.), to enclose in a watertight and airtight container

seam (n.), a line formed where two parts join

sear (v.), to scorch

se - cant (*n.*), a trigonometric function, the ratio of the hypotenuse of a right triangle to the side adjacent to a given acute angle

se-cond (*n.*), one sixtieth of a minute of time or of degree or arc

sec-tion (*v.*), to cut a solid to reveal a plane surface; (*n.*), a diagram of a plane which was revealed by a cut through a solid

sec-tor (*n.*), a pie-shaped section of a circle

sed-i-ment (*n.*), dregs, the material that settles out of a liquid suspension

sed - i - men - ta - ry (*adj.*), *see* sediment; *also* rocks formed by the sedimentation process

sed-i-men-ta-tion (*n.*), the act of depositing sediment

sed-u-lous (*adj.*), diligent

seep-age (*n.*), liquid that oozes through a material

see-saw (*adj.*), alternating

seg-ment (*n.*), a part; (*v.*), to cut into parts

seg - re - gate (*v.*), to put into separate groups

seis - mic (*adj.*), referring to earthquakes

seis-mo-graph (*n.*), an instrument that measures earthquakes and vibrations in the earth

seis-mol-o-gy (*n.*), the study of vibrations in the earth

seiz-ing (*adj.*), the locking together of moving parts

se-lec-tiv-i-ty (*n.*), ability of an electronic circuit to discriminate between frequen-

cies that are close together

se - le - ni - um (*n.*), a chemical element, Se

self- (*prefix*), directed toward or by itself

self-lim-it-ed (*adj.*), limited by its own nature

sel - syn (*n.*), a type of motor that turns exactly in accordance with the rotation of another separate part

se-man-tics (*n.*), the study of the meanings of words

semi- (*prefix*), half

semi-au-to-mat-ic (*adj.*), referring to a mechanism that operates partially automatically and partially as guided by an operator

semi-con-duc-tor (*n.*), a material that has an electrical conductivity midway between that of a metallic conductor and an insulator

semi - met - al (*n.*), a material having only some of the qualities of a metal

sem-i-nar (*n.*), a meeting held for the exchange of information on a given subject

sen-sor (*n.*), a device that reacts to physical phenomena (light, heat, sound, etc.) by giving off a useful response

sen-so-ry (*adj.*), referring to stimulation received by the human senses (sight, hearing, touch, etc.)

sep-a-ra-ble (*adj.*), able to be separated

se-pia (*n.*), a brown reproduction of a draftsman's drawing

se-ques-ter (*v.*), to set apart

se-ri-al (*adj.*), arranged in a

given sequence, belonging to a series

se-ries (n.), a group of things in progressive order; the name of a group of mathematical expressions that have a significant sequence; (adj.), in a row; *also* referring to an electronic circuit

ser-pen-tine (adj.), in a twisted, winding path.

ser-rat-ed (adj.), notched

ser-vo (n.), *see* servomotor

ser-vo-mo-tor (n.), a motor that turns exactly in accordance with a controlling mechanism

set (n.), a group the members of which have a particular interrelation; (v.), to put into a particular position or condition

set-up (n.), the way in which the elements of a mechanism or system are arranged

sev-er (v.), to cut

shale (n.), a kind of rock formation

shear (n.), lateral stress

sheath (n.), something which encases

sheathe (v.), to provide with a sheath

shed (v), to flow off without penetrating

shell (n.), the orbit of an electron inside an atom

shim (n.), a thin piece of metal added to a structure to bring it to desired size; (v.), to build up a dimension by adding thin sheets of metal

shock (n.), an electrical or mechanical jolt; (v.), to jolt

shock wave (n.), a compressed

wave in liquid or gas caused by something moving at great speed

short (n., v.), *see* short circuit

short cir-cuit (n.), an accidental, easy path for the flow of electrical current resulting in local overheating and burnout

shunt (n.), a path parallel or alternate to the main path for the passage of electrical current; *also* the electrical resistor used in providing an alternate path

shut-ter (n.), a movable plate that can open or close an opening

side band (n.), the range of frequencies on either side of a carrier frequency

si-de-re-al (adj.), referring to the stars

sieve (v.), to sift

sig-ma (n.), a Greek letter, Σ, σ

sign (n.), a symbol representing a word, letter or direction

sig-nal (n.), an arrangement of electrical waves that carries information

signal-to-noise ratio (n.), a measure of the amount of unwanted noise in a radio circuit

sil-i-ca (n.), the oxide of silicon, SiO_2

sil-i-cate (n.), a chemical radical containing silicon

si-li-ceous (adj.), containing silicon

sil-lic-ic (adj.), relating to silicon

sil-i-cide (n.), a silicon compound

sil-i-con (n.), a chemical element, Si; an important semi-conductor material

sil-i-cone (n.), a chemical compound of silicon which is similar to organic compounds

sil-i-co-sis (n.), a disease of the lungs caused by breathing silica dust

silk - screen (n.), a printing method

si - lo (n.), a deep cylindrical hole in the ground for storing a missile

sil-ver (n.), a heavy, precious metallic element, Ag

sim-u-late (v.), to set up a situation which copies another

sim-u-la-tor (n.), a device in a laboratory that duplicates conditions that may actually occur

si-mul-ta-neous (adj.), at the same time

sine (n.), a trigonometric function, the ratio of the side opposite an angle in a right triangle to the hypotenuse

sine wave (n.), a wave whose intensity fluctuates up and down in cycles

sin-gu-lar (adj.), unusual, individual

sink (n.), a place into which materials or energy may drain

si-nus-oi-dal (adj.), referring to phenomena which may be represented in the form of sine waves

si-phon (n.), an arrangement of tubes or pipes for drawing liquid out of a container

site (n.), a particular location

size (v.), to fill the pores of a material

siz-ing (n.), a material used to fill pores

skel-e-tel (adj.), see skeleton

skel-e-ton (n.), the basic, underlying structure

skel-e-ton-ize (v.), to reduce something to its basic underlying structure

sketch (v.), to make a simple drawing; (n.), a simple drawing

sketchy (adj.), incomplete

skew (adj.), slanted, oblique; not parallel; (v.), to make something deviate from a straight line

skid (n.), a platform used in loading of material

skin ef-fect (n.), conduction of high frequency electricity on a metal surface

slab (n.), a thick plate

slack (n.), a loose or relaxed portion

slag (n.), the glassy material that floats to the top of liquid metal during its refinement

slake (v.), to allow to absorb moisture

slate (n.), a kind of rock

slide (n.), a sliding part of a machine

slip (n.), material used in making ceramic and porcelain ware

slip - page (n.), the difference between the expected amount of power and the actual output

slip ring (n.), a part of a rotating machine used to conduct electrical current

slit (n.), a narrow opening used in optics

sludge (n.), sediment

sluice (n.), a channel for drawing away water

slur-ry (n.), a thin mixture of solids in a liquid

small sig - nal (n.), low power operation

smoke (n.), a suspension of solid particles in a gas

smol - der (v.), to burn slowly without flame

smooth - bore (adj.), having a smooth inside surface

smoth-er (v.), to suppress by depriving of oxygen

snarled (adj.), all tangled up

snor-kel (n.), a tube for conducting air into something submerged in a liquid

soap (n.), a family of organic chemical compounds

soap-stone (n.), a soft rock

sock - et (n.), an opening for holding a part

so - da (n.), the chemical, sodium carbonate

so-da ash (n.), see soda

so-di-um (n.), a chemical element, Na

sol (n.), a kind of liquid solution

so-lar (adj.), referring to the sun

so-lar cell (n.), an electronic device that converts light to electricity

so-lar-ize (v.), expose to the sun

sol-der (v.), to join pieces of metal by melting and freezing another metal around them; (n.), the metal which will be melted for soldering

sole (n.), the bottom or base of something

so-le-noid (n.), a coil of wire used to open and close electrical switches

so-lid-i-fi-ca-tion (n.), freezing or hardening

sol - i - dus (n.), the range of temperatures below which an alloy or other mixture of materials is solid

sol-u-ble (adj.), able to be dissolved; or able to be explained

so - lute (n.), that which dissolves in a solution

so-lu-tion (n.), a mixture containing a dissolved substance; also the answer to a problem

solv-able (adj.), able to be explained

sol - vent (n.), a substance in which another substance is dissolved

so-nar (n.), an electronic system that detects objects on or under the surface of water by the use of sound waves

sonde (n.), a class of instruments used for making high altitude measurements, particularly for weather analysis

son-ic (adj.), referring to audible sound

so - no - buoy (n.), a buoy that transmits sonar information

so-no - lu - mi - nes - cense (n.), giving off light as a result of sound

soot (n.), a very fine black powder formed by combustion

sorb (v.), to take up by absorption or adsorption and retain

sor-bate (*n.*), that which is sorbed

sor-bent (*n.*), that which sorbs

sorp-tion (*n.*), the process of sorbing

sort (*v.*), to separate into categories

sound (*v.*), to find out the depth of something

space charge (*n.*), the level of voltage in a region

spall (*v.*), to break off small chips

spar (*n.*), a supporting strut

spark (*n.*), an electric current conducted through a gas with a sudden flash

spark gap (*n.*), the space between two conductors across which a spark flashes

spa-tial (*adj.*), relating to space

SPDT (*n.*), single pole, double throw; a type of electric switch

spe-cif-ic (*adj.*), special for a particular use

spec-i-fi-ca-tion (*n.*), a set of plans, diagrams, or instructions for making a mechanism or for carrying out a job

spe-cif-ic grav-i-ty (*n.*), the weight of a unit volume of a substance as compared with the weight of the same volume of another substance

spe-cif-ic heat (*n.*), the amount of heat required to raise the temperature of one gram of a substance one degree

spec-i-fy (*v.*), to make a specification

spec-tral (*adj.*), relating to a spectrum

spectro- (*prefix*), spectrum

spec-tro-gram (*n.*), a picture of a spectrum

spec-tro-graph (*n.*), a machine for measuring spectra

spec-trom-e-ter (*n.*), an instrument for measuring the intensity of spectral lines

spec-trum (pl. spec-tra) (*n.*), the range of frequencies of any given periodic wave system (such as light waves, electromagnetic waves); also the separation and arrangement of parts of a wave in the order of their possession of a specified quality

spec-u-lar (*adj.*), mirror-like

spec-u-late (*v.*), to consider a question; to guess

sphe-noi-dal (*adj.*), a crystal system

spher-i-cal (*adj.*), relating to a sphere

spher-oid (*n.*), an object which resembles a sphere

sphe-roi-dal (*adj.*), *see* spheroid

spie-gel-ei-sen (*n.*), a type of crude iron alloy

spig-ot (*n.*), faucet

spill-age (*n.*), that which spills over

spin-dle (*n.*), the rod onto which something is wound

spi-nel (*n.*), a class of minerals

splice (*v.*), to join two wires or cables by intertwining their strands

spline (*n.*), a keyway

spon-ta-ne-ous (*adj.*), happening by itself, without outside stimulus

spo-rad-ic (*adj.*), occurring occasionally and without regularity

sport (*n.*), something that deviates from normal

sprock-et (*n.*), a gear tooth on a wheel

sprue (*n.*), a hole in a mold through which liquid metal will flow to make a casting

SPST (*n.*), single pole, single throw; an electrical switch

spur (*n.*), a sharp projection

spu-ri-ous (*adj.*), false

square (*n.*), a four-sided figure having all right angles and all sides equal; (*v.*), to raise to the second power, to multiply an expression by itself

square root (*n.*), a factor of a number that, multiplied by itself, yields that number

square wave (*n.*), an electrical wave form

squee-gee (*n.*), a blade or roller used to squeeze liquid from the surface of flat objects

sta-bil-i-ty (*n.*), the condition of being unchanging

sta-bi-lize (*v.*), to put into an unchanging condition

sta-bi-liz-er (*n.*), that which makes something stable

sta-ble (*adj.*), unchanging

stage (*n.*), a single electronic circuit in an electronic system

stag-ing (*n.*), scaffolding

stag-nant (*adj.*), not flowing, standing still

sta-lac-tite (*n.*), a mineral deposit hanging from the roof of a cave

sta-lag-mite (*n.*), a mineral deposit extending from the floor of a cave

stamp (*v.*), to cut, bend, or emboss a material by means of a sudden impact with a die

stamp-ing (*n.*), that which has been stamped

stand by (*v.*), to be ready to act

standing wave (*n.*), a wave which appears to stand still because its portions having zero amplitude remain in the same place

stan-nate (*n.*), a salt of tin

stan-nic (*adj.*), relating to a compound of tin; (*n.*), a radical of tin

stan-nous (*n.*), a radical of tin

staple (*n.*), a U-shaped pin used in fastening

star (*adj.*), referring to a type of electronic circuit

state (*n.*), a condition something is in

stat-ic (*adj.*), unmoving; (*n.*), electrical disturbance

stat-ics (*n.*), the branch of mechanics that deals with bodies at rest

sta-tis-tic (*n.*), a single datum or piece of information

sta-tis-tics (*n.*), the branch of mathematics that deals with the collection, organization, and interpretation of masses of numerical information

stato- (*prefix*), resting; *also* at equilibrium

sta-tor (*n.*), the part of a machine that stands still

sta-tus (*n.*), condition

steady state (*adj.*), a constant condition

stea-rate (*n.*), a salt of stearic acid

stear - ric (*adj.*), relating to a kind of organic acid

ste-atite (*n.*), the mineral soapstone

steel (*n.*), an alloy of iron

sten-cil (*v.*), to print a pattern by painting over holes in a form

step-up (*adj.*), a type of transformer connection

stereo- (*prefix*), solid, three-dimensional

ste-reo-chem - is - try (*n.*), the branch of chemistry that deals with the arrangements of atoms in space

ste - reo - graph (*n.*), a picture which makes an object look solid

ste - re - og - ra - phy (*n.*), the process of making stereographs

ste-reo-scop-ic (*adj.*), relating to the ability to see objects from several vantage points at the same time so that they appear three-dimensional

ste - reo - type (*n.*), something typical, or conforming to a pattern

still (*n.*), an apparatus used for distilling liquids in order to purify them

stip-u-late (*v.*), to make a requirement

stip-u-la-tion (*n.*), a requirement

stock-pile (*v.*), to save up; to store

stoi-chio-met-ric (*adj.*), in definite proportion; referring to the balance of factors in chemical equations

stop (*n.*), a device for limiting movement

stor-age (*n.*), a type of electronic circuit; *also* the computer memory

stor-age cell (*n.*), an electrolytic cell, a battery

strain (*n.*), the amount something stretches as a result of an applied force; (*v.*), to cause to stretch or change dimension

strat-a-gem (*n.*), a clever tactical maneuver

strati- (*prefix*), in layers

strat - i - fy (*v.*), to arrange in layers

strato-sphere (*n.*), the layer of atmosphere starting seven miles up from the earth

stra - tum (pl. stra-ta) (*n.*), a layer

stream-line (*n.*), a contour constructed so that fluids can flow easily around the object

stress (*n.*), a force which may strain an object

stri-at-ed (*adj.*), covered with fine, parallel grooves or lines

strip (*v.*), to remove a layer

strobe (*n.*), a stroboscope

stro-bo-scope (*n.*), an instrument that shows a moving object as though it were standing still

stro-bo-tron (*n.*), the tube used in a stroboscope

stron-tium (*n.*), a chemical element, Sb

struc-ture (*n.*), the physical make-up of a material

strut (*n.*), a structural member

sty-lus (*n.*), a needle-like tool

sty-rene (*n.*), an organic chemical compound

sub- (*prefix*), under

sub-atom-ic (*adj.*), particles smaller than atoms

sub-class (*n.*), a subdivision of a class

sub-con-trac-tor (*n.*), a company that works for another company which is under contract for a whole job

sub-ject (*v.*), to cause something to undergo a certain action

sub-li-ma-tion (*n.*), the change of physical state from solid to gas

sub-or-din-ate (*adj.*), in a lower class

sub-ox-ide (*n.*), an oxide containing a comparatively small amount of oxygen

sub-script (*n.*), a number or symbol written a half space below a mathematical, physical, or chemical expression

sub-sid-iary (*adj.*), aiding or secondary

sub-son-ic (*adj.*), moving at less than the speed of sound

sub-strate (*n.*), an underlying base material upon which materials are deposited

sub-stra-tum (*n.*), a layer just under the surface

sub-tra-hend (*n.*), the number which is to be subtracted from another number

suc-ces-sion (*n.*), the order in which something happens

suc-ces-sive-ly (*adv.*), in order

su-crose (*n.*), an organic chemical compound; a sugar

suc-tion (*n.*), the act of applying a partial vacuum

suf-fuse (*v.*), to spread over

sulfa- (*prefix*), relating to sulfur

sul-fate (*n.*), a radical of sulfur

sul-fide (*n.*), a compound of sulfur

sul-fo-nate (*v.*), to convert into sulfonic acid; (*n.*), a salt of sulfur

sul-fone (*n.*), a sulfur compound

sul-fon-ic acid (*n.*), a sulfur-containing acid

sul-fo-nyl (*n.*), a sulfur radical

sul-fur *or* sul-phur (*n.*), a chemical element, S

sul-fu-ric (*adj.*), pertaining to sulfur; a sulfur radical

sum (*n.*), the result of adding; (*v.*), to add

sum-ma-rize (*v.*), to make a summary

sum-ma-ry (*n.*), concise summing-up of what has been presented

sum-ma-tion (*n.*), the sum

sum-mer (*adj.*), an electrical circuit, used especially in computers

sump (*n.*), a container for drained fluids

sun-spot (*n.*), a mark on the surface of the sun

super- (*prefix*), in addition; greater than

su-per-a-ble (*adj.*), able to be overcome

su-per-con-duc-tiv-i-ty (*n.*), electrical conduction in the absence of resistance which

occurs at very low temperatures

su - per - cool (*v*.), to cool so rapidly that a substance remains liquid below its freezing point

su - per - fi - cial (*adj*.), only on the surface

su-per-flu-ous (*adj*.), extra, unneeded

su-per-heat (*v*.), to heat a substance above its boiling point and still keep it liquid

su-per-het-ero-dyne (*adj*.), a kind of electronic system (a radio usually) which subtracts out the signal frequency from other frequency ranges

su - per - phos - phate (*n*.), a chemical mixture of phosphorus compounds

su-per-sat-u-rate (*v*.), to dissolve more solute into a solvent than it can normally hold

sup - er - script (*n*.), a number written a half space above an expression

su-per-sede (*v*.), to take the place of

su - per - son - ic (*adj*.), faster than sound

su-per-struc-ture (*n*.), a structure added as an extension of a basic structure

sup-plant (*v*.), to take the place of

sup - ple - ment (*n*.), something that is added to something else; also the angle which, when added to another angle, equals 180°

sup-ple-men-ta-ry (*adj*.), *see* supplement

supra- (*prefix*), above

sup-pres (*v*.), to inhibit

sur- (*prefix*), over

sur-face (*v*.), to make smooth

sur-veil-lance (*n*.), watching by electronic means

sur - vey (*v*.), to measure and stake out a piece of land

sus - cep - ti - bil - i - ty (*n*.), an electrical quality of a dielectric

sus-pend (*v*.), to hang; to postpone

sus-pen-sion (*n*.), a system for hanging something; *also* a liquid, solid, or gas in which solid matter floats without settling out

swage (*v*.), to shape metal by hammering

sweep (*v*.), to examine a surface electronically; *also* an electronic circuit

switch-ing (*adj*.), an electronic circuit

swiv-el (*n*.), a device for allowing a part to pivot

sym-bol (*n*.), a mark or letter used to represent something

sym-bol-ize (*v*.), to show with symbols

sym-met-ri-cal (*adj*.), balanced

sym - me - try (*n*.), a state of balance

sym-po-sium (*n*.), a meeting to discuss a particular subject

symp-tom (*n*.), something that indicates that a particular phenomenon exists or has occurred

syn- (*prefix*), with

sync *or* synch (*n*.), synchronization

syn-chro (*n*.), a selsyn or synchronous motor

syn-chro- (*prefix*), referring to synchronization

syn-chro-nism (*n.*), the quality of occurring simultaneously

syn-chron-i-za-tion (*n.*), the act of occurring simultaneously

syn-chro-niz-ing (*adj.*), a type of electronic circuit

syn-chro-tron (*n.*), an apparatus for giving very high speeds to charged particles

syn-drome (*n.*), a set of symptoms typical of a particular condition

syn-the-sis (*n.*), the construction or production of something from its essential, basic parts

syn-thet-ic (*adj.*), artificial

sys-tem (*n.*), an assemblage of items and groups of items that forms a meaningful whole

sys-tem-at-ic (*adj.*), consisting of a system; organized

sys-tem-a-tize (*v.*), to put into a system

T

tab (*n.*), a projecting piece

tab-u-lar (*adj.*), data arranged in regular rows and columns

tab-u-late (*v.*), *see* tabular

ta-chom-e-ter (*n.*), an instrument for measuring the speed of rotation

tac-o-nite (*n.*), a kind of mineral

tac-tic (*n.*), a method of procedure

tac-tile (*adj.*), perceptible by touch

tail-ings (*n.*), that which is left over, useless residue

tail-stock (*n.*), part of a lathe

tal-ly (*n.*), the counting up, the score; (*v.*), to count up; to make correspond

tamp (*v.*), to press by a series of blows

tan-dem (*adj.*), in order, one behind the other

tan-gen-cy (*n.*), state of being tangent

tan-gent (*n.*), the ratio of the length of the side opposite an acute angle in a right triangle to the side adjacent; (*adj.*), the intersection of a line with a curved surface at only one point; *also* referring to a grazing contact

tan-gen-tial (*adj.*), relating to that which is tangent; *also*, veering off at a different angle or approach, divergent

tan-gi-ble (*adj.*), able to be touched, real

tank (*n.*), a type of electronic circuit

tan-nic ac-id (*n.*), an organic acid

tan-nin (*n.*), an organic chemical compound

tan-ta-lum (*n.*), a chemical element, Ta

tap (*v.*), to machine threads into a hole; *also* to remove fluid from a container; (*n.*), a tool used to make threads in a hole

tape (*v.*), to record on magnetic tape

ta-per (*n.*), a gradual lessening of dimension of a rod; (*v.*), to make a gradual lessening in a dimension

tap-pet (*n.*), a small lever used in engines

tare (*n.*), the weight of a container deducted from the total weight to give only the weight of the contents of the container; *also* a counterweight

tar-get (*n.*), the object in a vacuum tube which is struck by a stream of electrons

tar - tar - ic ac - id (*n.*), an organic acid

tar-trate (*n.*), a salt of tartaric acid

tau (*n.*), a Greek letter, τ

taut (*adj.*), tight

taut- (*prefix*), same

tax (*v.*), to strain the capabilities of

tax- (*prefix*), arrangement

taxi (*v.*), to move an airplane at low speed on the ground

tax-on-o-my (*n.*), the study of the principles of classification

tech-ne-tium (*n.*), a chemical element, Tc

tech-ni-cal (*adj.*), organized in accordance with scientific thinking

tech-ni-cal-i-ty (*n.*), a detail having significance only to a specialist

tech-ni-cian (*n.*), one who can apply the material of engineering and science

tech-nique (*n.*), a procedure, or way of doing something

techno- (*prefix*), technical

tech-no-log-i-cal (*adj.*), relating to technology

tech-nol-o-gy (*n.*), the means used to attain a given purpose; *also* application of scientific findings for useful purposes

tec-ton-ics (*n.*), the branch of geology dealing with the effects of great pressures on the earth's crust

tele- (*prefix*), at a distance

tele - com - mu - ni - ca-tion (*n.*), sending messages over great distances

teleg - ra - phy (*n.*), use of the telegraph to send and receive messages

tele-me-ter (*v.*), to send measurements by an automatic instrument from a distance

tel-lu-ride (*n.*), a compound of tellurium

tel-lu-ri-um (*n.*), a chemical element, Te

tem - per (*n.*), the springiness of a piece of metal; (*v.*), to subject metal to heat to enhance its mechanical qualities; *also* to make an argument less strong

ten-a-ble (*adj.*), capable of being defended by reason

te-na-cious (*adj.*), hard to pull apart, holding tightly

te-na-ci-ty (*n.*), *see* tenacious

tend (*v.*), to move in a particular direction

te-net (*n.*), a principle on which something is based

ten - or (*n.*), the general tendency

ten-sile (*adj.*), relating to tension

ten-si-om-e-ter (*n.*), an apparatus for measuring tension

ten - sion (*n.*), the pull or stretch; *also* the amount of voltage difference or potential that may exist between two points

ten - sor (*n.*), a mathematical expression

ten-ta-tive (*adj.*), uncertain

ten-u-ous (*adj.*), thin; flimsy

ter-bi-um (*n.*), a chemical element, Tb

term (*n.*), a part of a mathematical expression separated from the other parts by plus or minus signs; *also* the end; *also* a provision or condition

ter - mi - nal (*n.*), the place to which electrical connections are made on an electrical component

ter-mi-nate (*v.*), to close or to end

ter-mi-nol-o-gy (*n.*), the definitions and symbols used in a given activity; the nomenclature

ter - mi - nus (*n.*), the place at which something ends

ter-na-ry (*adj.*), threefold

ter-res-tri-al (*adj.*), referring to the earth

ter-tial (*adj.*), third

ter-ti-ar-y (*adj.*), of the third rank

tetra- (*prefix*), four

te-trag-o-nal (*adj.*), having four angles

tet - ra - he - dral (*adj.*), having four sides

tet-ra-va-lent (*adj.*), having a chemical valence of four

tet-rode (*n.*), an electrical device having four active ele-

ments

te-trox-ide (*n.*), an oxide having four atoms of oxygen

tet-ryl (*n.*), an organic chemical compound

tex - tu - al (*adj.*), relating to a text

tex - ture (*n.*), the way something is put together, especially at the surface

thal-li-um (*n.*), a chemical element, Tl

the-o-rem (*n.*), a principle that can be demonstrated by using known facts

the-o-ret-i-cal (*adj.*), speculative, abstract, not necessarily based on experiment

the-o-ry (*n.*), a speculation, a principle with some basis in fact

ther-mal (*adj.*), relating to heat

therm-ion (*n.*), a charged particle emitted from a red-hot substance

therm-ion-ic (*adj.*), referring to electrically charged particles emitted from hot surfaces

therm-is-tor (*n.*), an electrical component that changes its electrical resistance as a function of temperature

Ther-mit (*n.*), a type of bomb

thermo- (*prefix*), heat

ther-mo-cou-ple (*n.*), a device made of two dissimilar pieces of metal which generates an electrical voltage as a result of temperature changes at the metal junction

ther-mo-dy-nam-ics (*n.*), the physics of heat and energy

ther - mo - elec - tric - i-ty (*n.*),

electrical current generated by heat; *also* a technique of cooling electricity (the Peltier effect)

ther-mo-lu-mi-nes-cence (*n.*), giving off light as a result of heat

ther-mo-pile (*n.*), a device consisting of many thermocouples, generates substantial current

ther-mo-plas-tic (*adj.*), able to be formed when warm

ther-mo-set-ting (*adj.*), hardening as a result of heat

ther-mo-stat (*n.*), a device for maintaining a set temperature

the-sis (*n.*), a proposition

the-ta (*n.*), a Greek letter, θ

thi-a-zole (*n.*), an organic chemical compound

thin-ner (*n.*), a solvent which will dilute a solution

thio- (*prefix*), sulfur

thio-phos-phor-ic ac-id (*n.*), a chemical compound

thio-sul-fu-ric ac-id (*n.*), a chemical compound

tho-ria (*n.*), thorium oxide

tho-ri-um (*n.*), a chemical element, Th

thu-li-um (*n.*), a chemical element, Tm

thy-ra-tron (*n.*), a type of electron tube

tile (*n.*), a slab made of ceramic

tim-bre (*n.*), a quality of a tone which makes it sound distinctive

tim-ing (*n.*), a sequence of occurrences preset for definite time intervals

tin (*n.*), a chemical element, Sn

tin foil (*n.*), a thin sheet of metal not necessarily of tin

tin-ny (*adj.*), made of light material; cheap

tip-off (*v.*), to pinch a piece of tubing thus cutting and sealing it

ti-ta-ni-um (*n.*), a chemical element, Ti

ti-trate (*v.*), *see* titration

ti-tra-tion (*n.*), the doling out of measured quantities of liquids until an indicator shows that a chemical balance is achieved in a solution

TNT (*n.*), an explosive, trinitrotoluene

tog-gle switch (*n.*), an electrical switch operated by flipping a small metal rod

tol-er-ance (*n.*), the amount a measurement is allowed to vary

tol-u-ene (*n.*), an organic solvent

tol-u-ol (*n.*), toluene (commercial grade)

tooth (*n.*), one of a set of projections on a gear

to-pog-ra-phy (*n.*), the representation of features of land on a map

to-roid (*n.*), a doughnut-shaped object

to-roi-dal (*adj.*), *see* toroid

torque (*n.*), a force that tends to produce rotation or twisting

tor-sion (*n.*), the stress in a material as a result of torque

tour-ma-line (*n.*), a silicate mineral

tox-ic (*adj.*), poisonous

trace (*n.*), a tiny amount

trac-er (*n.*), a radioactive

chemical used to indicate movements of chemicals

trac-tile (*adj.*), able to be stretched

tra-jec-to-ry (*n.*), the path taken by a projectile in flight

trans- (*prefix*), across

trans-ceiv-er (*n.*), a receiver-transmitter combination that uses many of the same electronic components for both receiving and sending

trans-con-duc-tance (*n.*), a property of vacuum tubes, abbreviated mu or G_m

trans-duc-er (*n.*), a device that receives a signal in one form of energy and changes it to another form

trans-fi-nite (*adj.*), beyond finite values

trans-for-ma-tion (*n.*), a mathematical operation

trans-for-mer (*n.*), a device that changes the current-voltage distribution of alternating electricity

tran-sient (*n., adj.*), something that comes and goes; short-lived

tran-sis-tor (*n.*), a small electronic component made of semiconductor material, that performs the jobs done by radio tubes

tran-sis-tor-ize (*v.*), to change an electronic system from tubes to transistors

tran-si-tion (*n.*), a change from one state or place to another

tran-si-to-ry (*adj.*), temporary

trans-late (*v.*), to move something from one place or form to another

trans-la-tion (*n.*), the movement of something from one place or form to another

trans-lu-cent (*adj.*), transmitting light in a diffuse manner

trans-mis-sion (*n.*), the sending of signals

trans-mit (*v.*), *see* transmission

trans-mit-ter (*n.*), the electronic system that sends out signals

trans-mu-ta-tion (*n.*), the changing of one element into another

tran-spon-der (*n.*), radio system that automatically responds when it receives a signal

trans-pose (*v.*), to change the relative position of mathematical expressions

trans-ura-ni-um (*adj.*), having a greater atomic number than uranium

trans-verse (*adj.*), lying across

trap (*n.*), a crystalline defect in a semiconductor that prevents carriers of electricity from moving through

trap-e-zoid (*n.*), a four-sided figure having only two parallel sides

tra-verse (*v.*), to move across

tri- (*prefix*), three

tri-ad (*n.*), a group of three

tri-an-gle (*n.*), a three-sided plane figure

tri-an-gu-lar (*adj.*), relating to triangles

tri-an-gu-late (*v.*), to make triangles

tri-clin-ic (*adj.*), relating to a crystal form

trig-o-no-met-ric (*adj.*), referring to trigonometry

trig - o - nom - e - try (*n.*), the branch of mathematics that deals with properties of triangles on surfaces and in solids

tril-lion (*n.*), a million times a million, or a thousand billion, 10^{12}

tri-no-mi-al (*n.*), a mathematical expression having three terms

tri - ode (*n.*), a three-element vacuum tube or semiconductor device

tri-ox-ide (*n.*), an oxide containing three atoms of oxygen

trip - ler (*n.*), a type of electronic circuit

trip-let (*n.*), a group of three

tri-ti-um (*n.*), an isotope of hydrogen

tri-va-lent (*adj.*), having a valence of three

-tron (*suffix*), an instrument or device

tro-po-sphere (*n.*), a layer of the atmosphere below the stratosphere

trough (*n.*), a channel

troy weight (*n.*), a system of units of weight based on a pound having 12 ounces

true (*adj.*), well lined-up, accurate

trun-cate (*v.*), to cut off a part and replace it with a flat plane; to shorten by cutting

tube (*n.*), a hollow pipe; *also* an electronic device capable of rectifying and amplifying

tub-ing (*n.*), something having the shape of a hollow pipe

tu-bu-lar (*adj.*), tube-like

tum-ble (*v.*), to throw objects around inside a barrel in order to round off their corners and smooth off rough surfaces

tuned (*adj.*), a type of electronic circuit

tung-sten (*n.*), a chemical element, W; *also called* wolfram

tur-bid (*adj.*), muddy, obscured

tur-bine (*n.*), an engine run by the flow of liquids or gas

turbo- (*prefix*), turbine

tur - bu - lent (*adj.*), violently agitated

tur-ret (*n.*), a holder for tools in a machine

twin (*n.*), a crystal form in which two parts of a crystal are mirror images; (*v.*), to form a twin crystal

ty-ro (*n.*), a neophyte, a novice

U

ubiq - ui - tous (*adj.*), being everywhere at the same time

-u-lar (*suffix*), relating to

-u-lent (*suffix*), abounding in

ul-ti-mate (*adj.*), the farthest out, basic, fundamental, eventual

ul-tra- (*prefix*), beyond

ul - tra high fre-quen-cy (*n.*), a rapid electromagnetic wave, uhf

ul - tra - son - ic (*adj.*), sound waves of higher frequency than audible sound

ul - tra - vi - o - let (*adj.*), light waves of higher frequency than visible light but slower than X-rays

um-bra (*n.*), a shadow

un- (*prefix*), contrary to; not

un-coil (*v.*), to unwind

un-der-cut (*v.*), to cut away a portion of something so as to leave an overhanging region

un-du-late (*v.*), to move in waves

uni- (*prefix*), single; one

uni-fy (*v.*), to make into a single system

union (*n.*), a joint between several things; a piece of plumbing used to make pipe joints

uni-po-lar (*adj.*), having only one electrical or magnetic pole

unique (*adj.*), the only one; without similarity

unit (*n.*), an independent part of a system

unit cell (*n.*), the smallest atomic arrangement of a crystal

uni-va-lent (*adj.*), having a valence of one

uni-verse (*n.*), a particular environment in which an experiment is carried out

un-sta-ble (*adj.*), not stable; unsteady, fluctuating

up-si-lon (*n.*), a Greek letter, υ

ura-ni-um (*n.*), a chemical element, U

-ure (*suffix*), process

urea (*n.*), an organic chemical compound

ure-thane (*n.*), an organic chemical compound

-ur-gy (*suffix*), the art of dealing with material

us-age (*n.*), the amount used

V

va-cu-ity (*n.*), an empty space

vac-u-um (*n.*), the absence of material

va-lence (*n.*), the number of bonds available for chemical reaction which an atom or a radical may have; the number of electrical charges on an atom or radical

val-id (*adj.*), sound, true

val-i-date (*v.*), to confirm

val-ue (*n.*), the amount of anything expressed mathematically

valve (*n.*), a mechanism that opens or closes a passage; *also* a radio tube (British); (*v.*), to open or close a passage

va-na-di-um (*n.*), a chemical element, V

vane (*n.*), part of a mechanism that can be moved by the flow of fluids

va-por (*n.*), a material in the gaseous state

va-por-ize (*v.*), to cause to turn into vapor

va-por pres-sure (*n.*), the pressure exerted by a vapor

var-ac-tor (*n.*), a semiconductor diode that has variable reactance

vari- (*prefix*), varied

vari-able (*n.*), a symbol in a mathematical expression that can assume any value

vari-ance (*n.*), the amount something varies from a predicted amount

vari-ant (*n.*), that which does not conform with a standard

va-ris-tor (*n.*), a resistor whose resistance changes as voltage changes vary (*v.*), to change

vec-tor (*n.*), a mathematical expression that represents both quantity and direction, often indicated by an arrow above the expression

ve-hi-cle (*n.*), a structure in which an experiment may be carried out; *also* an inactive medium in which another substance may be carried

vein (*n.*), a mineral deposit

ve-loc-i-ty (*n.*), the speed of movement

ve-neer (*n.*), a surface layer of good appearance

vent (*n.*), an opening to allow for the escape of gas; (*v.*), to make openings for the escape of gasses

ven-ti-late (*v.*), to expose to air

ven-tu-ri (*n.*), a structure in a pipe

ve-rac-i-ty (*n.*), truthfulness

ver-ba-tim (*adv.*), in the exact words

ver-i-fy (*v.*), to confirm, establish

ver-mic-u-late (*n.*), mica-containing mineral

ver-ni-er (*n.*), a fine adjustment, or measuring device, consisting of a small scale

ver-sa-tile (*adj.*), able to act in a variety of areas

ver-sus (*prep.*), against; *also* refers to connections between variables graphed as functions of each other

ver-tex (pl. ver-ti-ces) (*n.*), the point at the top

ver-ti-cal (*adj.*), straight up and down, perpendicular

ves-sel (*n.*), a container

ves-tige (*n.*), a trace of something; a scrap

via (*prep.*), by way of or by means of

vi-a-ble (*adj.*), workable

vi-al (*n.*), a small container

vi-bra-tion (*n.*), a set of repeated oscillations

vi-bra-tor (*n.*), a mechanism that vibrates

vi-bra-to-ry (*adj.*), *see* vibration

vid-eo (*n.*), that which can be seen in television

vid-i-con (*n.*), a camera used in television

vi-nyl (*n.*), an organic chemical radical; *or* a class of plastics

vir-tu-al (*adj.*), almost actual, but not in fact real

vir-u-lent (*adj.*), very harsh and strong

vis-cos-i-ty (*n.*), thickness or runniness of a liquid

vis-cous (*adj.*), *see* viscosity

vise (*n.*), a tool for holding parts while they are worked on

vi-su-al-ize (*v.*), to form a mental image; to imagine

vi-ti-ate (*v.*), to make ineffective

vit-re-ous (*adj.*), glassy

vit-ri-fy (*v.*), to melt and make into a glassy substance

void (*n.*), a vacuum; (*v.*), to empty; (*adj.*), empty

vol-a-tile (*adj.*), easily vaporized

volt (*n.*), the unit of electrical force or potential

volt-age (*n.*), the amount of electrical potential

vol-ta-ic (*adj.*), referring to

voltage

volt‑am‑pere (n.), a watt; or the unit of electrical power which is the product of volts and amperes

vol‑u‑met‑ric (adj.), referring to the measurement of volume

vor‑tex (n.), (pl. vor‑ti‑ces), a swirl of rotating liquid

vul‑can‑iza‑tion (n.), a thermal or chemical treatment of rubber to improve its properties

W

ware (n.), manufactured articles

warp (v.), to twist or turn out of shape

watt (n.), the unit of electrical power equal to volts times amperes

watt‑age (n.), the amount of electrical power

watt‑hour (n.), a unit of electrical energy

watt‑me‑ter (n.), an instrument for measuring power

watt‑sec‑ond (n.), a unit of energy

wave (n.), periodic movement, or variation, which transmits energy in passing through a medium

wave band (n.), a range of radio frequencies

wave guide (n.), a metal pipe for conducting microwaves of a given frequency

wave‑length (n.), the length, time, or period of a single wave

wear (v.), to cause a surface

to be ground away as a result of repeated rubbing; (n.), the result of wearing

web (n.), a thin portion between heavy sections

we‑ber (n.), a unit of magnetic flux

wedge (n.), a chisel‑shaped piece of metal, which tapers to a thin edge; (v.), to force in between

weight‑ed (adj.), extra importance given to some data

weld (v.), to join pieces together by local melting and freezing; (n.), the place where a welded joint was made

weld‑ment (n.), an object formed of welded pieces

well (n.), a deep container

well‑found‑ed (adj.), based on correct reasoning and valid data

wet‑ta‑bil‑i‑ty (n.), ability to be wetted

wet‑ta‑ble (adj.), able to be wetted

whisk‑er (n.), a fine wire

whorl (n.), a spiral, coiled curve

wil‑lem‑ite (n.), a mineral of zinc

wind‑ing (n.), the wound wire of an electrical coil or transformer

wire (v.), to connect electrical systems with wire

wir‑ing (n.), the wire connections in electrical circuits

wob‑ble (n.), an uneven, irregular motion

wolf‑ram (n.), a chemical element, W; also known as tungsten work-a-ble (*adj.*), referring to the ability of a material to be bent and formed

worm gear (*n.*), a type of gear

wrench (*n.*), a tool; *also* a violent, twisting pull

wrought (*adj.*), manufactured

X

xan-thene (*n.*), an organic chemical compound

xe-non (*n.*), a chemical element, Xe

xe-rog-ra-phy (*n.*), a method of image reproduction

xi (*n.*), a Greek letter, Ξ, ξ

X-ray (*n.*), a high-frequency electromagnetic wave

X-ray lu-mi-nes-cence (*n.*), giving off light as a result of X-ray impact

xy-lene (*n.*), an organic chemical solvent

xy-lol (*n.*), *see* xylene

Y

ya-gi (*n.*), a type of antenna

yaw (*v.*), to swerve

yield (*v.*), to give way under force; (*n.*), the amount of output of a process

yt-ter-bi-um (*n.*), a chemical element, Yb

yt-tri-um (*n.*), a chemical element, Y

Z

ze-ner (*n.*), a type of semiconductor diode

ze-nith (*n.*), the highest point

ze-o-lite (*n.*), a type of mineral

ze-ro (*n.*), the state of total absence of quantity; (*v.*), to find a lowest starting point

ze-ta (*n.*), a Greek letter, Z, ζ

zinc (*n.*), a chemical element, Zn

zinc-ate (*n.*), zinc compound

zinc blende (*n.*), a zinc mineral

zir-con (*n.*), a zirconium mineral

zir-co-nia (*n.*), zirconium oxide

zir-co-ni-um (*n.*), a chemical element, Zr

zone (*n.*), a region; (*v.*), to mark into regions

zy-mur-gy (*n.*), the study of the chemistry of fermentation

Index

Abcissa, 74
Acid, 19
Acoustics, 99–102
  summary, 102
Algebra, 65–80
  summary, 79
Amplification, 162–65, 167, 168
Antilogarithm, 45
Arrows
  in chemical equations, 11–16
    double, 14
    drawing of, 14, 76
    physical chemistry, 25, 26
Atomic number, 120
Atomic reactions, words relating
    to, 127
Atoms, 5
  structure, 119–24, 131–2
  subatomic particles, 119
Axes, coordinate, 75

Base
  mathematical, 39
  natural, 45
Battery, 136
Benzene ring, 33, 34
Bonding lines in organic chemis-
    try, drawing of, 33
Bonds, chemical
  ionic, 28
  organic, 31–34
Braces, 69
Brackets, 69

Calculus, 80–87
  summary, 86
c.g.s. (metric), system of units,
    94, 95
Chemical combinations, summary,
    16
Chemistry
  electro-, 26–31
  organic, 31–35
    structural equations, 34
    summary, 35
    symbols, 32–34
  physical, 22–6
    summary, 26
    symbols, 25, 26
  words relating to structure,
    16–21
Circuits
  applications, 139–41
  block diagram, 141
  diagram, 141
  electrical, 138–43
  electrons in, 134–8
  integrated, words related to,
    175
  varieties of, 141, 142
Coefficient
  chemical, 8, 9
  in mechanics, 93, 94
Combination, chemical, 6–8, 13–16
Components, electronic, 155–62
  structure of words relating to,
    156–8, 160–61
Compound, chemical, 6
Computors, 178–84
  language, 179–83

programming, 179-84
   words relating to, 182
Conduction, electric, 129
Conductors, 129-30
Cosine, 58-9, 62
Crystal
   growth, 117, 118
   morphology (shape), 114-17,
      118
   physics of, 112
Crystallography, 112-118
   words relating to, 117
Cube, mathematical, 40, 41
Curl, 77
Current, electric, 135

Decimals, 37-9
Decrement, 47
Denominator, 36
Derivative, 82
   higher than first order, 83, 84
   partial, 84, 85
      writing of, 85
Differential, fractions, writing of,
   83
Differentiation, mathematical,
   81-5
Dissociation, 12
Dissolving, 23-5, 29
Divergence (div), 77
Dynamics, 90, 93

Electricity, static, 27
Electrochemistry, 26-31
   summary, 31
   symbols, 29, 30
Electrode, 136
Electronic systems, 176-84
Electrons, 134, 141, 142-3
Elements
   abbreviations for, 4, 5
   chemical, 3
   summary, 5
   naming of, 4
Energy, 94, 95
   bands, 128
English system of units, 94-5
Equal signs
   in chemical equations, 11-14, 16
   varieties of, 67, 68
Equations
   algebraic, 66-8
   balancing of, 14, 15
   chemical, 11-16
   electrochemical, 30
   integral, 86
   ionic, 30
Equilibrium, in mechanics, 90, 92
Exponents, 39-46
   examples of, 44
   fractional, 42, 43
   negative, 42-44
   positive whole-number, 39
   precautions in using, 46
   techniques in writing, 39-46

Factor, algebra, 70, 71
Factorial, 47, 48
   symbol for, 47
Fluorescence, 103-105
Force, 93-5
   words relating to, 93
Fractions, 36
French curve, 75
Frequencies, electric, names of,
   148
Function, mathematical, 71-5

Geometry, 55-9, 60-65
   summary, 65
   words relating to, 61-65
Gradient (grad), 77
Graph, 72-5
   drawing of, 74, 75
Greek letters, drawing of, 59

Heat, 109-12
  generation of, 111
  summary, 112
  transmission of, 110
  units, 111
  words relating to, 110, 111
Hydraulics, 96-9
  summary 99
  words relating to, 97-9
Hydrocarbons, 32, 33
Hydroxide, 11
Hydroxyl, 10, 11

Increment, 47
  symbol for, 47
Indices, Miller, 116
Infinity, 46
  symbol for, 47
Insulators, 130
Integral
  multiple, 85
  sign, 85
Integration, 85, 86
  limits of, 85, 86
Ions, 27-30
Isotopes, 120

Language, chemical, 8
Lens, 107
Light, 102-109
  waves, 102, 103
  words relating to, 104, 106, 108
Limits of integration, 85, 86
ln, 46
log, 45
Logarithm, 44-6
  natural, 45

Magnetism, 150-55
  words relating to, 154

Matrices, mathematical, 78
Matter, states of, 22-5, 26
  changes of, 22-5, 26
Mechanics, 89-96
  equilibrium, 90-92
  objects of, 91
  quantum, 129
  statistical, 129
  summary, 95
  words relating to, 91-5
Metric (c.g.s.), system of units,
  94, 95
Modulation, 164, 165
Molecules, 7
Morphology, of crystals, 114-17,
  118
Movement, 90, 92
Multiplication, symbols for, 69
Music, physics of, 100, 101

Number, imaginary, symbol for, 49
Numbers, 36-55
  prefixes, 50, 51
  summary, 54
  use of in chemistry, 8-11
Numerator, 36

Ohm's law, 143-4
Optics, 102-109
  summary, 108-109
Ordinate, 74

Parentheses
  in algebra, 68-9
  drawing of, 69
  use of in chemistry, 10
Physics
  modern, 118-24, 126-33
    summary, 131-3
  quantum, 126

Plus-or-minus, 70
Potential, 137
Power, 94, 95
  mathematical, 39
  raising to a, 40
Prefixes
  chemical, 18-21
    and suffixes, summary, 21
  mathematical, 50-51, 55
    symbols for, 50
  numbers, 50, 51
Primes, in mathematical series, 53
Probability, 128
Programming computors, 179-84

Radiation, 105
Radical, chemical, 9-11
Radioactivity, 121
Radiochemistry, 124
Radio tubes, 162-8
Ratio, in trigonometry, 57-60
Reaction, chemical, 7
  symbols and numbers in, 8, 9
Right angle, 60
Roots
  drawing of symbol for, 41
  mathematical, 41
  sign, 41, 42
  square, 42

Scalar, 77
Semiconductors, 130
Series, mathematical, 51
Sine, 58-60, 62
Solid-State
  devices, 168-74
    words relating to, 170, 171
  physics, 129

Sound, 99-102
  waves, 100
  words relating to, 100, 101
Square, mathematical, 40, 41
Statics, 90-92
Subscripts
  in mathematical series, 51-3
  use of in chemistry, 9
Suffixes, chemical, 17-20
Summation
  limits of, 48, 49
  symbol for, 48

Tangent, 58-60, 62
Temperature scales, 112
Term, algebra, 70, 71
Thermodynamics, 109-112
Transducers, 174-6
  words relating to, 175
Transistors, 129-30, 168-74
  words relating to, 170, 171
Trigonometry, 57-62
  summary, 65
  words relating to, 60-62

Variables, 72
  dependent, 72
  independent, 72
Vector, 75-8
  drawing of symbols for, 76
  symbol for magnitude of, 77
Vibrations, 99, 100
Voltage, 136

Waves
  electrical, 145-50
  light, 102, 103
  sound, 100

28224

Freedman

Handbook for the technical and scientific
secretary

DATE DUE

DISCARDED			